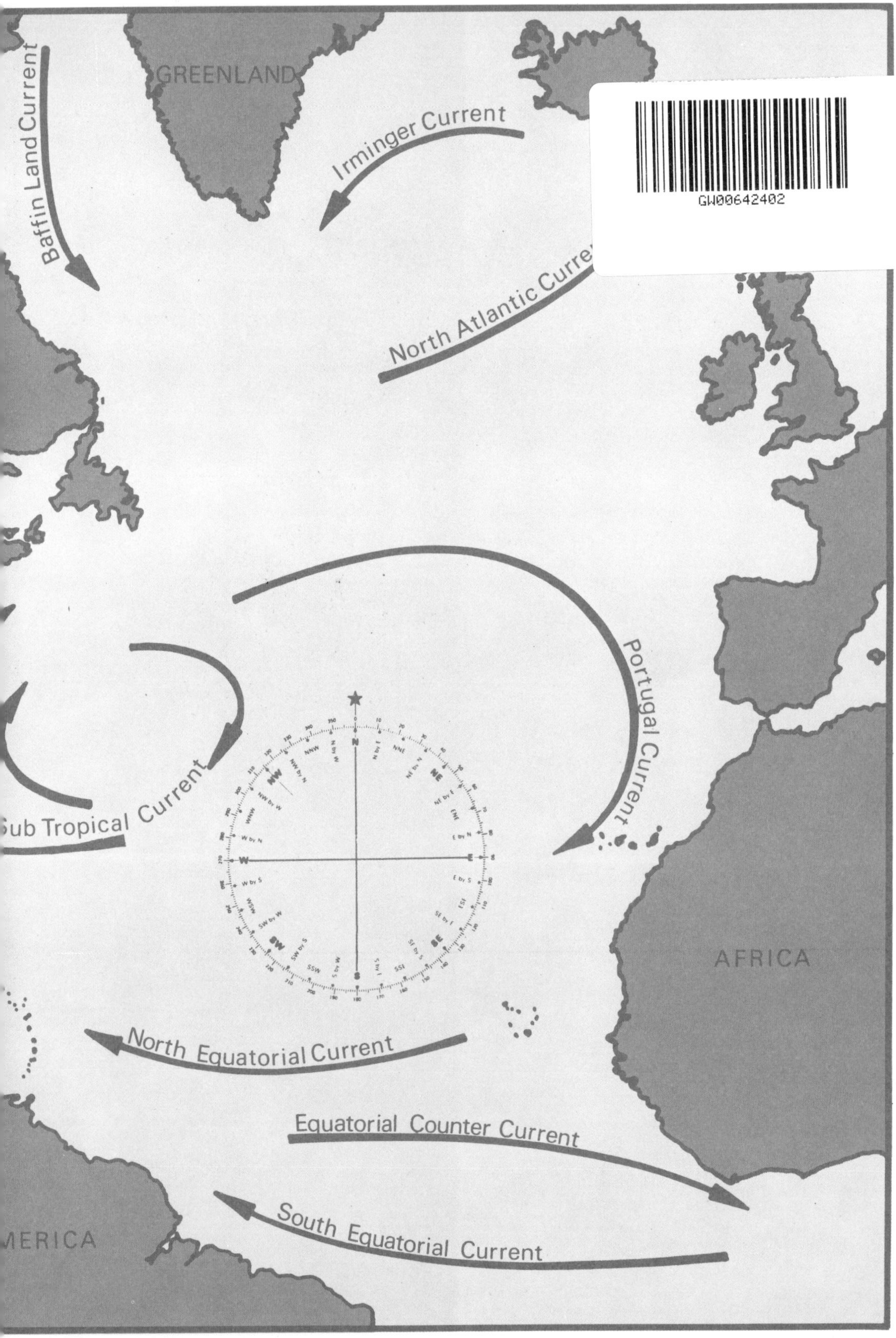

GREENLAND

Baffin Land Current

Irminger Current

North Atlantic Current

Portugal Current

Sub Tropical Current

AFRICA

North Equatorial Current

Equatorial Counter Current

South Equatorial Current

MERICA

BLUE WATER Y
NAVIGATIO

BLUE WATER YACHT NAVIGATION

Craig Coutts

CASSELL
London

Cassell Ltd
35 Red Lion Square, London WC1R 4SG
and at Sydney, Auckland, Toronto, Johannesburg,
an affiliate of
Macmillan Publishing Co., Inc.,
New York

First published in Great Britain 1979

ISBN 0 304 30451 4

Cover photograph
Australian Sailing Magazine

Set in 10/12 Century
by Jacobson Typesetters Ltd, Auckland, N.Z.
Printed and bound by KSL Singapore

Contents

Acknowledgments

I wish to thank the following for permission to reproduce material in this book:

The Hydrographer, Royal New Zealand Navy, for illustrations incorporating part of Charts NZ 532 and NZ 200 (extracts from the New Zealand *Chart Catalogue*); The Hydrographer, Royal Australian Navy, for a portion of International Chart No 602; The Controller of Her Majesty's Stationery Office for selected pages from the 1978 *Nautical Almanac*; AP 3270 Vols I and II; *Pacific Islands Pilot* Vol II and the *Manual of Seamanship* Vol II; the publishers Imray, Laurie, Norie and Wilson Ltd for extracts from the 1977 edition of *Norie's Nautical Tables*; The Hydrographer of the Royal Navy for Admiralty Charts Nos BA 5006 and 5216 and D6330; the Royal Yachting Association (UK) for extracts from the syllabus for the Yachtsmaster Ocean Syllabus, the Eiwa Bussan Co Ltd and the East Berkshire Boat Co, UK, for the photograph of the 'Saura' and 'Ebbco' sextants, W & G Precision Instruments Pty Ltd for the illustration of the Douglas protractor.

Introduction

It seems to me that most books about celestial navigation are written on the assumption that the navigator will always have clear skies, calm seas and good horizons. When it comes to advice on what to do in bad weather, in dangerous waters or when the calculations just will not work out, there is usually a deafening silence. *Blue Water Yacht Navigation* discusses some of the practical difficulties encountered by yacht navigators, and advice is given on overcoming these problems.

Though the book is mainly for the newcomer to celestial navigation, it can also be used by those who already have a passing knowledge of the subject. Sufficient background information is given for understanding the function of the instruments and tables used in navigation, but the emphasis is on the practical side of yacht navigation at sea.

The study of navigation has been divided into coastal and celestial or ocean-going navigation; over the years the belief seems to have developed that the two are essentially different, each to be learned separately and with little in common. When the land dips below the horizon, it seems, coastal navigation stops and ocean-going navigation begins. This misunderstanding is regrettable, for celestial navigation is not only an extension of coastal practice, but it depends on it. The first section of the book is therefore devoted to revising elementary coastal navigation techniques, as well as dealing with some that are more advanced, though not necessarily more difficult.

Mathematics is a basic tool in both coastal and celestial navigation, but anybody with commonsense and a reasonable grasp of arithmetic can learn to use the necessary books of tables.

Despite the fears of some beginners, celestial navigation is no longer a difficult subject. Once the principles have been mastered, it is most satisfying to predict that a given piece of land will appear above the horizon at a certain time, and for it to do just that. It is very pleasant during any voyage to know with certainty where one is, and not have to worry about where one might be.

Although *Blue Water Yacht Navigation* should enable the reader to understand the calculations and procedures needed, the only place to really learn navigation is at sea. Speaking from personal experience, the first ocean voyage is the best. Good sailing.

Craig Coutts
Auckland 1979

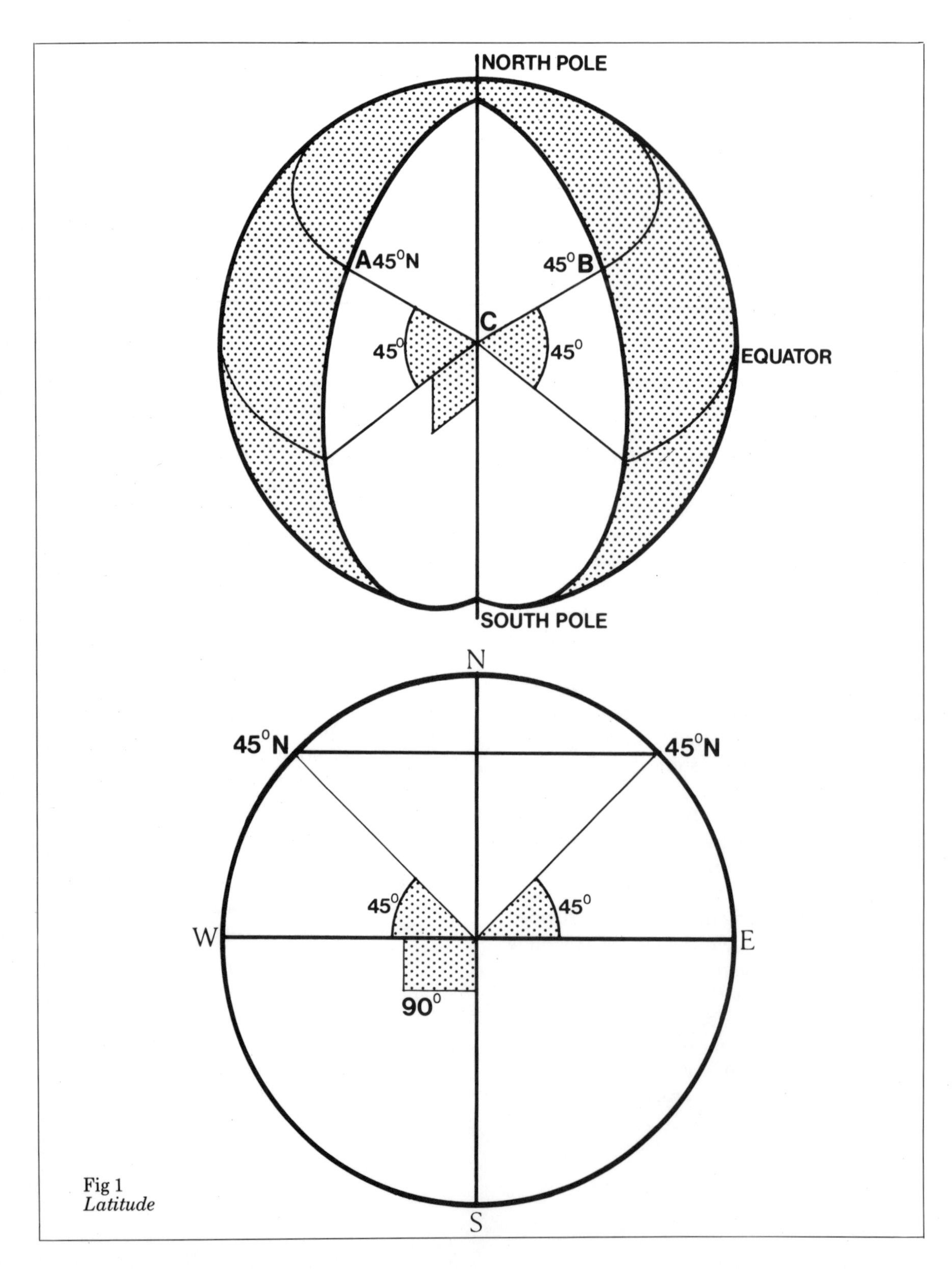

Fig 1
Latitude

Chapter One

The Basics of Navigation

TERMINOLOGY

The earth is a sphere, slightly flattened at the Poles, and for practical navigational purposes it can be regarded as looking like any schoolroom globe of the world. These globes have vertical and horizontal lines, which cross each other at right angles.

Any straight line joining the North and South Poles is called a meridian. These therefore run due north and south, and cut the east-west lines (called parallels) at right angles, or angles of 90 degrees. The line drawn across the centre of the earth is the equator.

Latitude

The lines drawn across the face of world maps are called parallels of latitude. Latitude itself is the angular distance of a place north or south of the equator.

Fig 1 shows the North and South Poles and the equator. The centre of the earth is marked C. A line has been drawn from the South Pole to C, and the angle at the centre of the earth between this line and a line through the equator is a 90-degree angle. The latitude of the South Pole is 90 degrees south, so the North Pole's latitude is 90 degrees north.

Fig 1 also shows two places in the northern hemisphere marked A and B. The line through each place to the earth's centre is shown, and in both cases the angle is 45 degrees. Each place has the same latitude, i.e. 45°N. Thousands of places on the earth's surface have a latitude of 45°N and a line joining all places that have the same latitude is a straight line, running east-west parallel to the equator; this is called a 'parallel of latitude'. To say that a place has a latitude of 30°S is to know that it lies somewhere on the parallel of latitude of 30°S. A vertical line is needed to get the exact position of the place on the globe.

Longitude

Until the late nineteenth century, major seafaring nations used the meridian through their capital city as the zero line. However, for reasons of international consistency, a particular meridian had to be chosen as the

Fig 2
Longitude

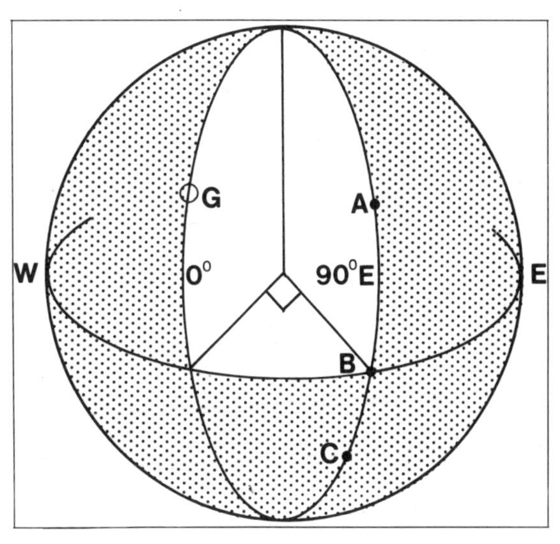

starting point for the numbering of the vertical lines necessary to complete the line grid on the map. In 1884, at the initiative of the United States, the meridian through Greenwich, England, was agreed as the zero meridian or 'prime' meridian.

Longitude is the angular distance of a place east or west of the Greenwich meridian. Fig 2 shows the earth with a cutaway section at the equator. A, B and C are all east of Greenwich, and they all lie on the same meridian. G indicates Greenwich. The angle shown at the centre is 90 degrees, so the longitude of all three places is 90° E.

Defining position using latitude and longitude

The position of any point on the earth's surface can be defined by its latitude north or south of the equator and its longitude east or west of Greenwich. Latitude and longitude, as we have seen, are angular measurements, and in any angular measure, there are 60 minutes of arc in a degree. Position is always given in degrees, minutes and tenths of a minute, and by convention latitude is given first. When writing down a position it is not strictly necessary to use the words 'latitude' and 'longitude', as this is evident from the use of north, south, east or west.

For instance, a typical position is 31°15′.4 N, 63°46′.9 E, which in words is: 'Thirty-one degrees, fifteen minutes point four north, sixty-three degrees, forty-six minutes point nine east'.

As the earth is a sphere, the distance covered when changing latitude by one degree in a north-south direction is the same anywhere on the surface.

To enable a straight conversion from angle to distance, the nautical mile has been chosen for use in navigation. A nautical mile is the distance on the earth's surface represented by one minute of latitude, or arc. As there are 60 minutes in a degree, so there are 60 nautical miles in one degree of latitude.

Fig 3
The great circle

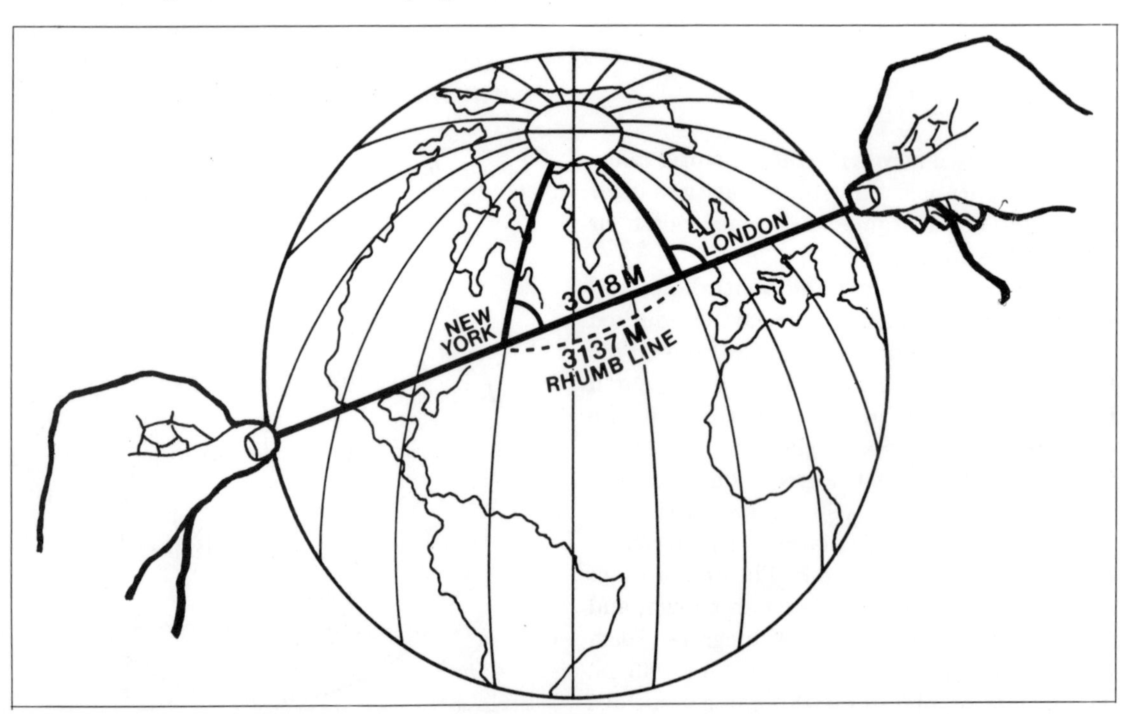

Fifteen point four nautical miles would be written either as 15.4M or as 15′.4.

The International Nautical Mile is 1 852 metres; kilometres are not used when measuring distance at sea.

Speed at sea is measured in knots, and one knot = 1 nautical mile per hour.

The great circle

If the earth were sliced right through along the equator, or down any meridian, it would be cut neatly in half through the centre. Any circle around the earth which, if cut, would go through the centre, is the largest circle that can be drawn around the sphere, and is called a 'great circle'. In Fig 3, the piece of string stretched across the globe is part of a great circle, and also the shortest distance between two points on the sphere.

DIRECTION

In everyday life, direction is indicated roughly by saying that one town is north of another or that the sun rises in the east and sets in the west.

In navigation, however, direction must be indicated far more precisely. At sea there are no convenient AA signposts or any other reference points to be seen. The north-south meridian is taken as the zero or datum line and the angle in degrees measured clockwise from north is used to measure true direction.

Fig 4
Measuring true direction

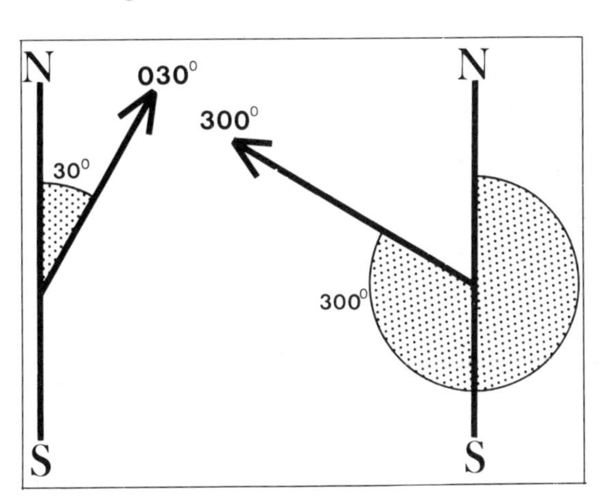

Bearing

The direction in which a place or object lies from a vessel is called the true bearing. As there are 360 degrees in a circle, bearings are numbered from 0 to 360 degrees. Courses and bearings are always given in three figures, e.g.

direction	written as	spoken as
north	000°	zero zero zero degrees
four degrees to the right of north	004°	zero zero four degrees
east	090°	zero nine zero degrees
twenty-one degrees clockwise from E	111°	one one one degrees
south	180°	one eight zero degrees
west	270°	two seven zero degrees

Course

The course of a boat at any moment is the angle between the north-south meridian through the boat and the direction in which the bow is pointing. To go from one place to another at sea, it is convenient to steer a constant course.

Look again at Fig 3. The great circle may be the shortest distance between New York and London, but note that to travel along it a boat would have to be on a north-easterly course at the start, and by the time it reached journey's end the course has changed to east. To sail along a great circle track means a number of alterations of course.

Rhumb line

A rhumb line cuts all meridians at the same angle. On the assumption that there are no currents or other off-setting factors, a boat can move along a rhumb line track by steering one constant course. However, the rhumb line distance on the earth is usually longer than the great circle distance between the same two points. For all coastal sailing and ocean voyages of less than 600 miles, the difference is negligible. As the equator is a great circle, an east-west course along the equator is also a rhumb line. Similarly all meridians are parts of great circles, so a north-south course anywhere in the world means that the boat is following both a rhumb line and a great circle track.

TOOLS USED IN COASTAL NAVIGATION

The basic tools in coastal navigation are parallel rulers, dividers, a pencil, an eraser, a chart table, a speedometer, called a log, a chart, and a magnetic compass.

Fig 5
Rhumb line: Angle A is the course

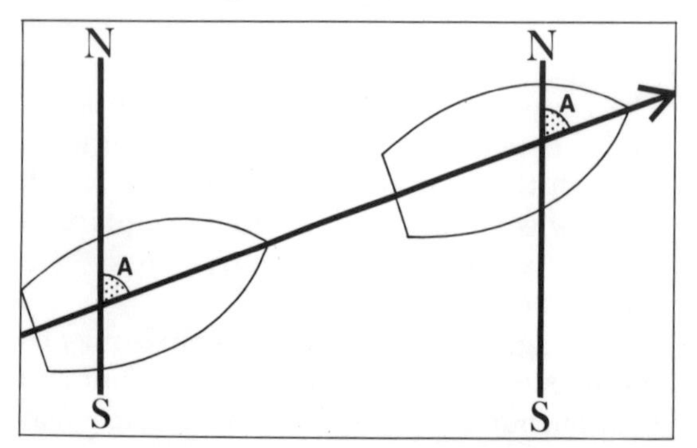

Parallel rulers consist of two rules connected by pivotal cross pieces. They are used to draw parallel lines in draughting or chartwork. The rulers can also be stepped across the face of a chart for measuring courses or bearings.

There is a second type of parallel rule called a roller rule, and this has two metal wheels fitted so it can be rolled across the surface of the chart. Either type of parallel rule is suitable, but the roller rule should have two edges and be a little heavier than the same-sized pivotal variety.

Dividers are used to measure distances in chartwork. Either the straight or the bow type is suitable, but they should be large enough to open out to at least 20-22 centimetres.

Pencils with B or 2B leads should be used, but no softer as they will smudge. Hard pencils can score the surface of a chart and are difficult to erase.

You will need at least two good erasers.

The chart table is probably any convenient flat surface, either built into the boat's hull, or perhaps the saloon table adapted for use at sea. Much of the time afloat will be spent at this working surface, so it should be made as comfortable as possible.

The log in most newly constructed boats is built into the hull, and both the boat's speed and the distance travelled register on a dial in the cockpit. How this information is used by the navigator and how to check the log's accuracy are explained in Chapter Two.

A chart is primarily concerned with showing the coastline and the sea. Its main purpose is to give the sort of information necessary to get the navigator from point A to point B. Charts show prominent coastal features, navigation lights and marks, depth of water, rocks, shoals and mudflats.

Charts **must** be differentiated from maps – maps are primarily concerned with the land areas of the world. Maps show states and nations, towns and cities, mountain ranges and other features of the land.

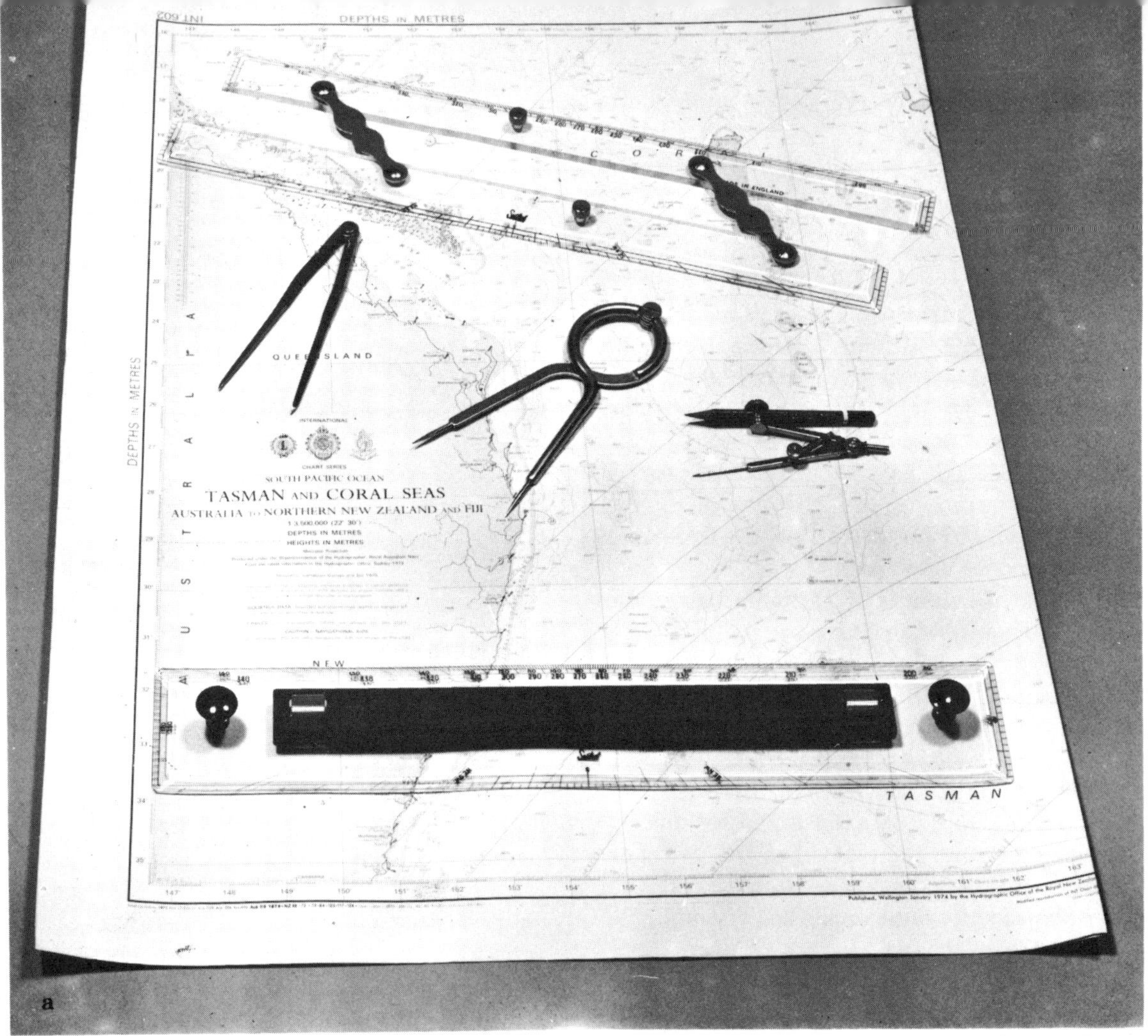

Fig 6
Basic coastal navigation instruments

a: *Top to bottom: Parallel rulers, straight dividers, bow dividers, compasses, roller rulers*
b: *A hand bearing compass*

Magnetic compasses are instruments used to indicate direction. There are two main types, a fixed and a hand bearing compass. A fixed compass is used to determine the course of a boat. Many sorts are available, and the navigator should be guided by a marine supplier in choosing the model most suitable for his or her use. A portable type called a hand bearing compass is used to determine the bearings of prominent shore objects, and this type is mainly discussed in this book.

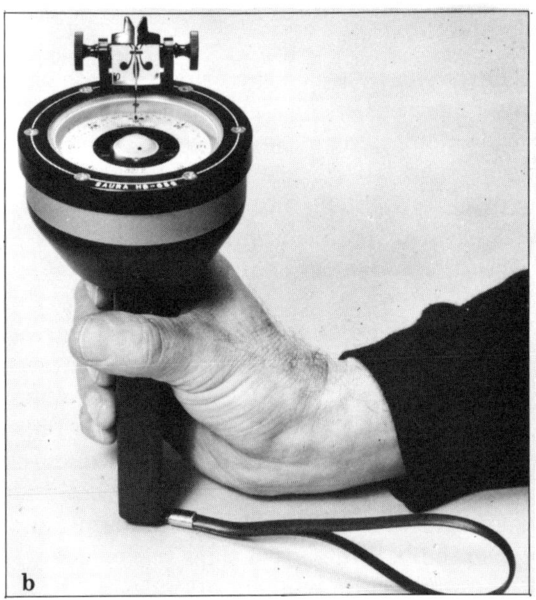

THE CHART

Drawing up a chart

The problem for the chartmaker is to represent the rounded surface of a sphere on the flat plane surface of a piece of paper. This cannot be done without some distortion or stretching. Luckily the chartmaker can choose the distortion his customer will be willing to accept in order to see any specific features needed to use the chart for a particular purpose.

The navigator needs to find the following characteristics in a chart:

(a) Countries should be easily recognizable, i.e. they should retain the same shape as on a globe.

(b) The parallels of latitude and meridians of longitude should cross at right angles, as on the globe.

(c) The direction and distance between any two places should be ascertained by merely drawing a straight line between the two. For most purposes this line should cut the meridians at the same angle, i.e. it would give the rhumb line course.

The chart might look like Fig 7.

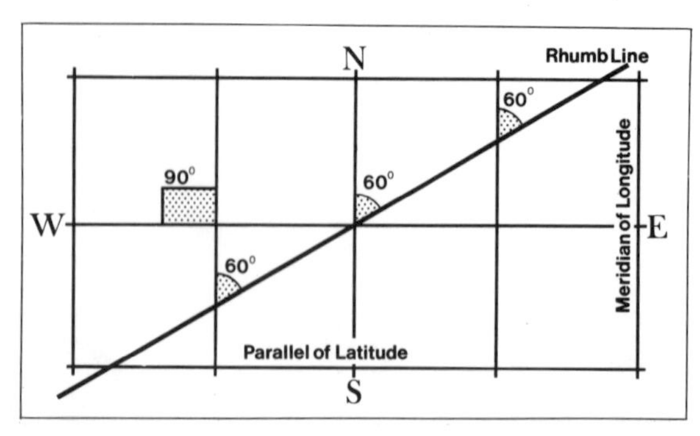

Fig 7

Projections

The system by which the world or areas of it are represented on a chart is called a projection. There are several sorts of projections used in charts, each one having particular problems and particular uses.

The main problem with all projections is distortion. On the equator, a degree of longitude and a degree of latitude are the same length, i.e. 60 miles. If two ships started at different points on the equator and moved due north, they would slowly come closer together until they met at the North Pole, because this is the point at which meridians of longitude converge. The distance between meridians of longitude therefore lessens, and for example if these two ships reached 70°N, they would be only about 20 miles apart, or only one-third the length of a degree of latitude.

The Mercator projection

Until the mid-sixteenth century, charts were made on the assumption that the world was flat. Meridans did not converge, but were drawn exactly the same distance apart (see Fig 7) and of course this led to quite large errors in position.

A Flemish geographer called Mercator realised that if longitude meridians ran vertically, i.e. the length of a degree of longitude was constant on a chart, then the length of a degree of latitude would have to be increased to keep the same proportion between the two as on the globe. The effect of lengthening the latitude scale to compensate for the constant longitude scale is that land masses are 'stretched' the closer the latitude approaches 90 degrees. On a map or chart using the Mercator projection, the land masses retain their shape, though towards the polar regions they are larger than they actually are on the globe.

The first chart using the Mercator projection was published in 1569. Today most wall maps or school atlases use this projection, as do most charts for use by sea navigators. The main advantage of the Mercator chart, as far as the navigator is concerned, is that a straight line joining any two places is the rhumb line between them, and the angle at which this line cuts any

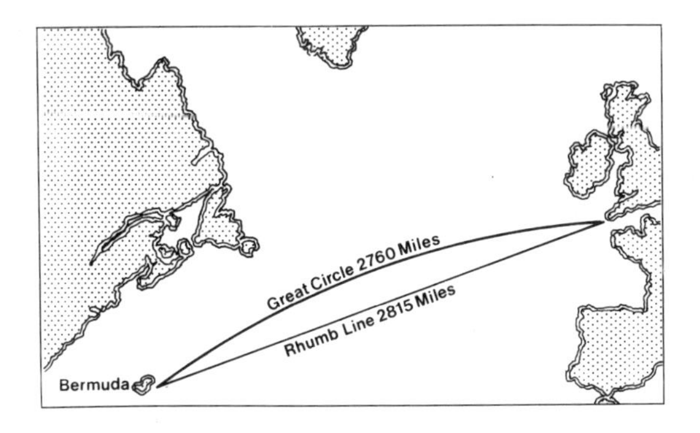

Fig 8
The difference between a great circle track and a rhumb line on a Mercator chart

meridian is the course to steer to go along the line.

Mercator projection charts are useless in polar regions, because the latitude scale and land mass distortion become too great. Most maps stop at about latitude 70 degrees north or south.

The gnomonic projection

Gnomonic charts are used in polar regions and as great circle charts. A straight line between any two points on the chart represents the shortest distance between the two. The method of transferring these tracks to a Mercator chart for navigational purposes is explained in Chapter Nine.

Measuring distance on a chart

Remember that one minute of latitude is equal to one nautical mile. Distance on a chart is measured by opening a pair of dividers until the points are on the two places, the distance between which is being measured, and moving the dividers to the nearest side of the chart to measure the distance on the latitude scale. The latitude scale is printed up and down each side of a chart, as shown in Fig 9. If the dividers cover, say, 6 minutes of latitude, then the distance being measured is 6 nautical miles. If a long distance is being measured, the dividers should be set at a convenient distance apart (say 5 or 10 miles) and stepped off along the line joining the two places.

Look at Fig 8. While the rhumb line is a straight line on the Mercator chart, a great circle track appears as a line which curves towards the nearest Pole. Even though the great circle track can be shorter by several hundred miles on a long trans-Atlantic or trans-Pacific voyage, sheer distance is not necessarily the most important consideration for yachts. For instance, by sailing the rhumb, the boat may stay in a favourable wind pattern; the great circle might take the boat into an area of head winds or perhaps no wind at all. The fact that the great circle curves towards the Pole and therefore takes the vessel into high latitudes may have other dangers. In the Round-the-World Race in 1977-8, the yachts were so far south that some reported being among small icebergs!

The longitude scale that runs across the top and bottom of a chart must *never* be used to measure distance.

The compass rose

On a chart, compass roses are used for measuring courses or bearings. In Fig 10, the outer circle of figures indicate true directions, measured 0° to 360° clockwise from north. Several roses are usually overprinted at convenient points on a chart.

Most true compass roses will have a smaller inner circle called the magnetic ring, used for measuring magnetic courses. This is necessary because the true and magnetic North Poles are not coincident, and a magnetic compass rarely indicates the direction of true north.

Magnetic variation

The angle between the direction of true north and that of magnetic north is called the magnetic variation. If magnetic north lies to the east of true north at a place, the variation

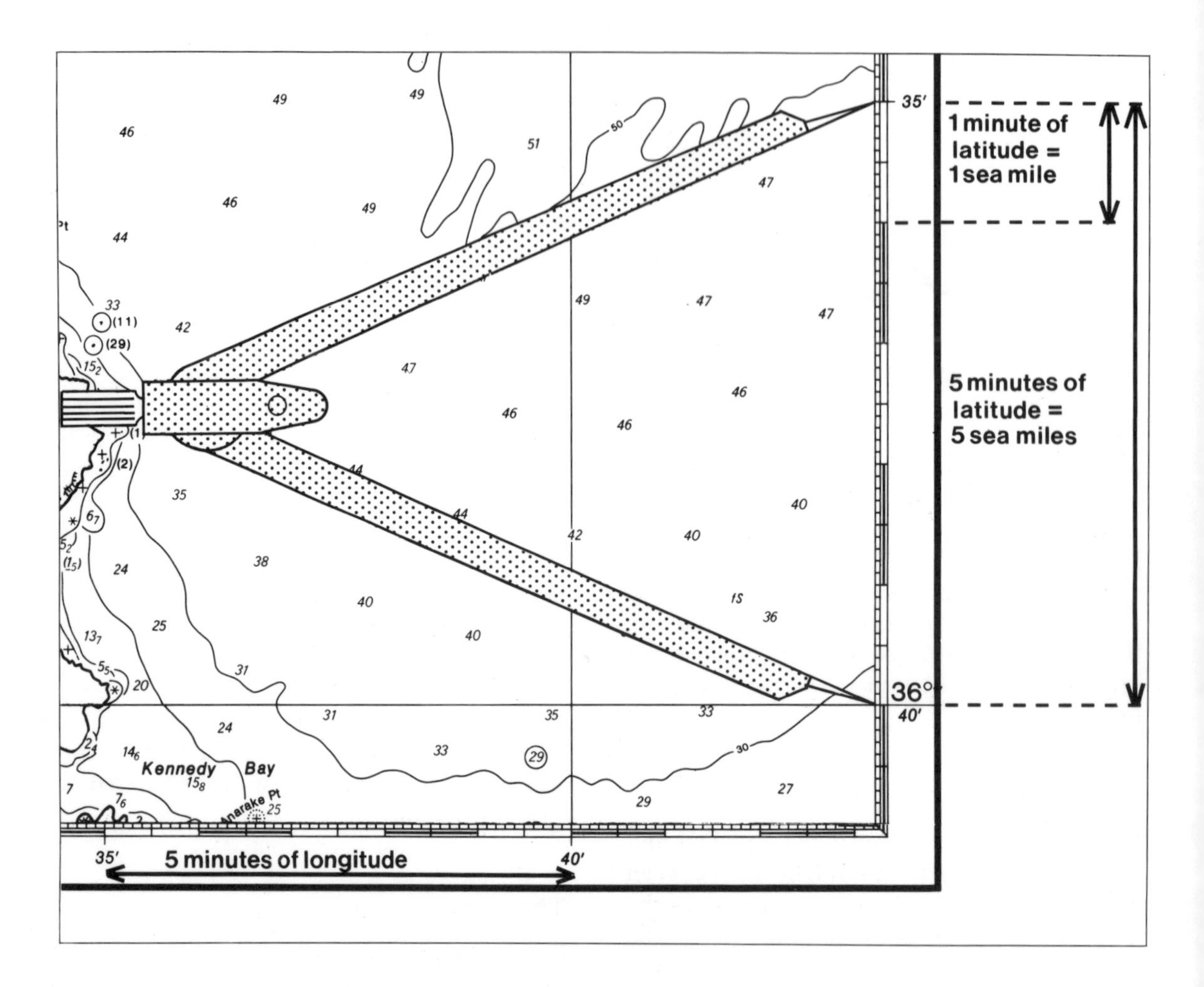

is called easterly, and westerly if it lies to the west of true north. The magnetic Poles move, thus variation changes slowly.

The magnetic ring of a compass rose is oriented so that the magnetic north/south line is lined up in the magnetic meridian. For practical purposes this can be considered as a line joining the North and South magnetic Poles. The value and annual change of variation is given in the magnetic ring on a chart. Fig 10 reads 'Variation 18°30'E (1974)'. Note that the inner ring is lined up to the east of true north.

Although a magnetic course can be measured directly from the rose, it is recommended that all working be done in true directions. As variation is known, the one can

Fig 9
Measuring distance on a chart

be converted to the other using the aide memoire:

'Variation East, magnetic least
Variation West, magnetic best.'

For example, if the true course is 060° and variation 10° East, the magnetic course is less than the true. Thus:

True course	=	060°
Variation	=	10° E –
Magnetic course	=	050°

If a magnetic bearing is taken, the true bearing can be found by reversing the procedure, e.g:
Shore mark bearing 320°M, variation 16°E.

Magnetic bearing	=	320°
Variation	=	16° E +
True Bearing	=	336°

In celestial navigation, all working is done in true bearings and directions.

Deviation

The steering compass in a boat may not show the direction of magnetic north correctly if it is influenced by magnetic materials in the hull or superstructure. Any difference in the direction of magnetic north and north as indicated by the compass is called deviation. The deviations alter with change of heading in the craft. These should be found by a compass adjuster, who will note them on a deviation card which should be kept adjacent to the steering position for easy reference. A hand bearing compass is usually free of any deviation as long as the navigator does not lean over the engine or up against steel wire rigging while using it.

Measuring the course on a chart

To measure a course on a chart, one edge of the parallel rulers should be aligned so that it joins the boat's starting point and destination. Then step the rulers over to the nearest compass rose so that one outer edge goes through the centre point of the rose. The reading on the outside circle where the same edge of the ruler cuts it is the course between the two points. To lay off a course on a chart from a given starting point, the procedure is reversed. Line one edge of the rulers from the centre point of the compass rose to cut the outer ring at the desired course or bearing. Move either of the outer edges to the starting point on the chart, and draw in the course line. Actually stepping the parallel rulers across the chart will prove tricky at first, but they can be walked from one end of the chart to the other and back again with a little practice.

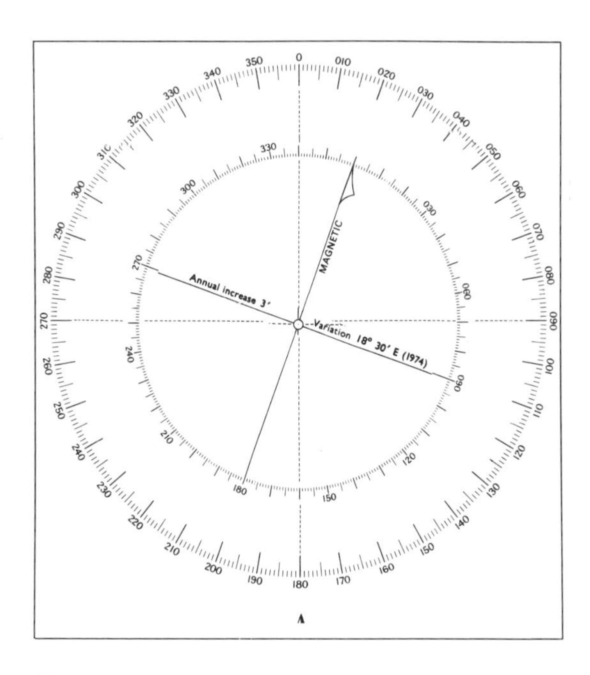

Fig 10
True and magnetic compass rose

TIMEKEEPING

In navigation, the day runs from midnight to midnight, i.e. from 0 to 24 hours. Although the division into two 12-hour periods using am or pm to identify the time of day serves well enough, it can be ambiguous and is therefore not sufficiently accurate for navigation.

For instance, finding the number of hours and minutes between 4.13 am and 11.02 pm cannot be done by subtracting one from the other. Although the reader can probably come up with the right answer (18h 48m) it takes some thought to work out.

In navigation, time is expressed in either four figures for hours and minutes or six figures if seconds are also included. Time is expressed or written in either a formal or informal manner, depending on the context. For example, a formal rendering is 10h 43m, or 15h 21m 10s; informally this is 1043, or, to the nearest minute, 1521. The hours are numbered straight through from 00 to 24. The following table should make this clear:

Time	24-Hour notation hrs mins	Spoken as
1.00 am	0100	oh one double oh
6.00 am	0600	oh six double oh
7.30 am	0730	oh seven thirty
10.43 am	1043	ten forty three
12.00 am	1200	twelve hundred
1.00 pm	1300	thirteen hundred
6.00 pm	1800	eighteen hundred
11.00 pm	2300	twenty three hundred
11.59 pm	2359	twenty three fifty nine

With this notation the question above can now be done by straight subtraction, i.e.

1101 pm	=	23h 01m
0413 am	=	04h 13m –
		18h 48m

If this is completely new to the reader, it will seem awkward at first. There is one point I must stress. There are 60 minutes in an hour and 60 minutes of arc in a degree. So the 13 minutes in this example were subtracted from (60m + 01m) or 61 minutes, to give the 48 minutes in the answer.

Time and longitude

The earth rotates once, i.e. it goes through 360 degrees of longitude every 24 hours. This is equal to 15 degrees of longitude every hour, or 1 degree every 4 minutes of time.

When the sun rises at Greenwich, it is already daylight in countries to the east of the United Kingdom, but still night to those in west longitudes. So places in east longitudes are said to be so many hours ahead of Greenwich, and others behind GMT (Greenwich Mean Time). The earth is divided into 24 zones, each 15 degrees of longitude wide with the initial zone centred on the Greenwich meridian. In the first zone to the east the zone time, as it is called, is one hour ahead of GMT and in each successive zone to the east the time changes by one hour. Each zone is given a number from –1 to –12 in east longitudes and +1 to +12 in west longitudes. The zone number indicates the number of hours by which the zone time must be increased or decreased to find Greenwich Mean Time, e.g. longitude 10°W is in zone +1. To find GMT if the zone time is 1120:

Zone time	1120
Zone +1	1+
GMT	1220

To find GMT in zone –10 at 0930 zone time on 16 May:

Zone time	09h 30m
Zone –10	10h –
GMT	?

Let's look at that a little more closely. I am quite certain that if the time on the reader's watch was 9.30 in the morning and somebody said, 'what time was it ten hours ago?' the answer would come quick as a flash, 'Half past eleven last night,' which would be quite correct. It is also the answer to the problem above. To do the calculation, we have to 'borrow' 24 hours, but don't be confused by the figures in problems like these.

Therefore:

Zone Time	09h 30m
	+24
	31h 30m
Zone	10 –
GMT	23h 30m on the previous day (15 May)

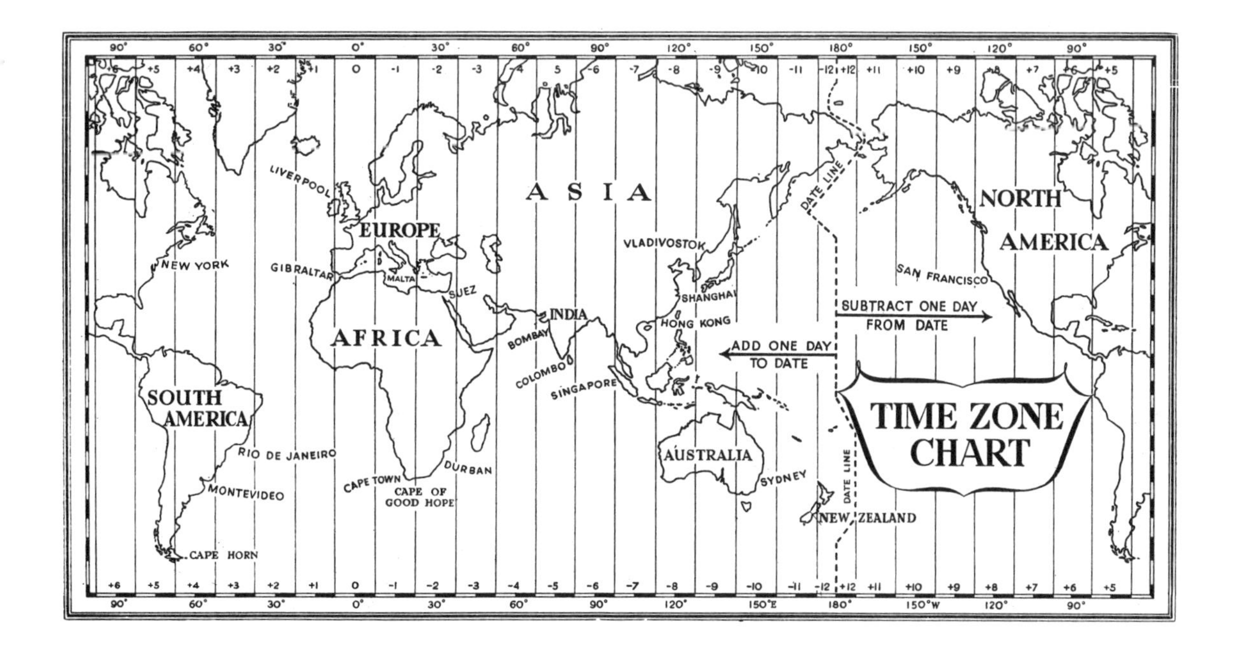

The zone time system for timekeeping at sea was introduced so that all vessels within certain defined limits of longitude would all keep the same time in the same way as do towns and cities on land even though they may be hundreds of miles apart.

The alternative is for each boat to set its clocks to be approximately correct by the sun, i.e. adjust the clocks to read 1200 hours when the sun is on the meridian or at its highest point in the sky each day. This means they must be advanced or retarded a few minutes daily. On the other hand, the clocks are adjusted exactly one hour when crossing from one zone into the next, and very few changes are needed, e.g. between England and the West Indies in the Atlantic or California and the Fiji Islands in the Pacific the clocks would be altered only four times.

Each system has its advantages, and in the end it comes down to personal choice. However, regardless of which system is used, there must be one timepiece on board which reads Greenwich Mean Time. It should have a sweep second hand and be used for navigational purposes only.

Fig 11
Time zone chart

Standard Time

Each country keeps its own Standard Time which is so many hours ahead of or behind GMT. These are listed in the *Nautical Almanac*. In general they will be the same as the zone in which the country is situated, but this is a political decision. In New Zealand, for example, the North Island lies wholly within zone −12 whereas most of the South Island is in zone −11. The New Zealand government has adopted 12 hours ahead of Greenwich as the Standard Time so that all clocks read the same nationwide. Some countries such as Australia, Canada or the United States cover such a wide band of longitude that there must be different Standard Times in different parts of the country, and clocks must be adjusted accordingly when moving from one part to another.

Summer Time

Summer Time or Daylight Saving Time is kept in some countries. Here the clocks are advanced on Standard Time, usually by one hour. Assume for example that the sun rises at 6 am and sets at 7 pm, giving thirteen hours of daylight. If Summer Time came into effect tonight, sunrise tomorrow would be at 7 am (new time) and sunset at 8 pm (new time). There would still be only 13 hours between sunrise and sunset, but the adjustment effectively means that an extra hour of daylight is available in the evening.

For the navigator, the crucial point is that by advancing the clocks, the time has been moved one zone to the east. If Standard Time had been 8 hours ahead of Greenwich (zone −8), it would now be 9 hours ahead (zone −9). If in west longitudes at say zone +8, this would mean that the clocks were now only 7 hours behind GMT, i.e. zone +7. In British Summer Time (BST) the country changes from GMT to one hour ahead of GMT, i.e. zone −1. On the other side of the world, when New Zealand changes each year to Daylight Saving, the clocks go from 12 hours ahead of GMT to 13 hours ahead, or zone −13.

Time checks

Many local radio stations broadcast periodic time checks on the hour, which consist of six 'pips'. The time is taken at the last pip. Similar time checks can be heard from Radios Australia, New Zealand and Fiji and can usually be received on an ordinary transistor radio, especially at night, anywhere in the Tasman and Coral Sea areas. For Pacific-wide coverage, Station WWVH (Hawaii) broadcasts on 5, 10, 15 and 20 Mhz. Station WWV (Fort Collins) covers most of the Atlantic on the same frequencies.

In the United Kingdom the signals are transmitted from Rugby call sign MSF on 2.5, 5 and 10 Mhz. BBC Radio time signals are given at frequent intervals throughout the day on Radios 1, 2, 3 and 4 and also on the BBC World Service.

Complete information is contained in the Admiralty *List of Radio Signals Volume 5*, which covers most of the world.

The dateline

The date or calendar line which roughly follows the meridian of longitude of 180 degrees is the boundary line between one date and the next. The line is diverted around groups of islands that lie on or near the meridian so that the day is the same throughout the group. A vessel sailing around the world will have adjusted clocks from time to time with the change in time zones, and when she crosses the dateline must make a further adjustment of one day. When crossing on an easterly course the date is put back a day; on a westerly course the date is put on a day.

Chapter Two

Finding the Boat's Position

But the principal failing occurred in the sailing,
and the Bellman, perplexed and distressed,
said 'he had *hoped, at least, when the wind blew due East,*
That the ship would not *travel due West.*
Lewis Carroll: The Hunting of the Snark

Navigation is the art of sailing a boat from one place to the next in safety. To do this, the rhumb line direction is first found from the chart and then the boat's position is checked from time to time to ensure that it is not in danger from reefs, rocks or other hazards. The various methods of position finding are explained in this chapter.

Dead Reckoning

Dead reckoning (DR) is a forecasting ahead of the boat's probable position, based on the direction of travel (course) and its speed (in knots).

You may dead reckon ahead for a minute, an hour, a day, or even longer. The accuracy of your forecast position will depend on how well the course is kept, your actual speed and other factors largely beyond your control which may set you off the intended track, such as wind and tidal stream.

The dead reckoning track is laid off on the chart by setting the parallel rulers to the intended course on the compass rose. One edge of the ruler is then moved to a known position of the boat and the course line drawn in.

In Fig 12 a vessel leaves a lighthouse at 1000 on a due east course, speed 4 knots. Using a pair of dividers, a distance of 4 miles is measured from the latitude scale of the chart, and the point 4 miles along the course line on the chart is marked. This would be the dead reckoning position of the boat after one hour, i.e. at 1100. The boat will move 2 miles in half an hour and this distance has been marked along the course to give the 1130 dead reckoning position. At this time the course has been altered to due south, or 180 degrees. A further half hour run has been laid off and the dead reckoning position (DR) for 1200 is shown. The boat then increases speed to 6 knots and steers 140° for 40 minutes. Course is then altered to due west (270°). Between 1240 and 1300 the distance covered is 2 miles at 6 knots, and the 1300 DR is shown.

The whole diagram to this point shows the dead reckoning track of the vessel from departing the lighthouse at 1000 to the

Fig 12
A dead reckoning track

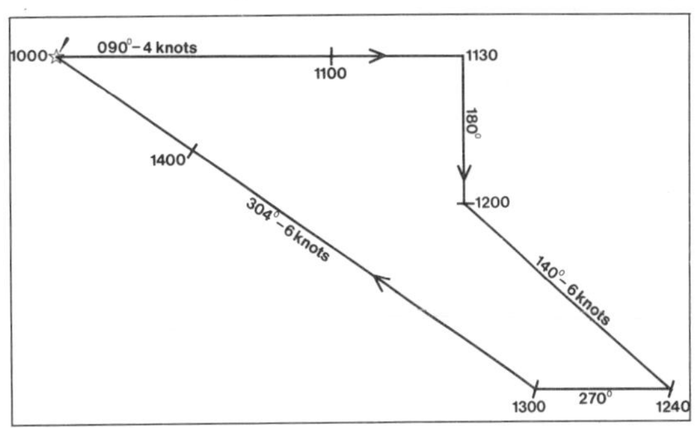

forecast position at 1300. It is unlikely that the vessel will be exactly at the position shown in the diagram. Over the three hours other factors may have influenced the boat's actual position. The helmsman may have been steering a degree or so off course on each leg. The drag from the barnacles on the bottom may have reduced the speed of the boat slightly below that used in the calculations.

Many logs have a 5 to 10 per cent error. If the speed indicated on the log is used in plotting the DR, the position might be slightly inaccurate because of this error. But that 1300 position shown is the best information available as to the boat's actual whereabouts at that time.

I agree that yachts do not travel on exact courses at exact speeds. Both courses and speeds may vary with wind shifts, and much of the time may be spent in tacking. For the moment, however, it is enough to understand what dead reckoning is, and how DR tracks and positions are plotted.

Looking at Fig 12 again, if at 1300 you decide to return to the starting point, the course to steer can be found by joining the dead reckoning position and the lighthouse as shown. This course measured on the compass rose would be 304 °, distance 8.4 miles. At 6 knots it would take 1 hour and 24 minutes to cover the distance. Arrival time would be 1424. This is called an estimated time of arrival, or ETA – estimated because it is based on a dead reckoning track, and a further dead reckoning or forecasting ahead. The more proficient a navigator becomes at plotting courses and reckoning ahead, the more accurate will his ETAs become.

Tidal stream

As we have seen, the dead reckoning track gives a good guide to position but it does not allow for outside influences acting on the vessel. A better forecast position can be found if any known tidal stream, ocean current, or anything else which tends to take the boat off its plotted track is taken into account.

Most coastal charts show tidal arrows at several points. These give the general direction of the flood or ebb stream and the rate in knots. There may also be more specific information on tidal stream directions and rates tabulated for any points which have a tidal diamond overprinted on the chart, as in Fig 13.

The rate and direction for spring and neap tides are shown for every hour from 6 hours before high water (HW) at a stated major port to 6 hours after the time of HW at the port.

Before continuing to discuss the mechanics of using the tidal stream information to estimate position, I would like to discuss a point which can cause uncertainty. When under way in a boat, whether moving or stopped and drifting, the log does not register, nor is it in any way affected by the tidal stream; only when moored to a jetty or at anchor will the rush of water under the boat's hull register on the log. The moment the lines are cast off or the anchor raised from the sea bed,the boat is free to move with the water and the log speed drops to zero. Water, boat, driftwood, and fish may all be moving quite quickly in the same direction, but only the boat speed through that water shows on the log.

The estimated position

Whenever a dead reckoning position is further refined by making allowance for the effect of tidal stream or other outside influences on the vessel's progress, the resultant forecast position is said to be an estimated position. It should be a more accurate measurement of the vessel's position than the straight DR.

If a vessel was heading on a general easterly course and there was a tidal stream setting to the south, the vessel would be set off the

Fig 13
A tidal diamond

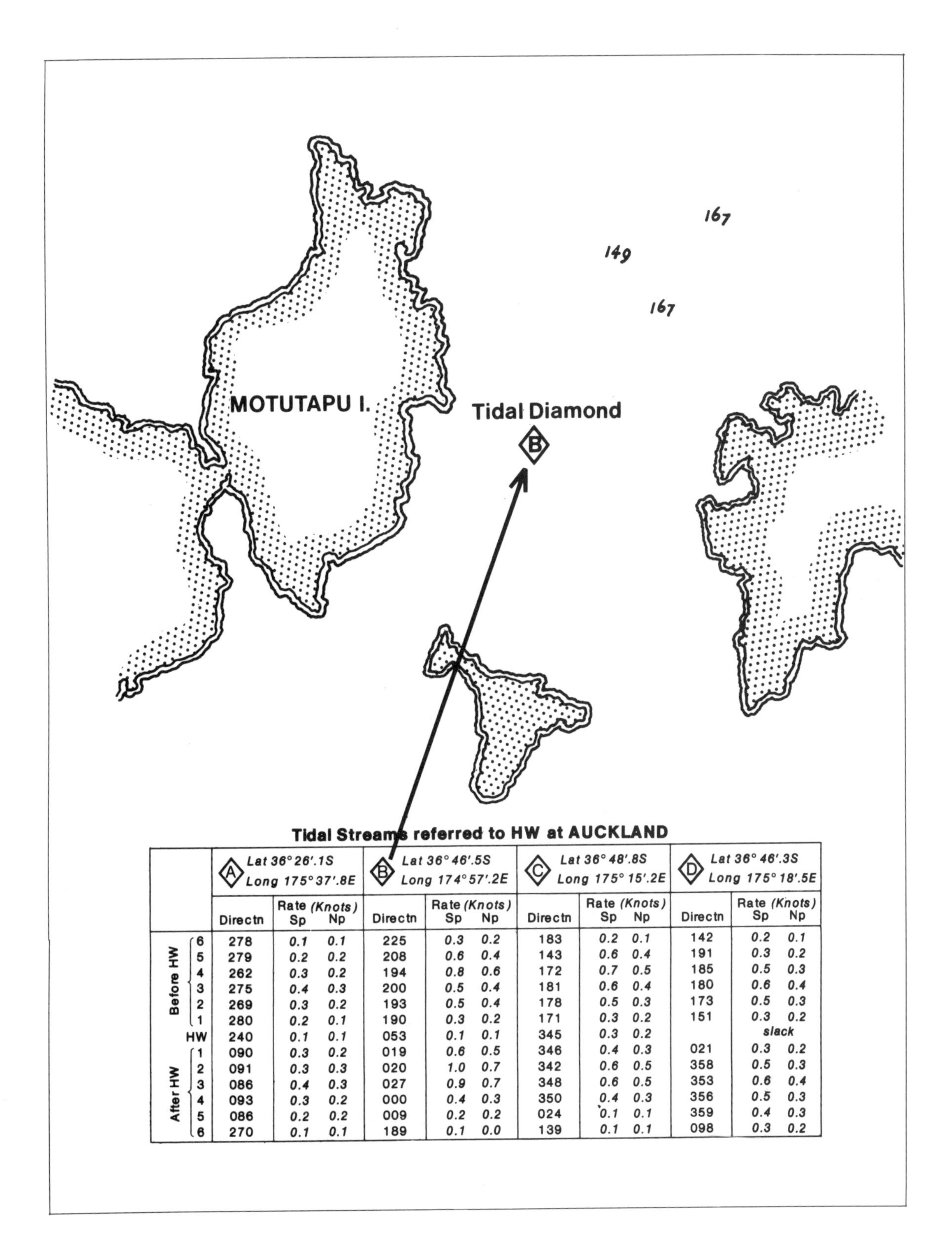

Tidal Streams referred to HW at AUCKLAND

	A Lat 36° 26′.1S Long 175° 37′.8E			B Lat 36° 46′.5S Long 174° 57′.2E			C Lat 36° 48′.8S Long 175° 15′.2E			D Lat 36° 46′.3S Long 175° 18′.5E		
	Directn	Rate *(Knots)* Sp	Np	Directn	Rate *(Knots)* Sp	Np	Directn	Rate *(Knots)* Sp	Np	Directn	Rate *(Knots)* Sp	Np
Before HW 6	278	*0.1*	*0.1*	225	*0.3*	*0.2*	183	*0.2*	*0.1*	142	*0.2*	*0.1*
Before HW 5	279	*0.2*	*0.2*	208	*0.6*	*0.4*	143	*0.6*	*0.4*	191	*0.3*	*0.2*
Before HW 4	262	*0.3*	*0.2*	194	*0.8*	*0.6*	172	*0.7*	*0.5*	185	*0.5*	*0.3*
Before HW 3	275	*0.4*	*0.3*	200	*0.5*	*0.4*	181	*0.6*	*0.4*	180	*0.6*	*0.4*
Before HW 2	269	*0.3*	*0.2*	193	*0.5*	*0.4*	178	*0.5*	*0.3*	173	*0.5*	*0.3*
Before HW 1	280	*0.2*	*0.1*	190	*0.3*	*0.2*	171	*0.3*	*0.2*	151	*0.3*	*0.2*
HW	240	*0.1*	*0.1*	053	*0.1*	*0.1*	345	*0.3*	*0.2*		*slack*	
After HW 1	090	*0.3*	*0.2*	019	*0.6*	*0.5*	346	*0.4*	*0.3*	021	*0.3*	*0.2*
After HW 2	091	*0.3*	*0.3*	020	*1.0*	*0.7*	342	*0.6*	*0.5*	358	*0.5*	*0.3*
After HW 3	086	*0.4*	*0.3*	027	*0.9*	*0.7*	348	*0.6*	*0.5*	353	*0.6*	*0.4*
After HW 4	093	*0.3*	*0.2*	000	*0.4*	*0.3*	350	*0.4*	*0.3*	356	*0.5*	*0.3*
After HW 5	086	*0.2*	*0.2*	009	*0.2*	*0.2*	024	*0.1*	*0.1*	359	*0.4*	*0.3*
After HW 6	270	*0.1*	*0.1*	189	*0.1*	*0.0*	139	*0.1*	*0.1*	098	*0.3*	*0.2*

intended DR track to the south. The most probable position after, say, one hour can be found as follows (see Fig 14):

Course 080°, speed 5 knots. Tidal stream setting 145° at 2 knots, (ebb stream arrow). Mark the DR track for 1 hour, line AB in diagram (Fig 14a). From B lay off the direction and distance that the tidal stream would offset the boat in 1 hour, 145° for 2 miles, line BC. C is the estimated position after one hour. (Fig 14b).

The boat will have moved along the line AC, and if there is no change in the tidal stream, the estimated position after two hours would be on the extension of the line for the distance CD equal to AC (Fig 14c).

Exactly the same method can be used to find an estimated position when out of sight of land in a known ocean current.

Leeway

If a vessel lies stopped in the water it will be blown down wind. When moving through the water, this effect is masked by the boat's own speed, but it is still present. The sideways movement through the water caused by a wind on the beam is called leeway. It can be estimated by checking the angle between the boat's wake astern and the fore and aft line, which is the course being steered. This angle of offset from the intended track should then be used in plotting estimated positions by applying it to the course steered; in the opposite direction as shown in Fig 16.

Fig 14
Plotting the estimated position

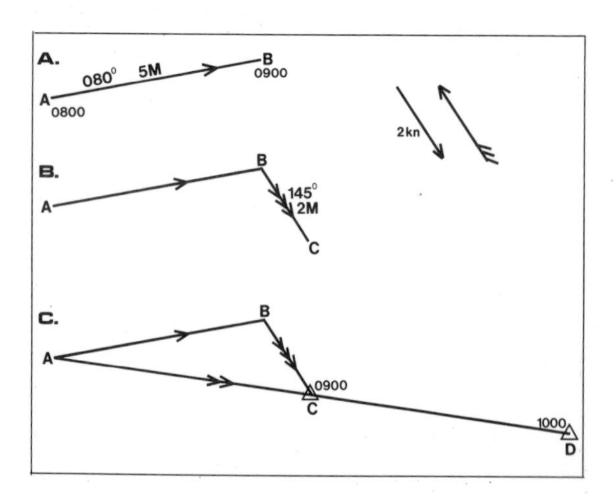

Allowing for tidal stream

While it is all very well finding an estimated position, there will be times when it is better, even essential, to make good a given course, no matter what effect the tidal stream is having on the vessel. This can be seen in Fig 17. The vessel is at point S and has to make good a course over the ground of 040 degrees to pass safely between the two dangerous rocks. The intended track is drawn in. From the starting point at S, draw in the direction the tidal stream is moving and the distance it would travel in one hour. In one hour the tidal stream would carry the vessel to this point if it were stopped in the water. Set one hour of intended ship's speed on a pair of dividers or compasses. With centre T, cut in to the intended track (point C in the diagram). Then TC is the course to steer to allow for the effect of the tidal stream.

Fig 15
a *No leeway*
b *Leeway present*

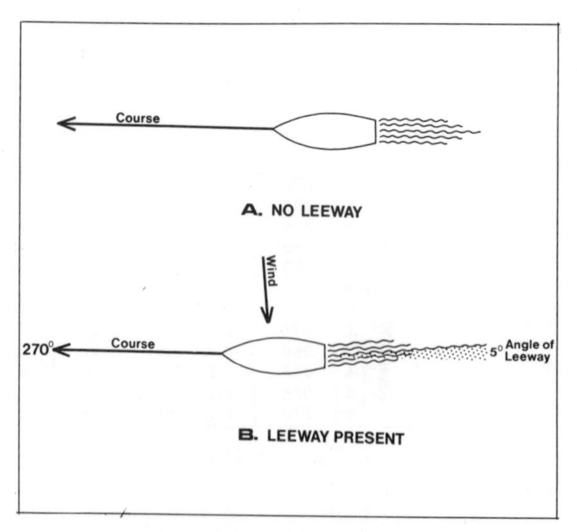

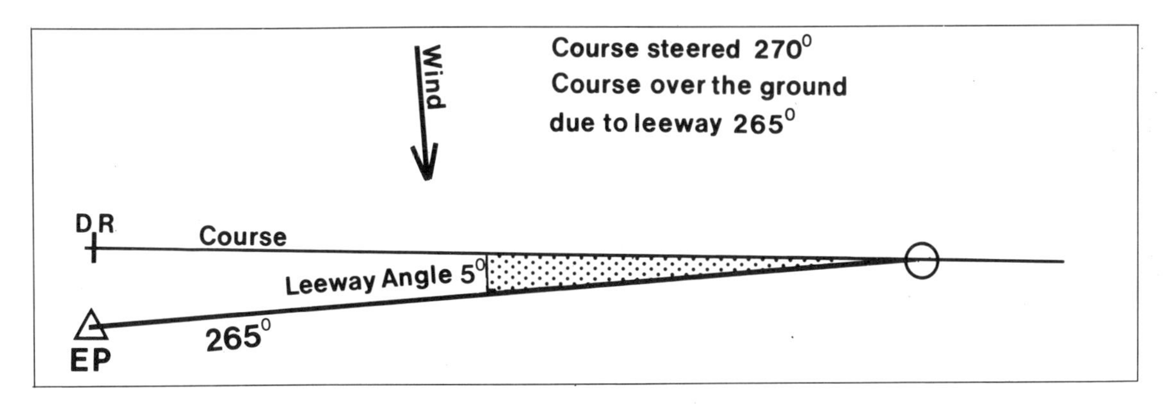

Fig 16
Estimated position using leeway angle

Fig 17
Finding course to steer to allow for tidal stream. The boat speed is 5 knots and the speed made good is 4.6 knots.

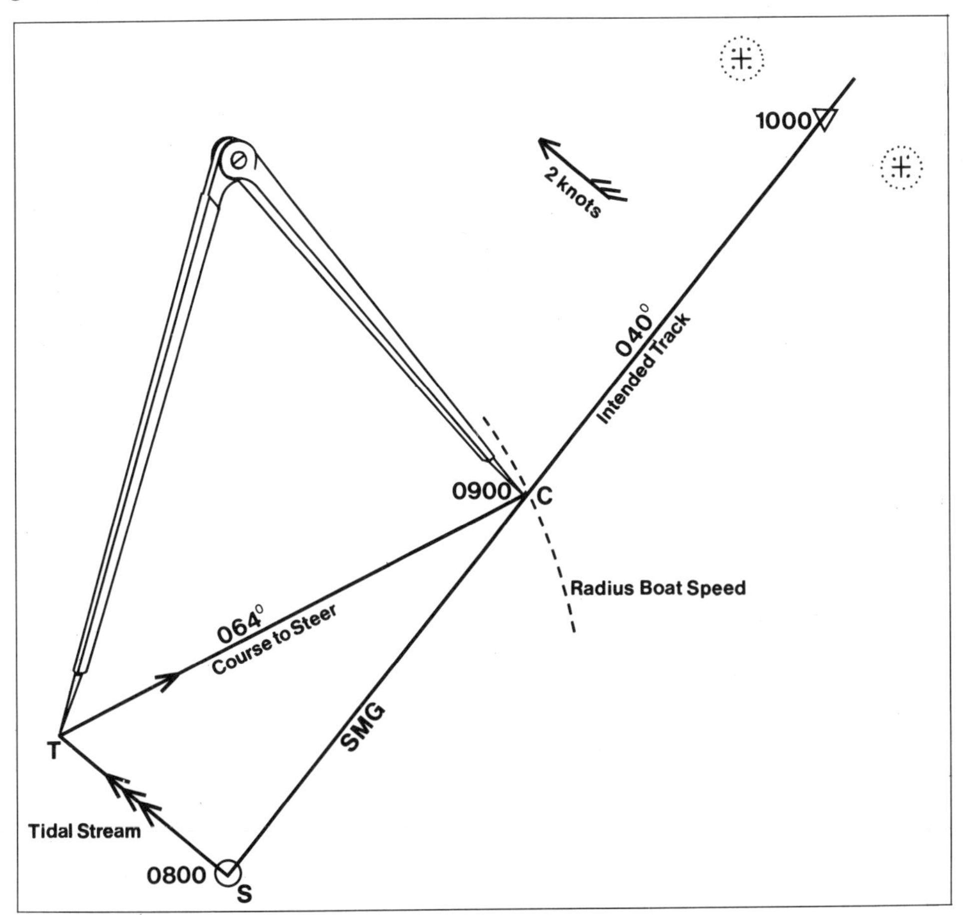

After one hour, the vessel should have reached point C on the desired track, having moved along the line SC on the chart. This is called the course made good (CMG) over the ground and the distance from S to C is the speed made good (SMG) in one hour. If the boat course and speed and the tidal stream remain the same, then so will the speed made good. As it is a combination of tide and boat movement any forecasting ahead using the SMG results in an estimated position, not a dead reckoning position.

In this example the SMG is 4.6 knots. The estimated position for 1000 based on this speed shows that the boat will be passing between the rocks at that time.

The slower a boat is moving, the greater the angle of throw-off needed to allow for the tidal stream. In the above example the difference between the intended track and the course the boat had to steer to make good the intended track was 24 degrees. Fig 18 shows that under the same set of circumstances, but with a speed of only 4 knots, the second vessel would have to throw off 30 degrees to achieve the same result.

Allowance for leeway

When the angle has been estimated, leeway can be counteracted by altering course the same amount towards the wind. In Fig 16, to make good an intended track of 270° an alteration to starboard to 275° would compensate.

POSITION AND POSITION LINE

The dead reckoning and estimated positions can be good guides to progress, and they may be correct, but their accuracy can only be checked by finding the vessel's actual position from time to time. The basis for finding the boat's position is the position line. A position line is a line on the chart on which the vessel lies or has lain. It can be straight, curved or irregular in shape. If two position lines are obtained at the same time and as the vessel lies somewhere on each line, then the point at which the two lines cut must be the vessel's actual position.

Finding two or more position lines is called fixing the boat's position. The most common method of doing this, or getting a fix, is by taking simultaneous compass bearings of two prominent charted objects such as lighthouses.

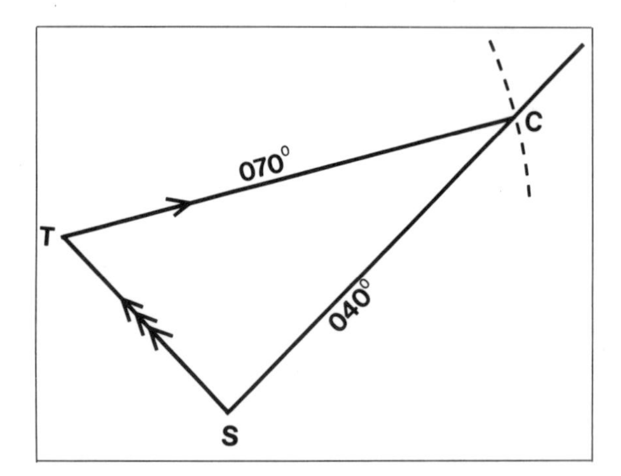

Fig 18
Allowing for tidal stream. The boat speed is 4 knots and the speed made good 3.5 knots.

Fig 19
A fix by cross bearings

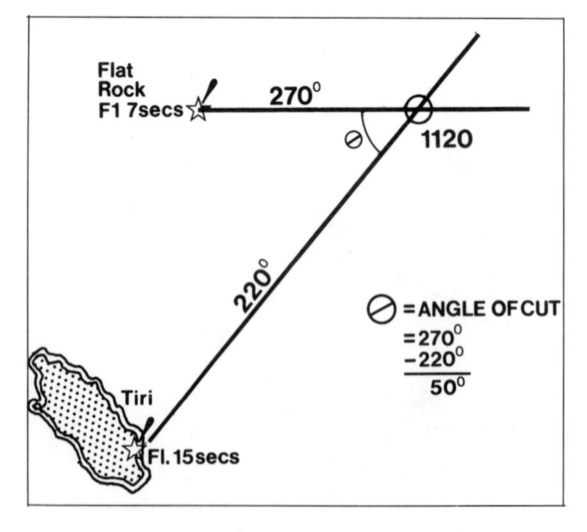

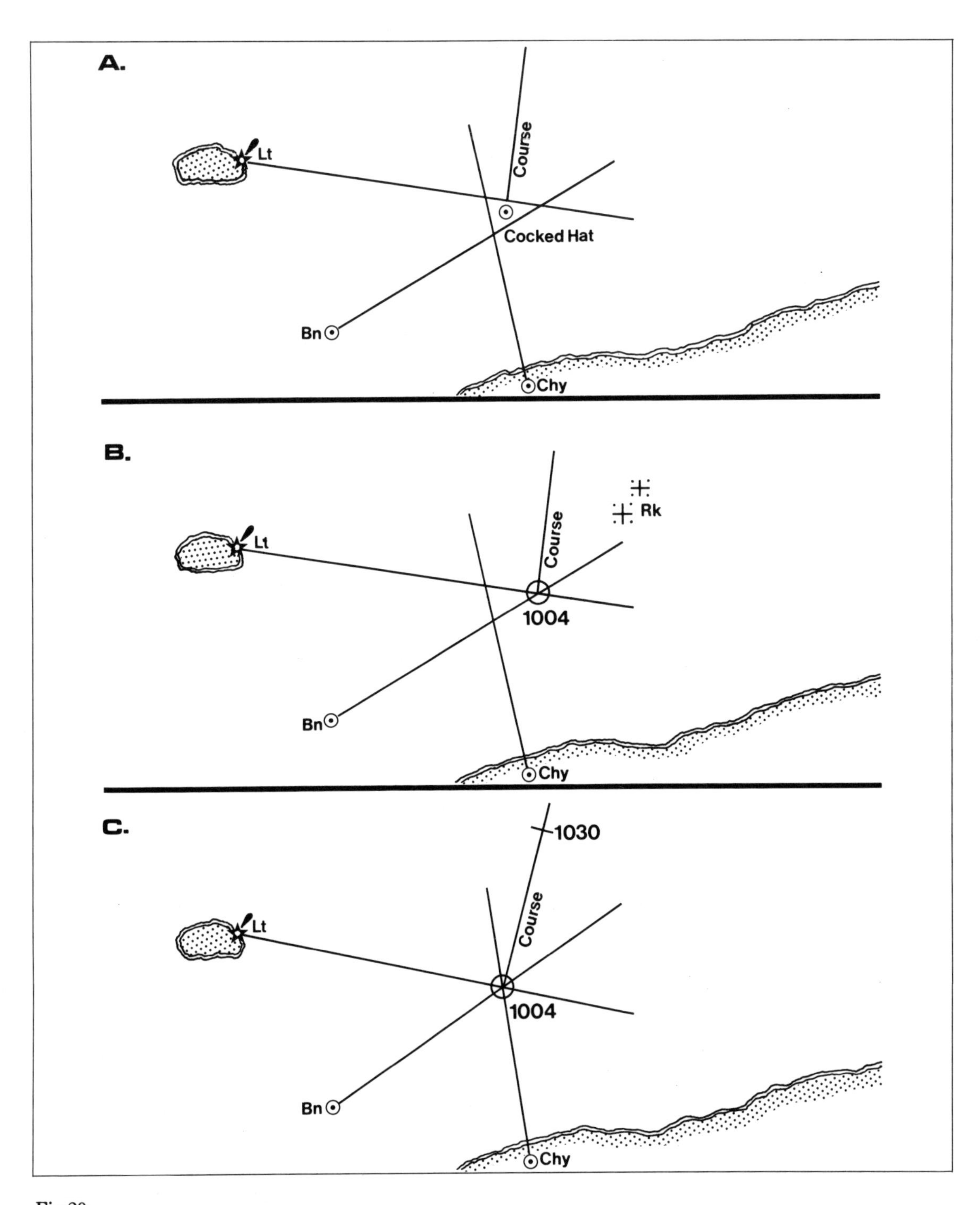

Fig 20
a *A cocked hat fix*
b *Setting a safe course from a cocked hat fix*
c *A good three bearing fix*

Look at Fig 19. Using a hand bearing compass and adjusting for magnetic variation, the navigator has found that the true bearings of Flat Rock and Tiri Lights are 270° and 220° respectively. The fix is identified by a circle where the bearing lines cross, and the time noted. To get the bearing lines, the navigator had to look from his position in the boat towards the two objects. To see Flat Rock, he had to look due west. If he had fired a rifle at the Light, the bullet would have moved along the line on the chart. So any bearings obtained are from the boat towards the object, and must be plotted as such.

Using a hand bearing compass in a pitching or rolling boat is not easy, and any bearings obtained may not be quite accurate. In this case the resulting fix would be slightly in error. To try and cancel out any such problem, it is usual to take the bearings of three charted objects at all times and if there is an error the three bearing lines will not cross at the same point. An example is shown in Fig 20a; the small triangle is called a cocked hat. The actual position is taken as being at the centre of the cocked hat, except if close to danger, when to be on the safe side the point closest to that danger is taken as being the position, as in Fig 20b.

The most accurate fix by cross bearings is if they are at right angles to one another, when any error in taking the bearing has the least effect on the plotted position.

Notice that in Fig 19, the phrase 'angle of cut' is used. This is the angle between any two position lines, and in Fig 19 the angle of cut is 50°. The minimum angle of cut acceptable to get a reliable fix is 30 degrees, especially if only two bearings are taken.

The object whose bearing is changing most rapidly should be taken last, and this moment should be used as being the time of the fix. This overcomes the practical problem of not being able to take the bearings at exactly the same time.

The running fix

Although a fix is usually described as being the point of cut of two or more position lines taken simultaneously, there are occasions when only one suitable object is visible. When coasting by night and when lighthouses are spaced well apart, only one may be visible at any given period. A position can be found using just one object by using a running or transferred position line fix, and this is done as follows.

Take and plot a bearing on the chart. Then wait until the bearing has changed by a minimum of 30 degrees, to get an acceptable angle of cut, and take and plot a second bearing. In both cases note the time and the log reading. Comparing these gives the distance covered between the two times, and the boat's course is known. The first position line is then transferred in the same direction and for the same distance that the vessel has travelled between taking the two bearings. As the vessel was somewhere on the first position line and as every point on that line has been moved in the same direction for the same distance, it effectively remains a position line. As the boat is somewhere on the line after transferring, the

Fig 21
A running fix

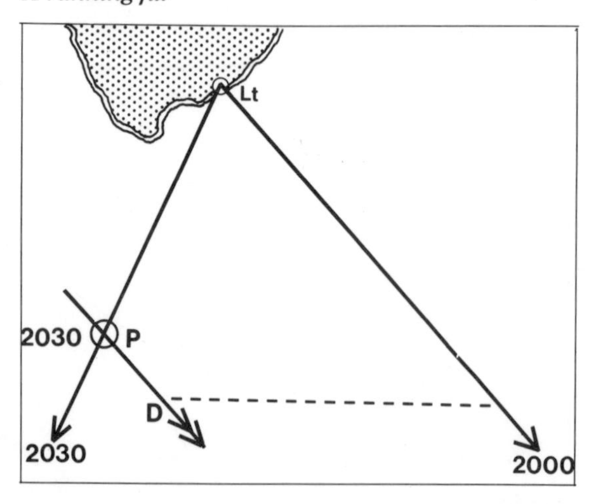

point at which it cuts the second bearing line is a fix.

In Fig 21, a bearing of the light was taken at 2000. A second bearing taken at 2030 has been plotted as shown. Then from *any* point on the first line lay off the boat's course and mark the distance travelled along it – point D in the diagram. Align the parallel rulers to the first line, and transfer it through point D. The point of intersection, P, is the fix at 2030. However, any tidal stream effect has not been taken into account, and if the vessel is in strong tidal waters the running fix should only be used as a guide to position, though a much better one than an inaccurate DR.

A transferred position line should not be transferred twice. If in Fig 22 a third bearing of the light was taken at 2115, then the 2030 position line would be transferred to give the running fix at that time.

I am convinced that a major part of the problem when learning coastal navigation is that the student ends up with too many lines drawn all over the chart. The moment this happens, the picture becomes confused, and attempting to understand the procedure being explained is well-nigh impossible.

A cardinal rule in chartwork is to erase all unnecessary lines as you go along (see Fig 23).

The next two fixes are included for the sake of completeness. They should *never* be used if there is any appreciable cross tide or if the boat is making much leeway.

Doubling the angle on the bow

The emphasis here is not on the use of true bearings but on the change of angle of a shore mark relative to the bow when the boat is on a steady course. Look at Fig 24. At 1400 the tower is 30° on the bow and by 1430 this angle has doubled to 60°. As the two bearings and the course line form an isosceles triangle the distance from the tower at the time the angle has doubled is equal to the distance run between the times of the two bearings. If any initial angle on the bow is doubled, the distance travelled by log is the distance from the object at the time of the second bearing.

Fig 22
The 2030 bearing line has been transferred

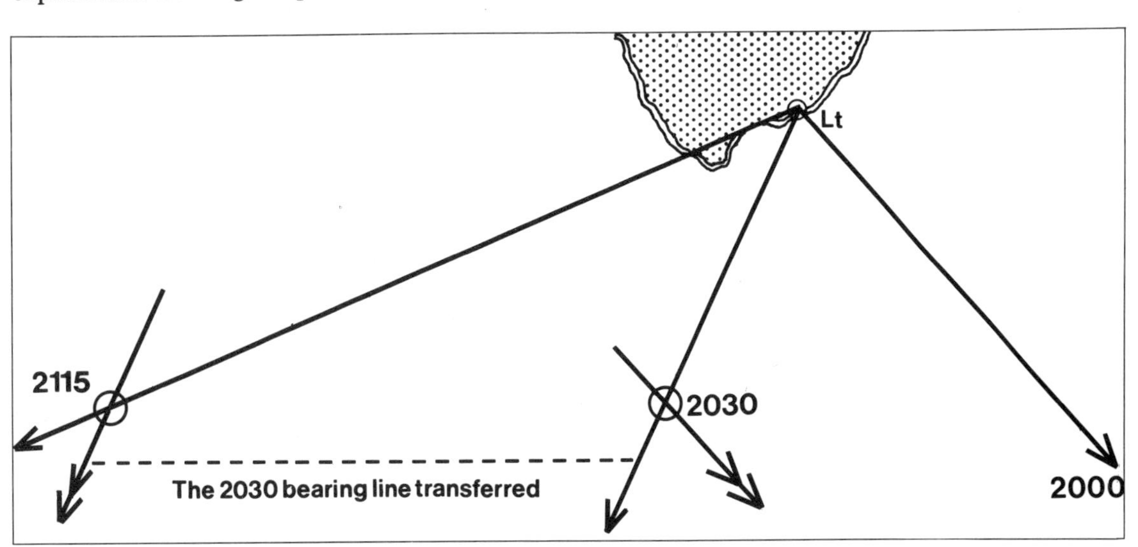

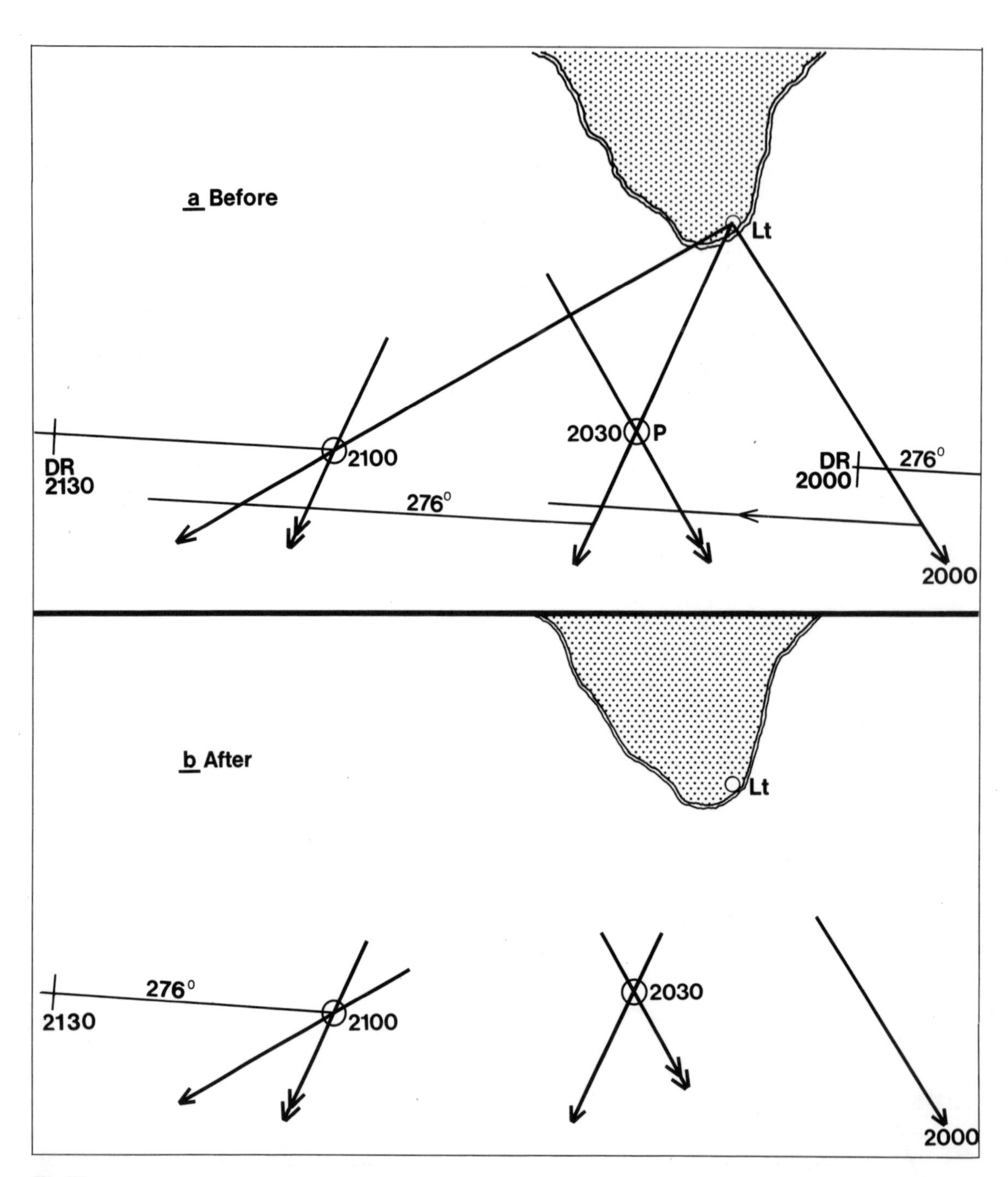

Fig 23
a *Before*
b *After*
Before and after erasing unnecessary lines on a chart

Four-point bearing

This is a special case of doubling the angle on the bow. If a fixing mark is 45 degrees (four points) on the bow and course is maintained until the object is 90 degrees on the bow – i.e. abeam – then not only has the angle been doubled but the boat will be the same distance off the mark as the distance run between bearings.

In theory a compass can be dispensed with by finding two pieces of standing rigging on the boat which when in transit with an object mean that it is 45 or 90 degrees on the bow. In fact, unless the boat is in calm water and perfectly steady, this procedure would result in a most inaccurate fix.

Running fix with change of course

Sometimes it may not be possible to steer one steady course between taking the first and second bearings during a running fix. The basis of the running fix is that the first position line is transferred to allow for the boat's movement between the times of taking the first and second bearings of the single fixing mark. Whether the boat remains on one course, or steers several courses in the period, the first position line must be moved to allow for the course or courses steered and the distance the vessel has moved along each course.

For example, a vessel on course 090°T at speed 6 knots finds the bearing of a light to be 220°T at 1115. At 1125 the vessel alters course to 170°T at the same speed. At 1145 the light bears 260°T.

To find the boat's position at 1145:

1 Plot the first bearing of the light on the chart.
2 Plot the second bearing.
3 From any point on the first position line, lay off the first course. The boat was steering 090° between 1115 and 1125, which is ten minutes. This is one mile at six knots.
4 Mark this distance along the first course line, AB in Fig 26.
5 From B lay off the second course (170°).
6 Between 1125 and 1145 the boat travels two miles. Mark this distance along the second course line, which gives point C.
7 Using the parallel rulers, transfer the first position line through C.
8 The position or fix is where the transferred position line cuts the second bearing taken at 1145, because the total movement of the boat has been allowed for.

Fig 24
Doubling the angle on the bow

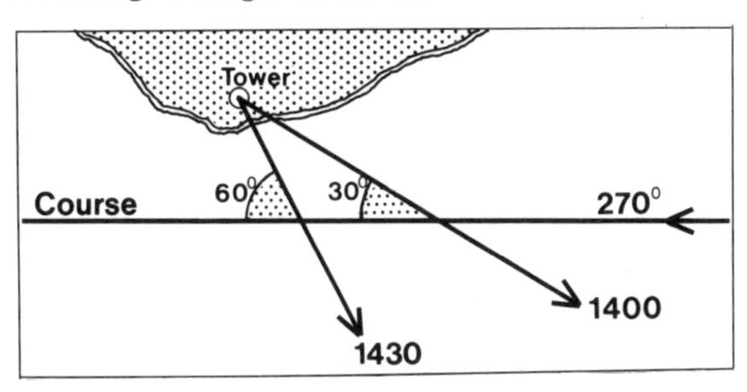

Fig 25
The four-point bearing

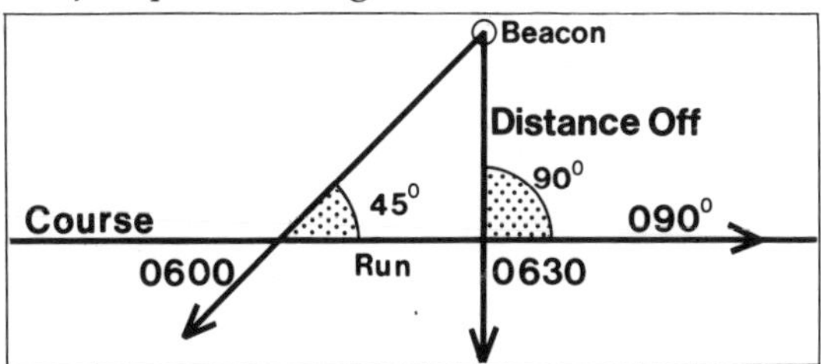

Fig 26
Running fix with change of course

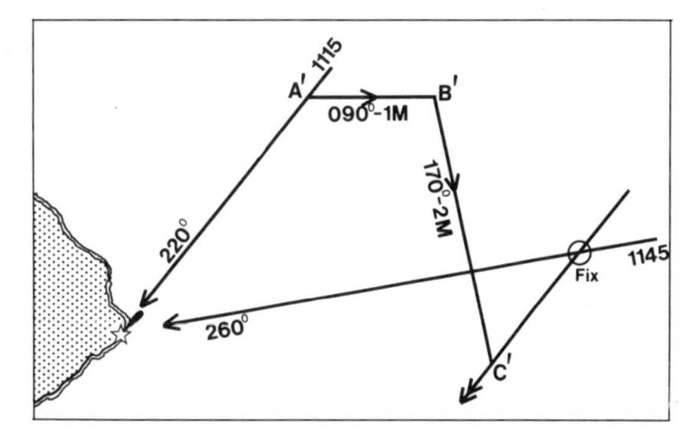

If three or more courses are steered between the times of taking the first and second bearings then the distance travelled on each course is calculated. The third course is laid off from the end of the second course line and so on.

The reader should understand that the line ABC in the diagram is not the dead reckoning track. A is any convenient point on the first position line. The above example is shown again in Fig 27, except that in this diagram the first course has been plotted from a different point A on the first position line. Comparison of the two figures will show that the 1145 fix is in exactly the same position in both diagrams and that the lines ABC and A′B′C′ are equal in length and direction.

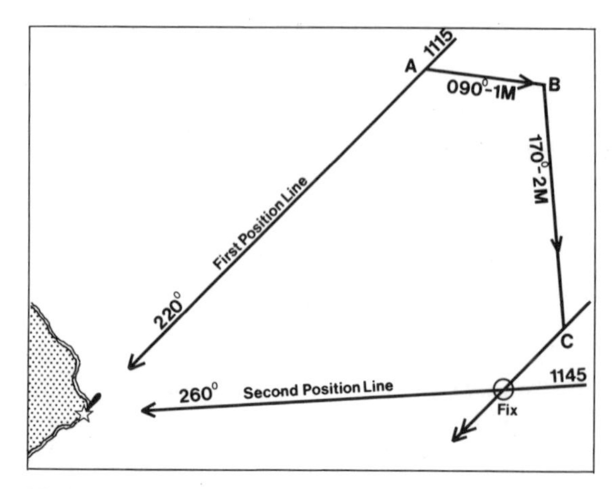

Fig 27
The course in Fig 26 has been plotted from a different point A on the first position line.

Transferring a position line to allow for tidal stream

This procedure is similar to the running fix with a change of course. The first position line is transferred to allow for the boat's movement and also the movement of the tidal stream. In Fig 28 a boat is steering 090°T at 8 knots. Tidal stream is estimated setting 130°T at 3 knots. At 0400 a lighthouse bore 062°T. At 0430 the same light was bearing 320°T.

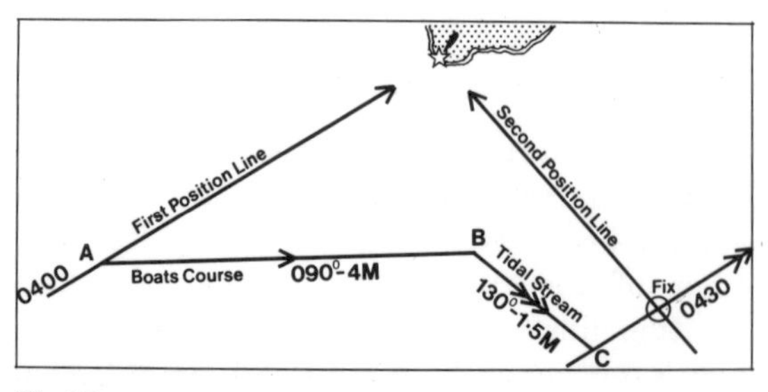

Fig 28
Transferring a position line to allow for tidal stream

1 A is any convenient point on the first position line.
2 AB is the boat's course and distance in 30 minutes – 090°, 4M.
3 BC is the direction and distance the tidal stream will set the boat in 30 minutes – 130°, 1.5M.
4 The fix is found by transferring the first position line through C.

The same construction is used if in a known ocean curren .

Frequency of fixes

I am sure that some readers have spent many years cruising in their own home waters with never a DR position or fix on their charts. I do not advocate that from now on it is mandatory to keep a constant track on the chart with a plethora of fix positions in well-known and presumably safe waters. However, only with practice comes proficiency in taking and plotting a fix. With proficiency comes confidence that your answers are right. There is little point in starting the procedure in unfamiliar, and perhaps dangerous, waters when you are not even sure if the positions you put on the chart are correct. A false sense of security is more dangerous than admitting that you haven't a clue where you are and proceeding with caution. So the place to learn and master the procedure is the well-known home cruising ground. Then when sailing further afield it will be with the calm assurance that you know what you are doing and, better still, that your

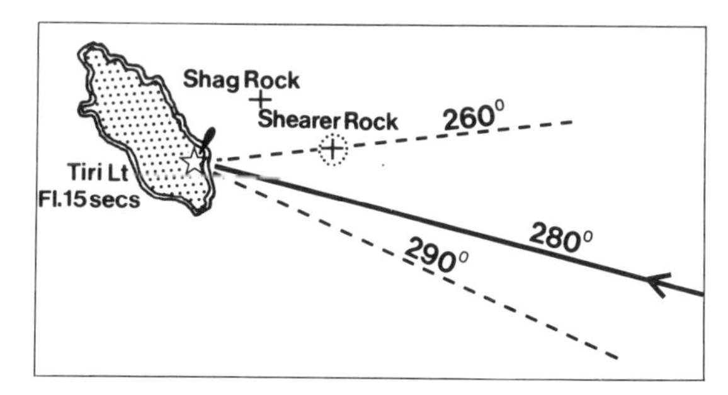

Fig 29
The clearing bearing

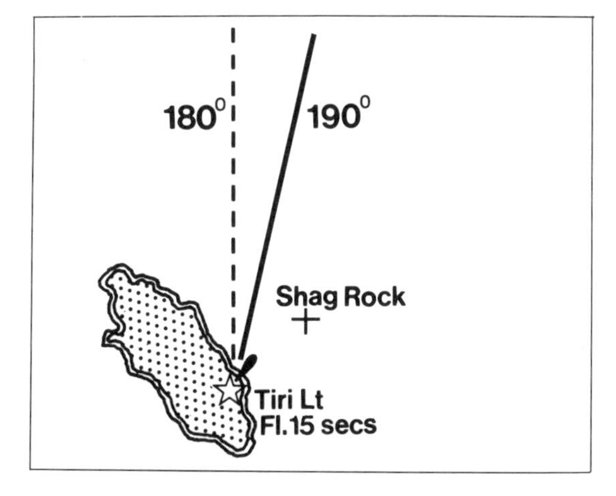

Fig 30
Clearing bearing 190° or less to pass Shag Rock

fixes are accurate. The name of the game in navigation is 'make it easy on yourself'.

When coasting offshore, the position should be checked hourly; if closer inshore, perhaps every half hour. When coming into unfamiliar estuaries and bays it may be necessary to fix every fifteen minutes. If in shoal waters with a strong tidal stream, it may be prudent to step the rate up even higher. The frequency of fixing is solely dependent on the particular situation.

Although fixing is the only way of finding your actual position, knowing where the boat is *not* can be very useful in certain circumstances. If sailing in a bay which has one underwater danger, being able to guarantee that the vessel is nowhere near it can be just as reassuring as knowing the vessel's exact position.

The clearing bearing

In Fig 29, if a boat was approaching Tiri Lighthouse from eastward, Shearer Rock could be a danger if one's exact position were not known. The dotted line shows that if the vessel were steering 260° with the light directly ahead, a grounding would be inevitable. On the other hand if the approach were made along the 280° track, the rock would be passed safely, leaving it half a mile to the north. If the light bearing ahead was 290°, the vessel would pass even further south of the danger. As long as the bearing of the light is 280°, *or greater*, the vessel must be in safe water.

If the vessel were approaching Tiri Lighthouse from the north, by keeping the light bearing 190° *or less*, the rock will be passed in safety.

At this stage you may think that taking a fix tells you where the boat is. It does not; it tells you where the boat *was*.

Once you have taken the bearings, you must plot them on the chart. An expert can plot three bearings in about 45 seconds. Until you are proficient in the use of the plotting instruments, it may take two or three minutes before those bearings are translated into three lines on the chart. In either case the resulting point of intersection or fix is history.

Granted, if you are in open water with the nearest danger some miles away, this fact is not particularly significant. But in shoal waters and close to hidden dangers, the navigator's first concern should not be where he was, or even is, but where he will be in the immediate future. So plotting the fix does not finish until a dead reckoning track based on the fix is laid off on the chart, and the navigator satisfies himself that the boat is quite safe on its present course.

Choosing your moment

The timing of a fix should not be a spur-of-the-moment decision. Time can be wasted in trying to identify indistinct objects prior to taking any bearings. Much time can be saved by actually planning the next fix as soon as the previous one is on the chart.

There are two ways of getting a position. The first is to wander up on deck with a hand bearing compass and look around for some prominent fixing marks. After wasting a minute or so searching, you may be lucky enough to find what you're after. Even then you may be left with a nagging doubt that the beacon or church spire you used when plotting on the chart was not the one you actually took.

The second method is to have a good look at the chart beforehand and decide what marks could be the most useful. While it may be convenient to take the bearings exactly on the hour or half hour, an additional few minutes' delay may mean that a more conspicuous mark is then visible, or that the angle of cut between two objects will have increased from the marginal 30 degrees to a more accurate 35 degrees. The accuracy of a fix is the prime concern – not the convenience to the navigator of the time that it is taken.

Having said that, and all else being equal, allowing exactly six minutes between two successive fixes gives a quick easy check on speed. Six minutes is one tenth of an hour, so the distance between these fixes in tenths of a mile equals the speed in knots. For example, if a boat travels .7 of a mile in six minutes, then the speed over the ground is 7 knots.

Transits

Any two objects that are in line as you look at them are said to be in transit. If the objects are marked on the chart, the vessel lies somewhere on the extension of the line joining the two, and is a position line. Harbour authorities set up pairs of marks which, when kept in transit, lead a ship down the centre of the main channel. The rear mark is higher than the front and each has its own distinctive light. A vessel can negotiate the channel at night by keeping these leading lights, as they are called, in transit.

The harbour chart usually has the line

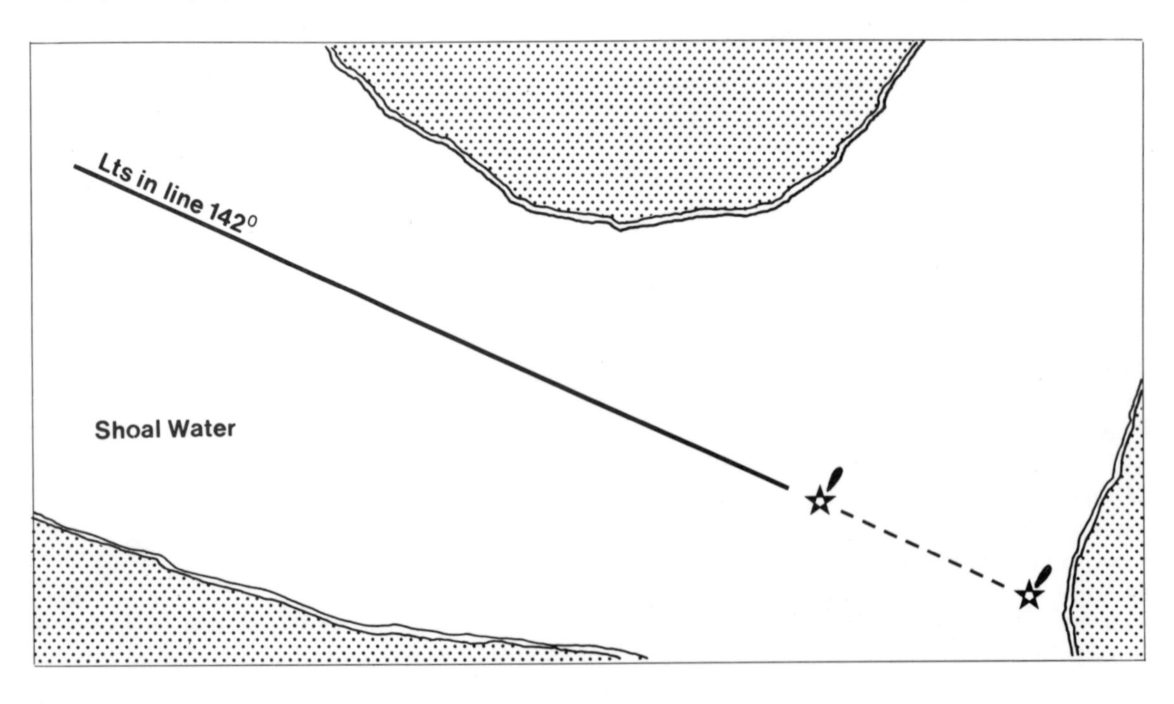

Fig 31
Keeping leading lights in transit

joining the lights printed with a caption such as 'Lights in line 142°' (see Fig 31). These leading marks have been set up for a specific purpose, but by selecting any two charted objects and merely watching until they come into line the navigator knows that he is on the seaward side of the line joining them. Moreover, if the boat is then steered to keep the objects in line, it must be moving along the transit.

In Fig 32 the line joining the tower and water tank is well to the north of the sunken rock. By keeping the two in line, the navigator can guarantee to clear the danger as the boat passes the unseen rock.

A transit can also be used in fixing as it gives a position line, independent of magnetic variation or any compass error. Indeed no instrument is needed other than the naked eye watching until the selected objects come into line.

A ship leaving harbour uses the same leading lights as it does when entering, but it keeps them in transit astern. Do not fall into the trap of vainly searching the chart for suitable objects ahead while completely overlooking a perfectly good pair of marks behind the boat.

Measured distance

The extreme accuracy of the moment of transit of two well-defined marks is used in defining a measured distance, usually one nautical mile, for checking speed by log. Two separate pairs of marks are set up on shore which, when in transit, show each end of the measured mile. Two runs are made, one in each direction, to compensate for the effect of tidal stream. The courses steered are at right angles to the line of the transits. The time taken for each run is noted and the speed by log recorded. The speed on each run is then found, and these two speeds averaged out to give speed through the water, which is what the log should have been showing. Any difference is converted to a percentage error, and this can be used to give true speed when using speed by the log for dead reckoning purposes.

Fig 32
Use of a transit to pass an unseen danger safely

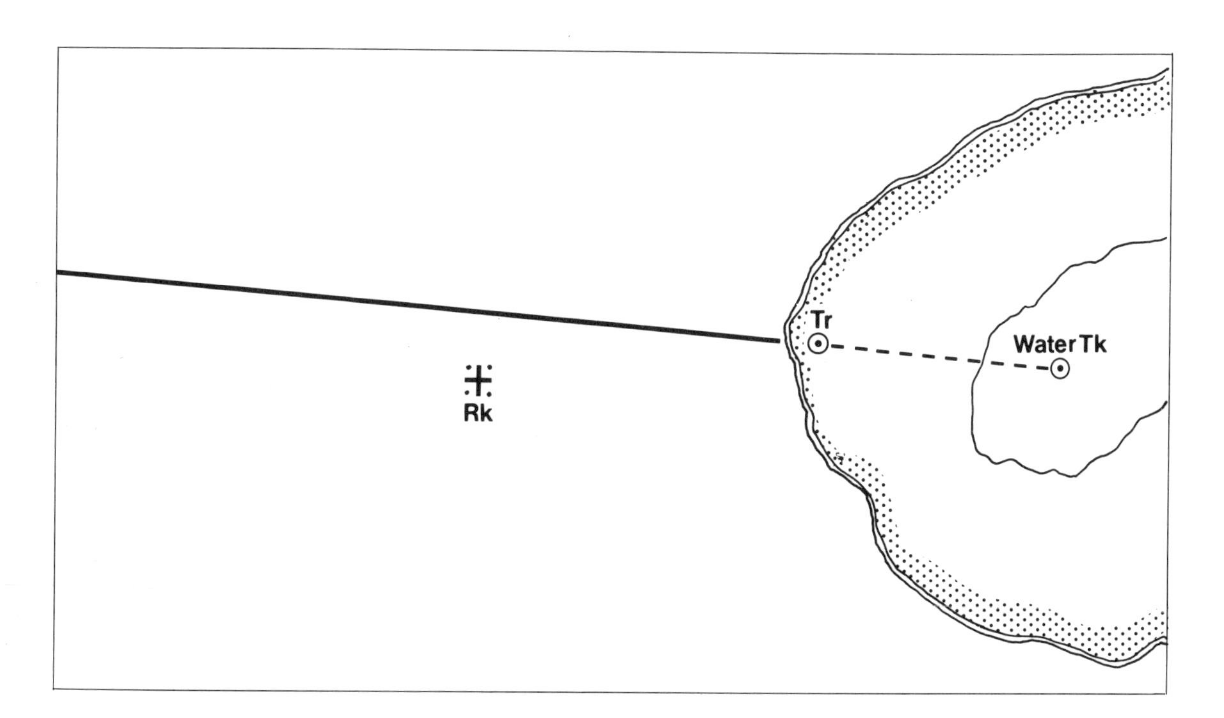

For example, say a boat does two runs over the measured mile. The first against the tide takes 12 minutes, the second 8½ minutes. The log shows a speed of 6.6 knots on both runs.

Speed on Run 1:	
one mile in 12 mins	5 knots
Speed on Run 2:	
one mile in 8½ mins	7 knots
Average	12 ÷ 2
Boat speed through the water	6 knots
Speed by log	6.6 knots
Log is over-reading by 0.6 knot	
i.e. .6 of a knot in 6 knots	10 per cent

The correct speed is found by multiplying the log speed by $\frac{100}{110}$

e.g. $\frac{6.6 \times 100}{110} = 6$ knots

Using total time and total distance to get the answer on the measured mile runs is *not* correct. Assume that a boat is actually doing 12 knots and the tide is 6 knots. With the tide against, the boat will take 10 minutes to run the mile, as it will only be effectively making 6 knots. When running with the tide it will be moving between the marks at 18 knots and take 3⅓ minutes.

Total distance	2 miles
Total time	13⅓ minutes
Apparent speed	9 knots

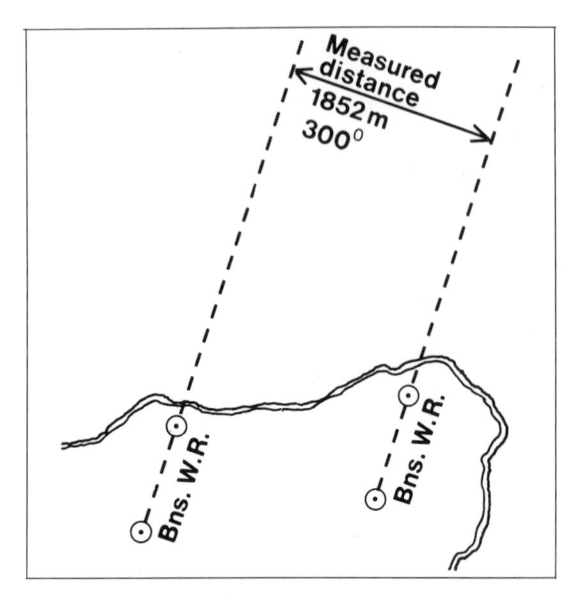

Fig 33
The measured mile

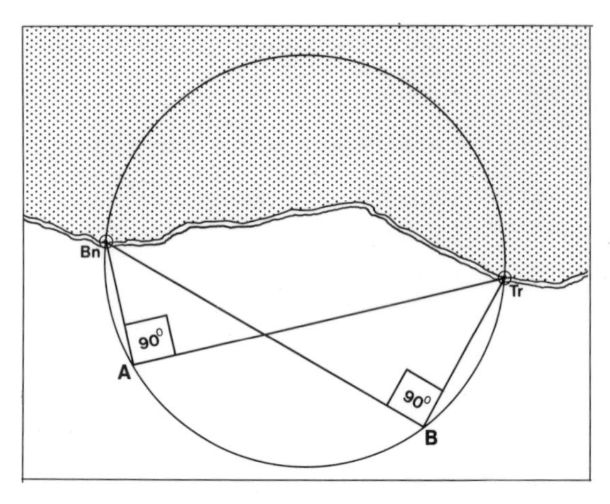

Fig 34
Horizontal sextant angles

COASTAL FIXING: SEXTANT METHODS

The use of a sextant in coastal navigation not only extends the range of fixing techniques available to the navigator but also gives greater accuracy in position fixing.

The angle between any two charted objects in roughly the same horizontal plane can be measured with a sextant which gives a circle of position or curved position line. In Fig 34 the angle between the tower and the beacon is 90° at both points A and B which lie on the circle shown. This circle passes through the two charted objects and the angle between them is 90° from any point on the circle. If three shore objects are selected and the angles between the centre and each outer object measured with a sextant, two position circles are obtained. The point of intersection is a fix.

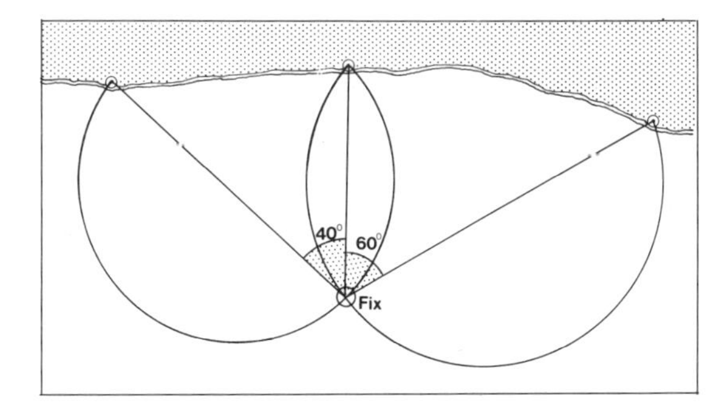

Fig 35
Horizontal angle fix using three marks

Plotting the fix

This can be done without drawing the circles on the chart. The two angles can be drawn on tracing paper, radiating from a common point as in Fig 36a. The paper is then placed over the chart, with the centre line on the centre object, and then adjusted so that each line crosses one of the fixing marks. The boat's position is then at 0 in the diagram and can be pricked through on to the chart with a point of the dividers.

More convenient methods of plotting this type of fix by using either a Douglas protractor or station pointer are given in Appendix 4. In addition a particular method of using the circles of position obtained from a horizontal sextant angle, which gives the fastest and most accurate method of manual fixing, is explained.

The advantage of this method of plotting a fix is that an extremely accurate fix is possible because the sextant can be read more accurately than a compass. Such a fix is independent of magnetic variation or compass error.

However, the system does have disadvantages – three suitable fixing marks must be chosen from the chart. The fix may also take longer to plot than would be necessary using other methods.

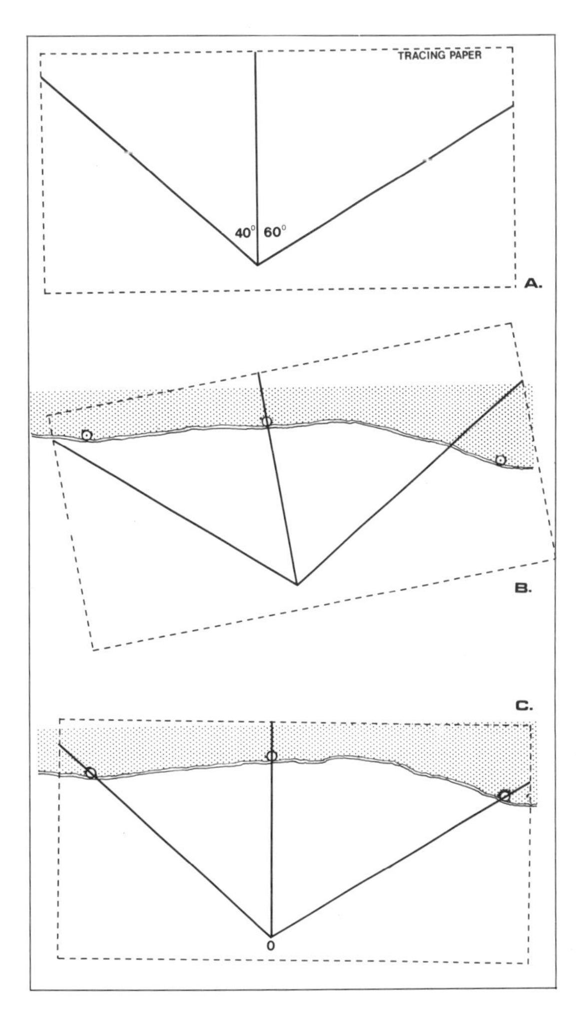

Fig 36
Stages in plotting a horizontal sextant angle fix
a *The two angles are drawn on tracing paper*
b *Place the paper over the chart with the centre line on the centre fixing mark*
c *Slide the paper until each line is over a fixing mark as shown. The fix is at the point 0.*

Choosing suitable fixing marks

Look at Fig 37. The three marks should either be in a straight line, or the centre mark should be closer to the observer than the other two. The angle between each set of marks should be a minimum of 30 degrees.

The reason for possible inaccuracy in the fix if unsuitable marks are used is explained in Appendix 4.

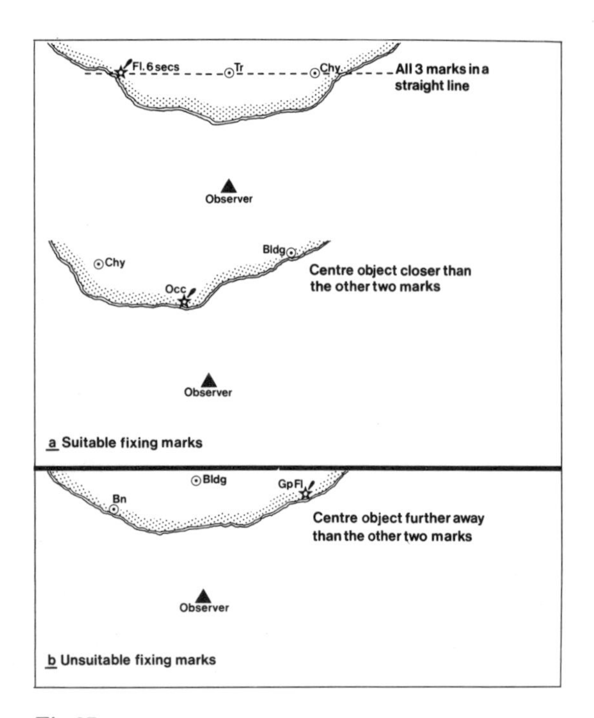

Fig 37
Horizontal sextant angles
a *Suitable fixing marks*
b *Unsuitable fixing marks*

Fig 38
Vertical sextant angle

Finding distance by vertical sextant angle

Most large ships and some yachts have the advantage of radar to measure distances from land or other vessels. The yachtsman can find the distance from a lighthouse as long as both the light and the shoreline below it can be clearly seen.

In Fig 38 SB is the distance from the point directly below the base of the light to the vessel, and is part of the right-angled triangle SLB. The side SL is the height of the light which can be found from the chart or light list. The angle at B, which is the angle between the light and the shoreline directly below it, can be measured with the sextant.

Any set of nautical tables will have a section called 'Distance by Vertical Angle' which gives the distance off from the sextant angle and height of the object in metres or feet. For example, the tables tell us that for a 91-metre light and an angle of 0° 50′, the distance is 3.4M. With the lighthouse as centre, and using a radius of 3.4M, a circle or part circle can be scribed on the chart. This is a curved position line, sometimes called a range arc.

There is a bonus here in that to take the vertical sextant angle the lighthouse was

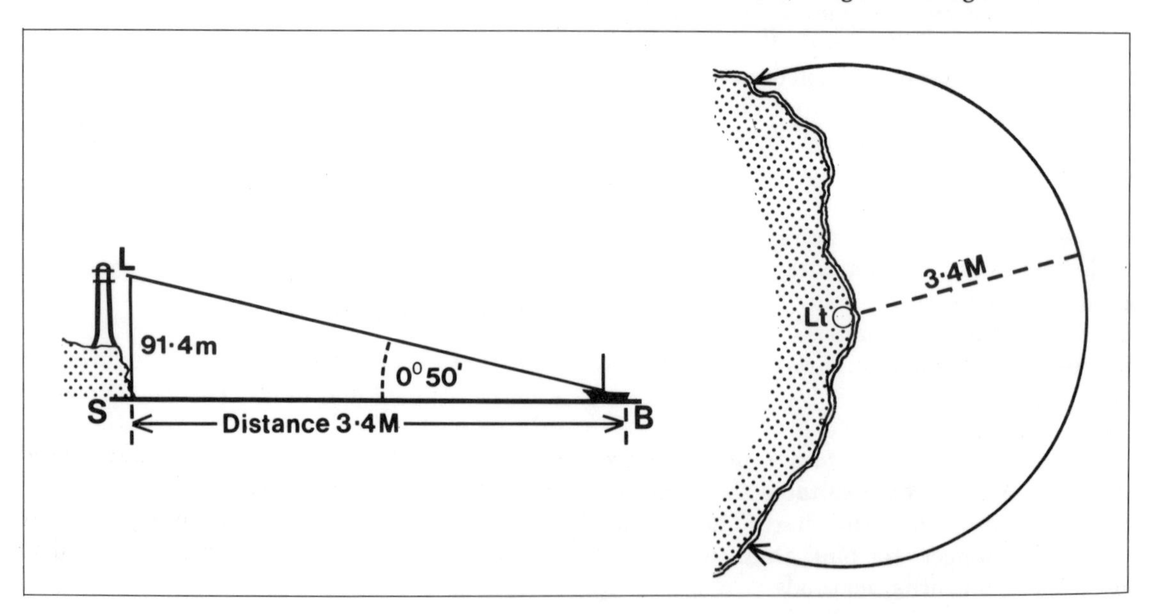

obviously visible, in which case a bearing can be taken at the same time. This results in a fix from *only one object*, consisting of a bearing and a range arc.

Rule of thumb

The following so-called 'five-six-five rule' can be used to find the distance if a set of tables is unavailable. However this can be used only with the older fathom charts where the heights of lights are given in feet.

$$\frac{\text{Height of the light in feet}}{\text{Sextant angle in minutes}} \times .565 = \text{Distance off in nautical miles}$$

Using the previous example we get:

$$\frac{300}{50} \times .565 = 3.39\text{M}$$

Fig 39
A fix from one object. The light is bearing 280° (T), range 3.4 M.

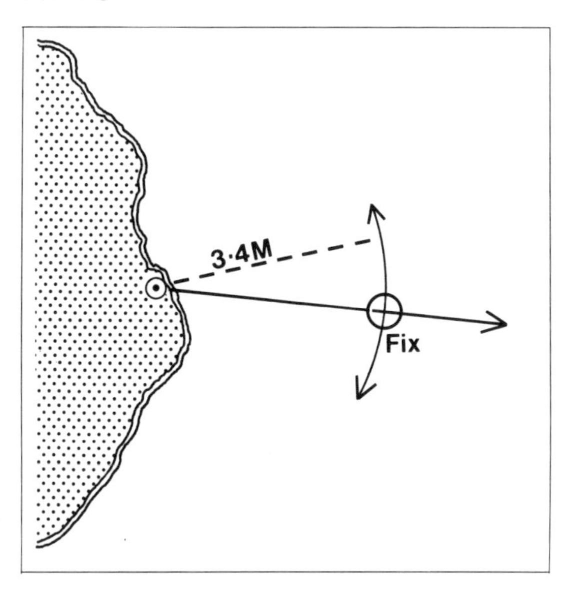

One of the minor drawbacks of the gradual replacement of the older fathom charts by the new metric series, where heights are given in metres, is that the navigator must learn two rules. When the height is in metres the formula for finding distance is:

$$\text{Distance off in miles} = \frac{h}{.54N}$$

where N = sextant angle in minutes
300 feet equals 91.44 metres, so the example would be worked as follows:

$$\frac{91.44}{(0.54 \times 50)} = 3.386 = 3.39\text{M}$$

Danger angle

Like the hand bearing compass, the sextant can be used to keep the vessel clear of a danger without the navigator having to spend time at the chart table plotting fixes in what might be a tricky situation. If there were rocks one mile to seaward of a light, as shown in Fig 40, the navigator might decide not to get closer than 2 miles from the coast. If the charted height was 300ft (91.4m) the vertical sextant angle at 2 miles would be 1°25′. This 'danger angle' is set on the sextant, and as long as the light does not come into coincidence with the shoreline, the vessel is outside 2 miles.

Fig 40
Danger angle

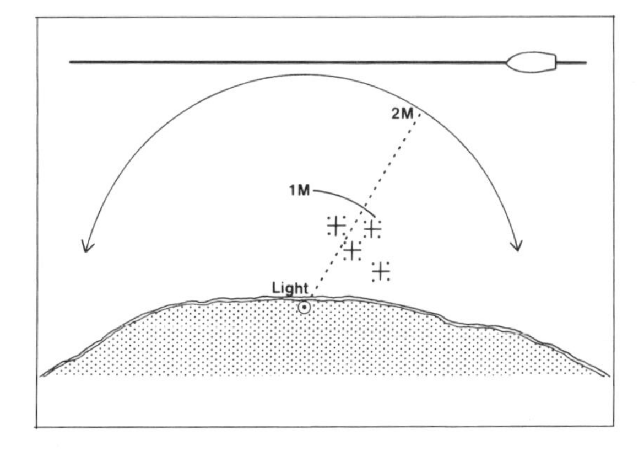

Height of tide

Charted heights are given above the level of mean high water springs, (MHWS) so as the tide falls, the height of the light increases. This can be ignored as the slight error introduced is on the safe side, i.e. the distance found by the vertical sextant angle shows that the vessel is closer to the danger than it actually is.

Other coastal fixes

As discussed earlier, the most common type of fix results from plotting two or more bearing lines. However the vessel's position can be found by the intersection of any two or more position lines, such as the curves of constant angle used in horizontal sextant angle fixing. The use of a sextant further extends the range of fixing methods available to the navigator, and the position in Fig 39 was found by crossing a straight line (bearing) with a curved position line (range arc).

In Fig 41, the navigator has used the distance from the two lighthouses to give a fix by crossing two range arcs.

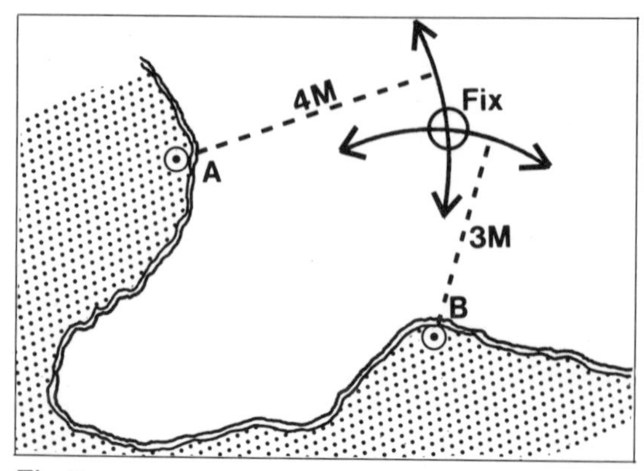

Fig 41
Range arc fix. Light A: range 4 miles. Light B: Range 3 miles

Big ships can fix by using radar to find the distance and crossing range arcs of prominent points of land fifteen or more miles away. While the average yachtsman does not have this aid to navigation, the principle of using range arcs should be established.

In Fig 42 the range arc of 5 miles radius is quite clearly a curve and part of a circle. However, it would not be apparent to the casual observer that the 15-mile range arc is curved and part of a circle of radius 15 miles centred on the light. It looks remarkably like a straight line. In other words, the greater the range, the less the curvature of any small section of the circumference of the range or position circle.

Fig 42
The difference in the curvature of the range or position circle circumference at a five mile and a fifteen mile range arc

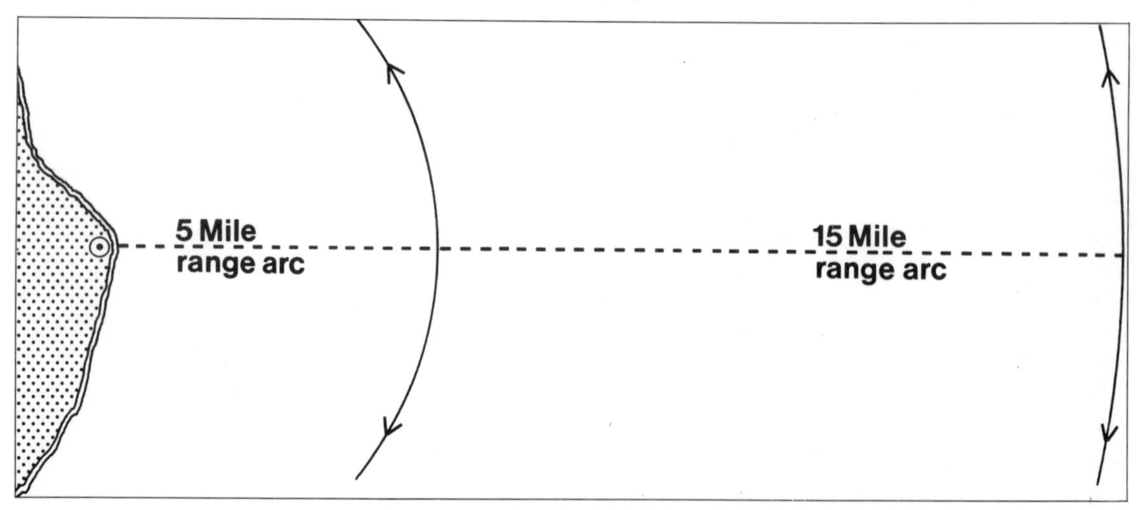

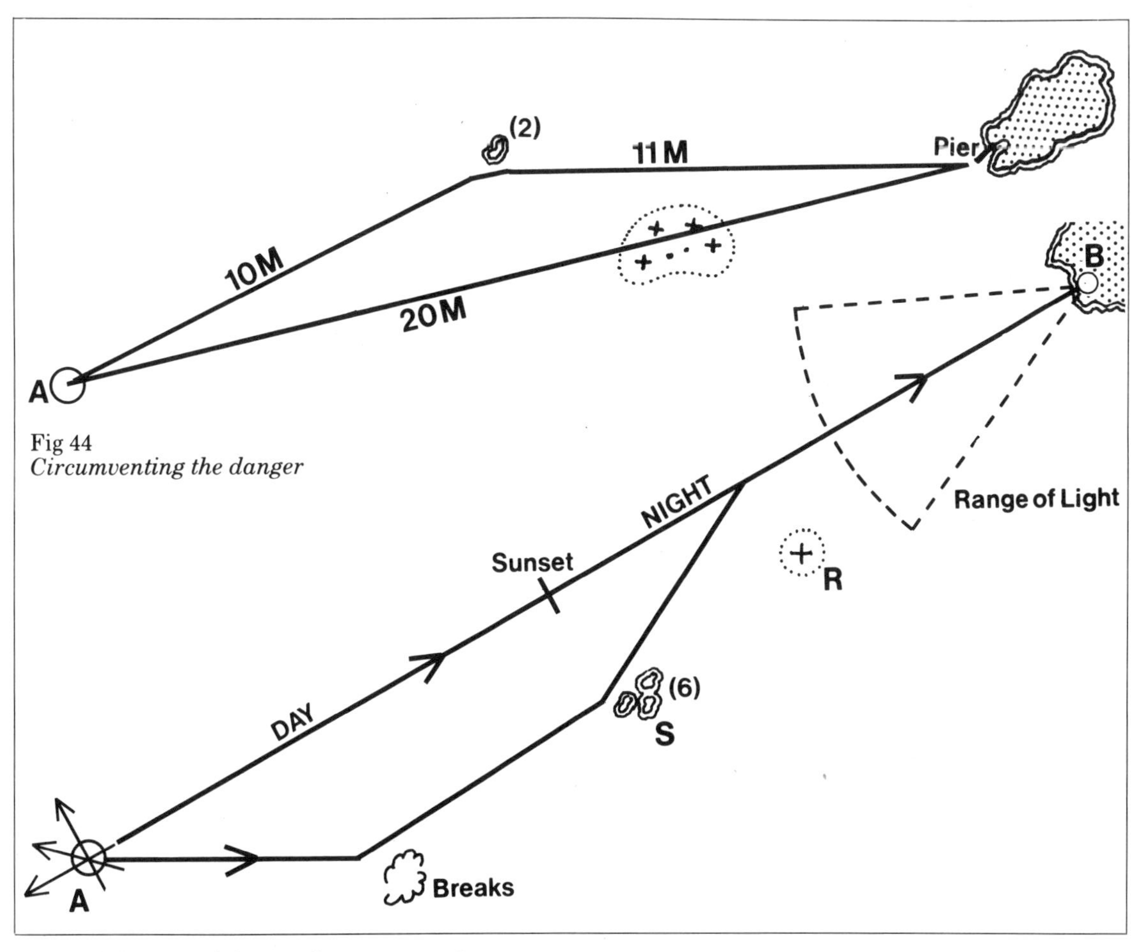

Fig 44
Circumventing the danger

Fig 43 *Direct track is over dangerous rocks*

Head for the rocks!

Up to now the emphasis has been on keeping the vessel in safe waters by using any or all of the position finding methods to keep a check on the track, and choosing courses to counteract the effects of tidal stream or wind. The guiding principle has been to keep away from dangers.

There is a saying that occasionally the best form of defence is attack. The same is true of navigation. The most worrying time afloat is when you are not quite certain of your position and you think the boat will clear that charted rock, but will it? If the danger is actually sighted, all doubt vanishes. You know exactly where you are, but I would agree that the last thing to do would be to go and find a rock a metre or so below the surface. The first time you'll see it is when you put your boat on it.

In Fig 43, the vessel is at fix A and is going to the island 20 miles away. The direct track is shown, but it passes over some dangerous underwater rocks. The navigator notices that 5 miles to the NW of the rocks there is a small islet with a chart height of 2 metres. It would not be visible from the direct track. The navigator sets course for the islet. He does not just get close enough to sight it, because even if he used it for a running fix, any unknown tidal stream would still leave the exact position in doubt. He passes perhaps no more than half a mile off. The total distance would be 21 miles, an increase of only 1 mile or 5 per cent. Increase in peace of mind, 100 per cent!

A different set of circumstances is illustrated in Fig 44. The line AB is the direct course to the destination. The problem here is to keep clear of the dangerous rock marked R. To complicate the issue, the rock must be passed in darkness, before the light is sighted.

Inspection of the chart shows that there is a small group of above-water rocks to the southwest at S. To fix the vessel's position en route by finding these would be a good idea by day, but again the DR track shows that they would have to be approached after sunset and to do this by dead reckoning from the starting position would not be safe. Further to the southwest is a small shoal, which breaks in all sea conditions, and at this stage of the journey it is still daylight. So course would be set to find the shoal.

Once sighted, the short distance to the rocks could be covered safely by dead reckoning. Another short leg by dead reckoning, based on the known position at S, enables the boat to pass the underwater rock in the dark with safety. So again, a small diversion from the direct track to deliberately find two dangers virtually guarantees that the main danger, the sunken rock, will be safely passed.

I must make it very clear that this procedure could only be adopted in good visibility. If visibility was restricted, or there was a large sea running due to a recent storm, the only safe track would be well to the north of all three dangers.

The transition period between coastal and celestial fixing

Imagine this scene. You are actually under way on your first ocean voyage. The coastline disappears and the hilltops seem to sink into the sea. Finally it happens – for perhaps the first time in your life there is nothing but sea and sky around you.

From the navigation point of view this is a danger period. The coast has been safely cleared, with perhaps a thousand miles of ocean between you and your destination. With no immediate problems on hand it is easy to fall into the trap of deciding to start the detailed ocean navigation later.

There is no one point at which it can be said that coastal navigation stops and ocean navigation begins. The basic techniques are exactly the same. The boat's position is forecast ahead by dead reckoning. In some ways this is made easier away from the coast because the boat may be on the same course, or at least on the same tack, for long periods. In one ocean race I sailed in, many boats were on the same tack for almost six days, except for one gybe. Log speed or distance by log must be as accurate as possible to help the navigator maintain a good dead reckoning track. The method of finding any log error by running the measured mile has been explained earlier (page 35).

The boat's actual position is again checked from time to time by fixes. The major difference between coastal and ocean navigation is that in ocean navigation the position is found by using the sun, stars, planets or moon to get two or more position lines on the chart. Some yachts have radio aids fitted, such as Loran C or Omega receivers. At the time of writing these retail at around $2 000, or £1 600, so most yachtsmen will be relying on the traditional methods of finding position at sea for many years yet. It may be a surprise to the reader to know that in at least one ocean racer world-beater fitted with Omega, and in many of the world's submarines fitted with complex navigation equipment, celestial sights of one form or another are used to give a check on the accuracy of the equipment.

The groundwork for celestial fixing should be laid when still within easy fixing distance from the coast, which could be an hour or more before losing the distinctive navigation marks.

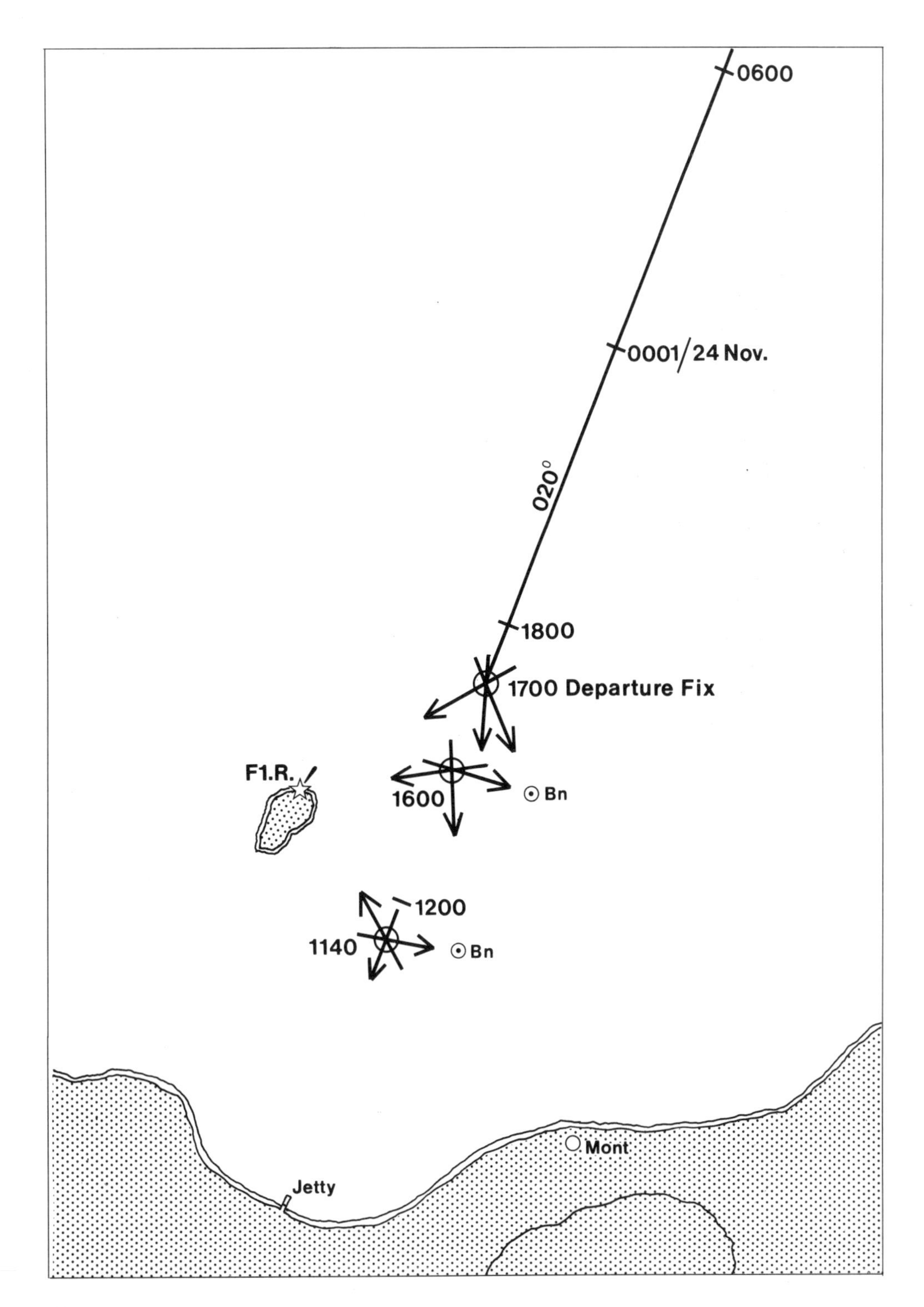

Fig 45
A good three bearing departure fix at 1700

One of the most important positions the navigator ever plots is called the 'departure fix'. It must be as accurate as possible, because the ocean dead reckoning track will be started from this point. This could well mean that the navigator ceases taking coastal fixes when land is still in sight, but any resulting fixes would be of doubtful accuracy. If the weather deteriorates, the navigator who has based his track on an accurate starting point is far more confident of his position the next day than the one who got a highly suspect position based on the bearings of a couple of mountain tops as the land finally disappeared, and who was banking on bringing his position up to date with celestial sights the following day.

Fig 45 shows a good three bearing departure fix at 1700. With the existing wind, the navigator expects to make a course of 020° true overnight. There is no hard and fast rule as to how often times should be entered against this type of dead reckoning track. The positions shown are exactly six hours apart at 1800 hours, midnight and 0600 the following morning. Some people may prefer to enter the times every four hours, but this is entirely a matter for personal choice. Other people might argue that the navigator cannot guarantee that the course and speed will be maintained overnight: surely it would be easier to wait until the following morning, and then work out a position for 0600 or 0800 based on what actually happened overnight. Fair enough, and I would admit that 90 per cent of the time the type of track illustrated would have to be amended, not just once but probably twice.

However, the whole point of a dead reckoning track on the chart is that the boat's position can be seen at a glance, and this is most important in an emergency. If the boat is breaking up around you, the last thing you have time for is to be fooling around with a pair of dividers and doing some mental arithmetic to get a position to send out in your Mayday call! If it were three o'clock in the morning, latitude and longitude could be read off *by eye* accurately enough for the emergency purpose as long as there was a dead reckoning track on the chart.

Chapter Three

Celestial Navigation

Celestial navigation is that branch of the art in which the sun or other heavenly bodies are used to find position. The end result of one observation is a single position line. As in coastal work, finding two or more position lines gives a fix.

Geographical Position (GP)

At any given moment there is one point on the earth's surface directly beneath the sun. It is the point at which a line from the *centre* of the sun to the centre of the earth would pass through the earth's surface, and is called the sun's Geographical Position (GP). Anybody who happened to be at the GP would have to look directly above him to see the sun.

Zenith

The point directly overhead is said to be a person's zenith. It follows from the last paragraph that if the sun is at your zenith, then you must be at the sun's GP. So the latitude and longitude of your position and the sun's GP would be the same.

Fig 46
The visible horizon depends on the observer's height of eye

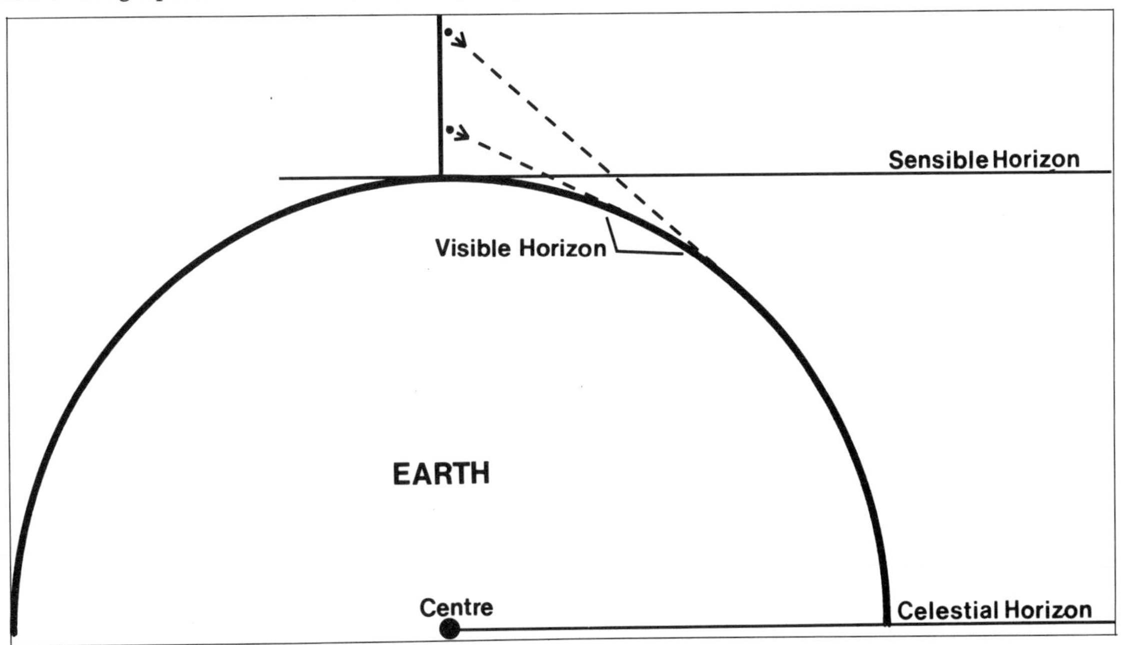

Altitude and horizons

Many readers will be familiar with the sea or visible horizon – the line where sea and sky appear to meet. The distance to the visible horizon varies with height of eye because of the curvature of the earth. The higher the observer, the further he can see over the curve, as shown in Fig 46. The sensible horizon is the tangent to the earth's surface at the observer's position directly in line with the sun. The angle between the sensible horizon and a person's zenith is 90 degrees (see Fig 47).

The angle between the sensible horizon and the sun above it from the observer's position is called the sun's altitude, and this angle is measured with a sextant. The altitude actually required is the angle at the centre of the earth between the sun and a line through the centre of the earth parallel to the sensible horizon. This is the true altitude above the celestial or rational horizon and is shown in Fig 48.

For the next and most important step towards the understanding of how a position line is found using the sun, it will be assumed that the true altitude at the centre of the earth and the altitude found by the navigator on the earth's surface are exactly equal. This can be done because the sun is so distant that all the rays of sunlight striking any part of the earth can be considered parallel. (The maximum error introduced by such an assumption approximates 9 seconds of arc or 0.15 of a nautical mile.)

Fig 49 is an expanded section of part of Fig 48. The line from the sun to the centre of the earth which determines the true altitude passes of course through the sun's GP. Now the relationship between the observer, the GP and the true altitude becomes rather interesting.

As the zenith is directly overhead, the extension of the line from the zenith through the observer leads to the centre of the earth. The angle between this line and the celestial

Fig 47
The angle between the sensible horizon and the observer's zenith is 90°.

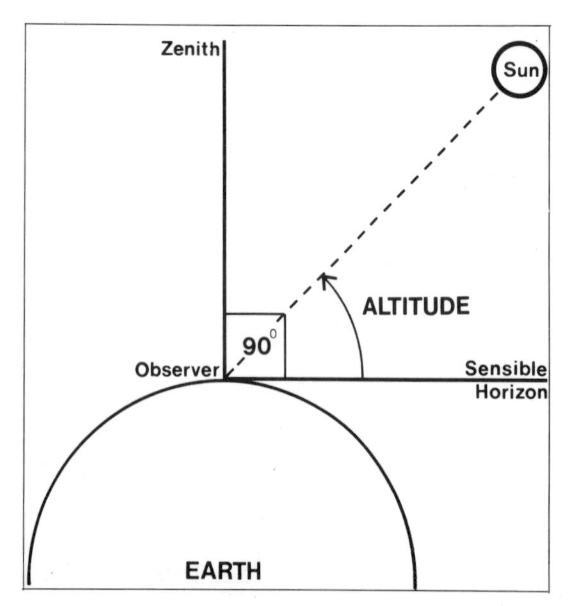

Fig 48
True altitude above the celestial or rational horizon

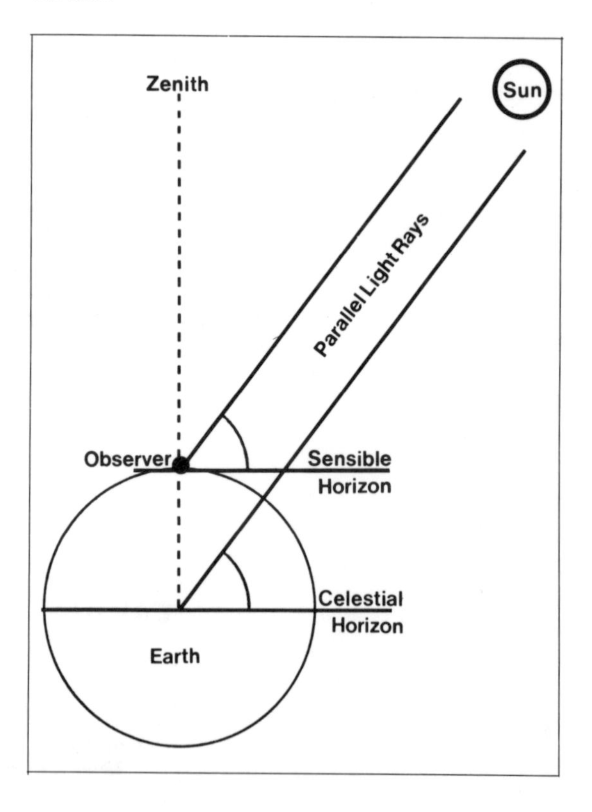

horizon is a right angle (90°). If the true altitude is subtracted from 90°, the angle D is found. But D is also the arc, or distance on the surface of the earth between the observer and the sun's GP. And this is where the logic of using latitude for measuring distance at sea really pays off, because angular distance (or distance along any arc) on the surface of the earth in minutes of arc equals linear distance in nautical miles. (One degree of latitude = 60 minutes of arc = 60 nautical miles.)

It will be explained shortly how the navigator can find the position of the GP for any given moment. In Fig 50, if the GP was plotted as shown, then by setting the dividers at the correct distance a circle could be drawn in. As every point on this circle is the same distance from the GP, it must pass through the observer's position. The end result is a position line consisting of a range circle.

Fig 49
Use of the true altitude to find the observer's distance from the sun's GP

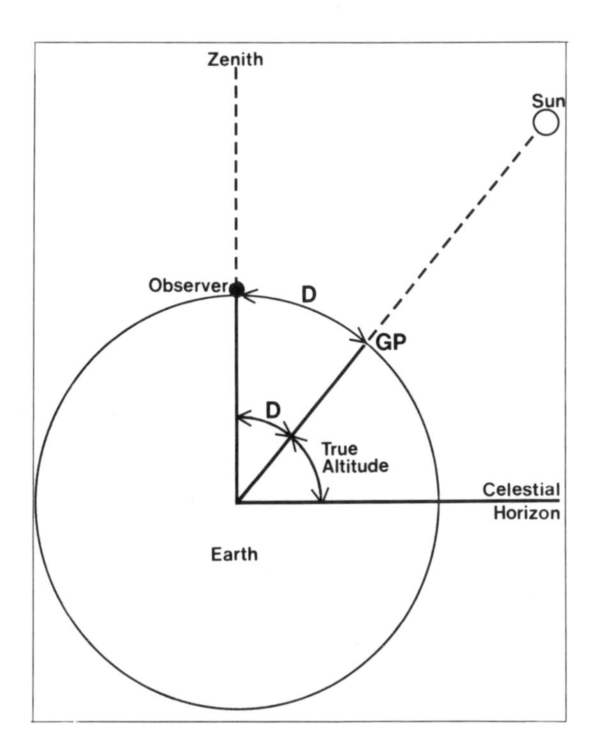

Declination

Position on the earth's surface is defined by latitude and longitude. The latitude and longitude of the sun's geographical position (GP) are called the declination and Greenwich hour angle respectively. Both are listed in various publications, of which the *Nautical Almanac* and *Reed's Nautical Almanac* are probably the most widely known. The *Nautical Almanac* is used for the examples given later in the text.

Declination is given in degrees and minutes north or south of the equator, just as is latitude, and can be plotted on a chart exactly the same way.

A few words on the relationship between the sun's declination and the seasons may help to show the reader that celestial navigation is based on practical events that affect our daily lives. The earth rotates around its axis of spin once a day and revolves around the sun once a year. Fig 51 shows that if the axis were perpendicular to the orbit, the

Fig 50
A celestial position line

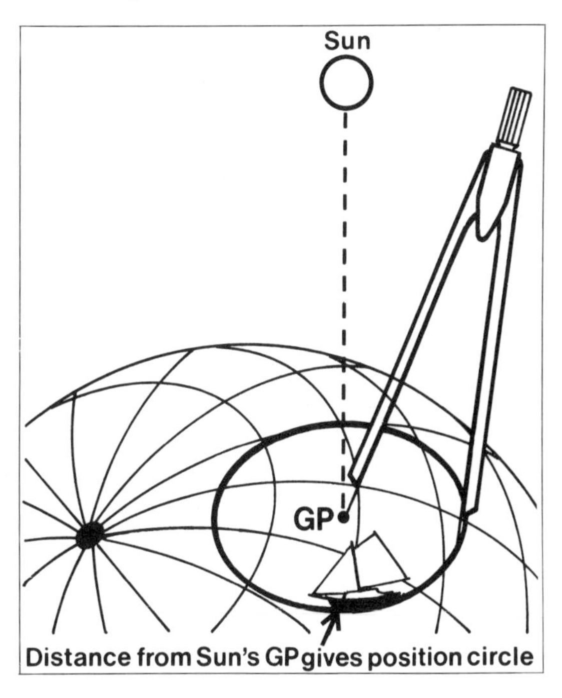

sun would always be over the equator and the declination would be a constant zero degrees. In fact the axis is inclined at an angle of about 23½° to the orbit.

The bottom diagram in Fig 51 shows this, and also the earth at two positions along the orbit six months apart. In June the declination or GP of the sun is in the northern hemisphere, giving the northern summer. The southern summer occurs when the earth has moved around the orbit to the position shown in December. Every year the declination and thus the GP of the sun changes between 23½°N and 23½°S, and the band of latitude across which it moves is called the tropics. The sun crosses the equator twice in the process, once on the way north on about 21 March and again on the way south about 22 September. These are called the equinoxes, meaning 'equal nights'. The sun reaches its maximum north and south declinations on 21 June and 22 December, and the change in declination is momentarily zero before it reverses direction.

These dates are the 'solstices' meaning 'sun standing still'. If the earth was not inclined on its axis and the declination remained constant there would be no seasons.

Greenwich Hour Angle

The declination, which changes only slowly, is determined by the position of the earth in its orbit around the sun. The Greenwich hour angle (GHA) or longitude of the sun's GP, is governed by the earth's daily rotation around its axis. The earth spins from west to east under the sun through one full circle or 360 degrees every 24 hours. Like longitude, GHA is based on the Greenwich meridian but unlike longitude it is measured from 0 degrees to 360 degrees westward from Greenwich.

Fig 51
Declination of the sun and the seasons

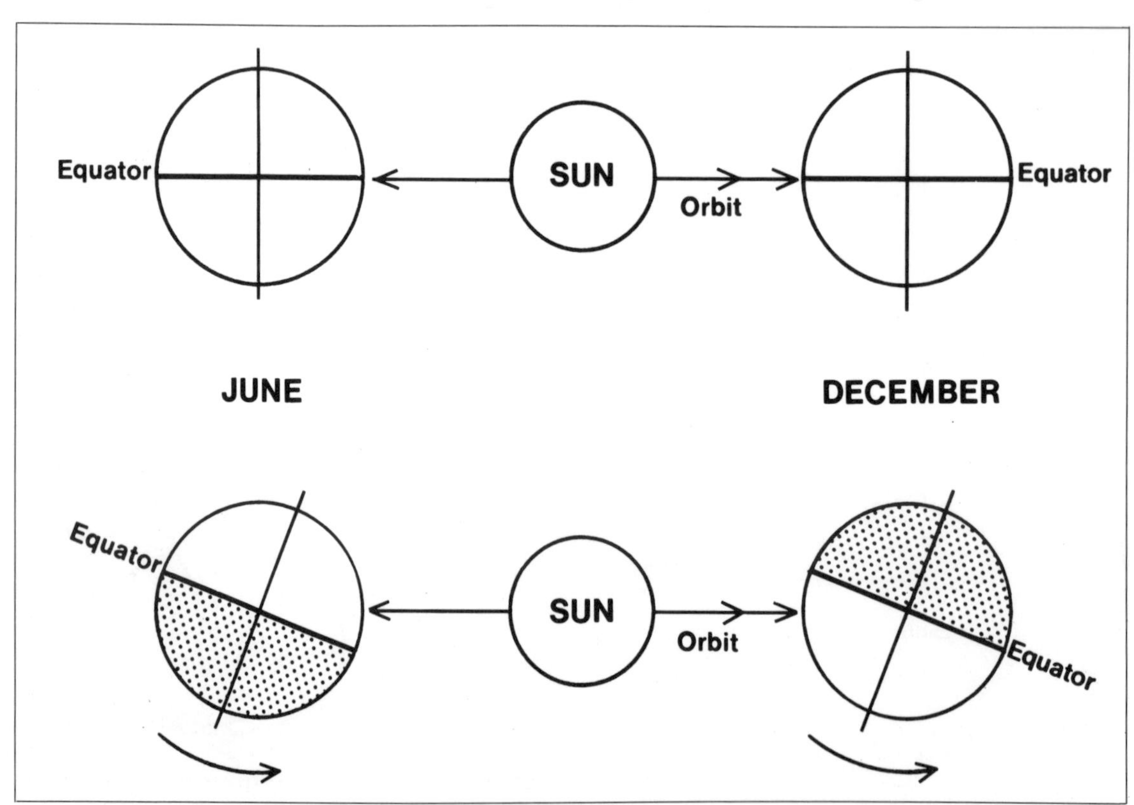

Fig 52 shows the earth viewed from above the North Pole. When the GP is on the Greenwich meridian, the GHA is zero degrees, and it is noon in London. (The exact meaning of noon is further discussed in Chapter Five.) Three hours later, the earth has turned through 45 degrees to the east and the GP is then on longitude 45°W. The GHA increases at a steady 15 degrees every hour, because the earth is rotating under the sun. One day later the GHA has increased to 360°W, the GP is therefore back over the Greenwich meridian and the cycle starts again.

Azimuth

The direction of the sun or any other celestial body from an observer is called the 'true azimuth'. The true azimuth is exactly equal to the true bearing from the observer to the body's geographical position on the earth. As with any true bearing it is measured clockwise from north 0° – 360°.

Fig 52
Greenwich hour angle – the earth viewed from above the North Pole

The celestial fix

It has been established that an observer can find both his distance from the sun's GP and that the sun's true azimuth gives the true bearing of the GP. The position of the latter could be plotted by declination and GHA. The reader might think that if a bearing of the sun was taken with a compass at the same time as an altitude was found, a fix could be plotted. Unfortunately, with the compasses now in use it is impossible to take a bearing with sufficient accuracy for this. If the sun's altitude was 40 degrees and the bearing taken was one degree out, the resulting fix would be in error by about fifty nautical miles.

So let's consider a stationary observer. Fig 50 showed that the navigator could find one position circle from one sunshot. Remember that the sun's GHA or longitude west of Greenwich is constantly increasing by 15 degrees each hour. After waiting perhaps two hours when the position of the GP has substantially changed, the navigator can find a second position or range circle. The point at which this cuts the first position circle is the celestial fix.

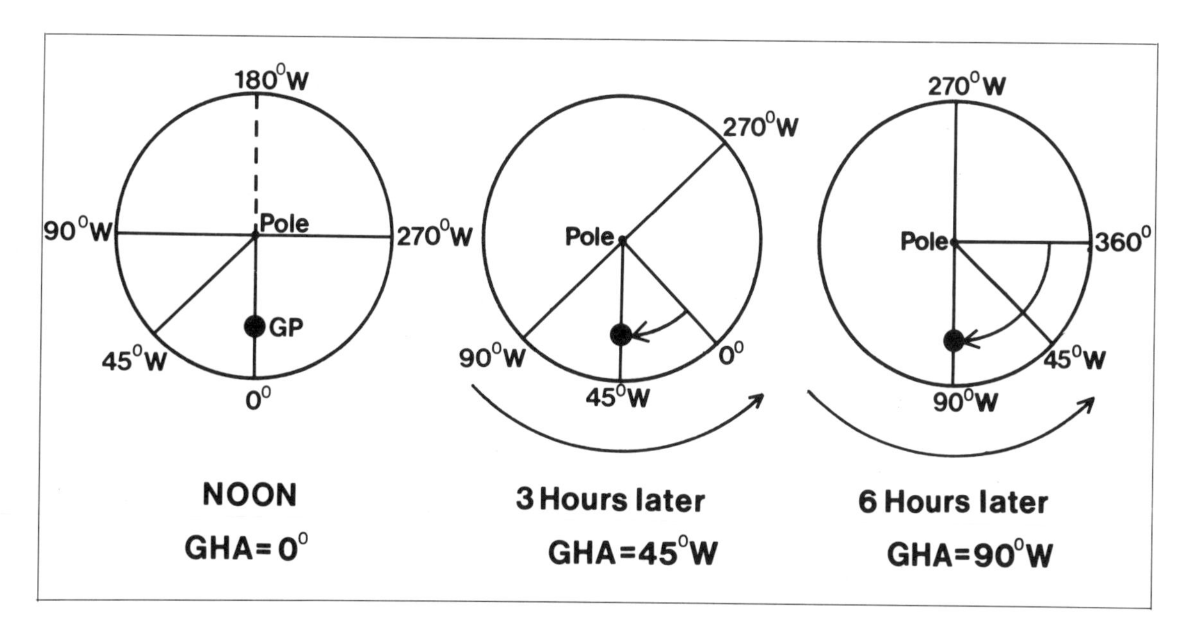

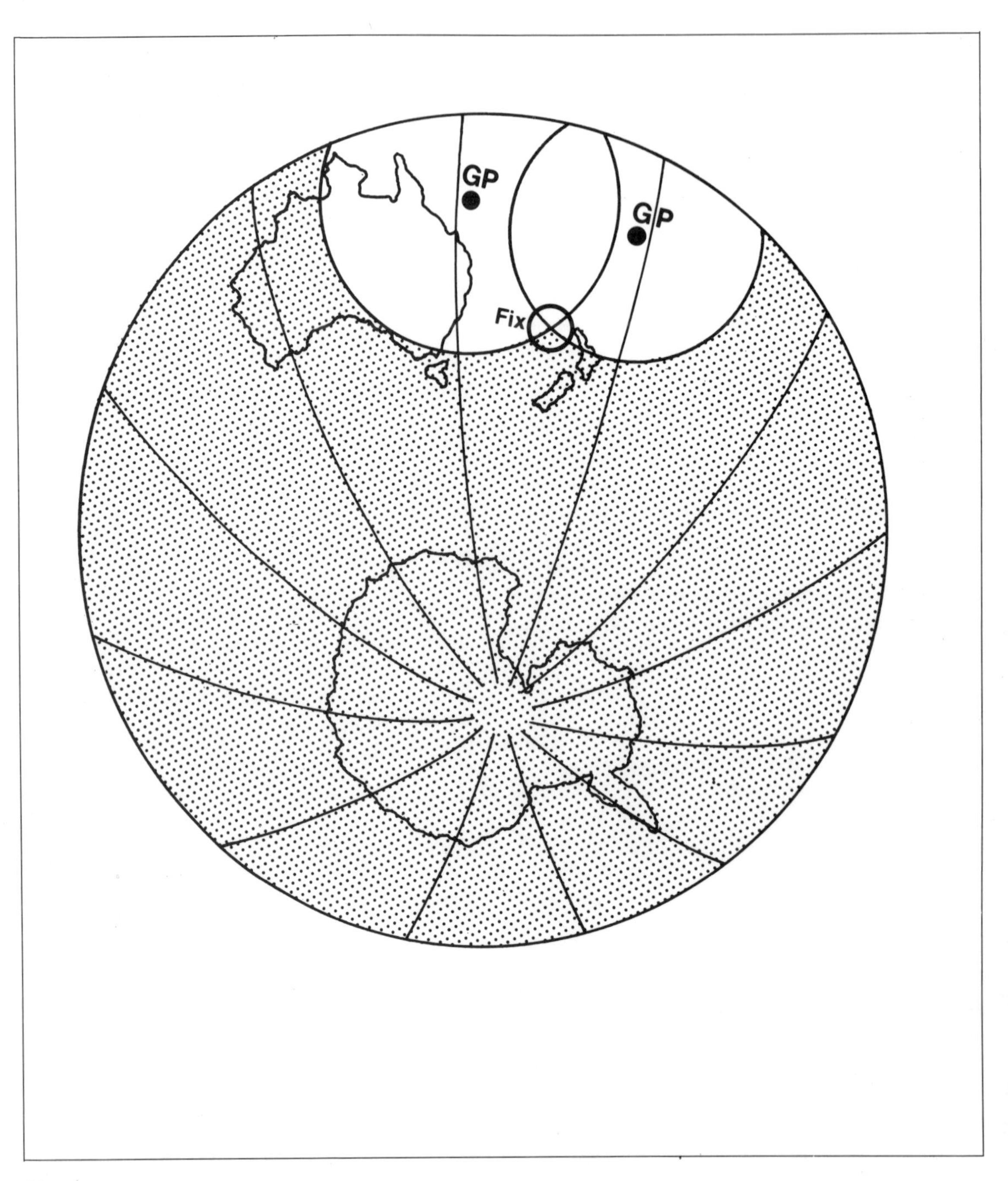

Fig 53
The celestial fix

Chapter Four

The Sextant

A sextant is an instrument used for measuring the angular distance or altitudes between any two objects. Its arc is roughly one-sixth of a circle, hence its name. In celestial navigation, the angle being measured is from the sun to the visible horizon directly beneath it, i.e. the altitude.

The principal parts of the sextant are shown in Fig 54.

The uses of the different parts of the sextant in Fig 54a are as follows:

1 The handle is always on the right hand side and held with the right hand when using the sextant. The instrument should always be held by the handle and never by any of the smaller parts; this could cause bending or distortion, resulting in altitude errors.

2 The arc is engraved with the scale, usually from 0 degrees to 120 degrees.

3 The index arm is the only moving part. It is pivoted at the top and moves across the scale.

4 The index mirror is mounted at the top of the index arm and therefore moves with it.

5 The clamp is pressed to release the index arm so that it can be moved freely, much like the button on a car hand brake. If this clamp is not released before trying to move the index arm on its pivot, there is a grinding noise.

6 The micrometer wheel is on an endless tangent screw and is used to give fine adjustments when finding the altitude.

7 The horizon mirror is secured to the frame of the sextant. One half is clear glass and the other half is a mirror.

8 The telescope is used to magnify the sun to assist in getting a more accurate reading. It can be removed quite easily.

9 The index mirror shades are hinged and can be moved over in front of the mirror to cut down the glare of the sun. They vary in density and a suitable shade or sometimes two shades should be selected before looking directly at the sun.

10 In bright sunshine at sea there can be quite a glare at the horizon, and the horizon shades are used if necessary to cut down this glare.

11 The screw in the centre of the horizon mirror is used for the correction of side error (see page 56).

In Fig 55, images seen through the telescope can come from one of two sources; firstly,

Fig 55
The principle of the sextant – direct and reflected images

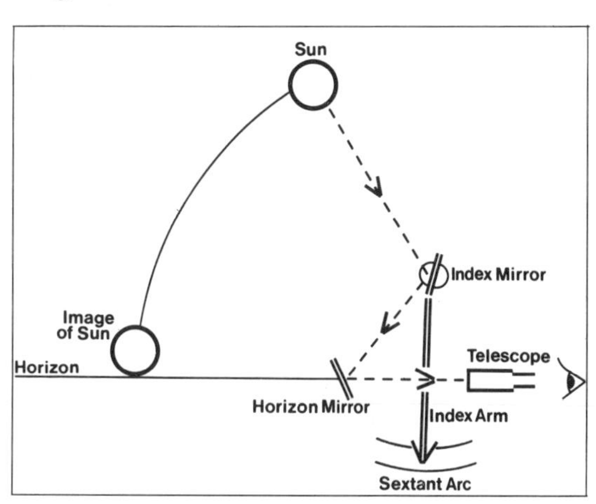

a

Fig 54
The sextant

a *1 Handle*
2 Arc
3 Index arm
4 Index mirror
5 Clamp
6 Micrometer wheel
7 Horizon mirror
8 Telescope
9 Index shades
10 Horizon shades
11 Side error correcting screw

b *Index scale and micrometer wheel. The sextant altitude shown is 65° 20′.0*

c *A reliable plastic sextant*

b

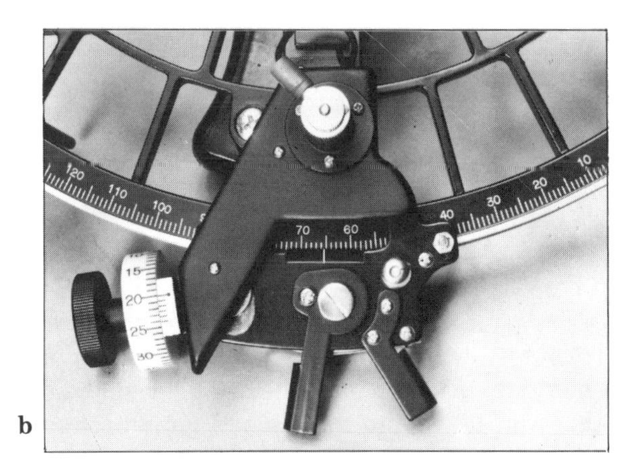

c

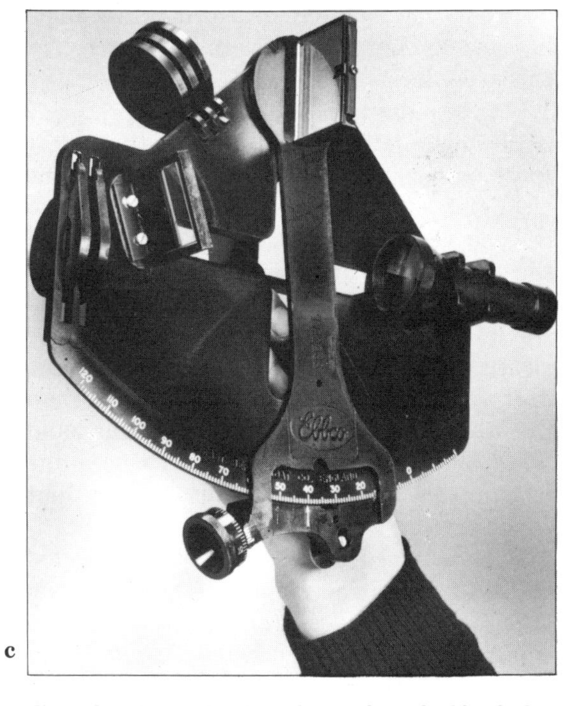

directly through the clear glass half of the horizon mirror so that the navigator sees whatever is directly in line with the telescope. Secondly, a ray of light from any object in line with the index mirror is reflected into the mirrored half of the horizon mirror and re-reflected back through the telescope to the eye of the observer. What he sees through the clear glass is called the 'direct image' and i the mirrored half the 'reflected image'.

Fig 56 shows what happens when the index arm is set at zero on the scale. In this state the

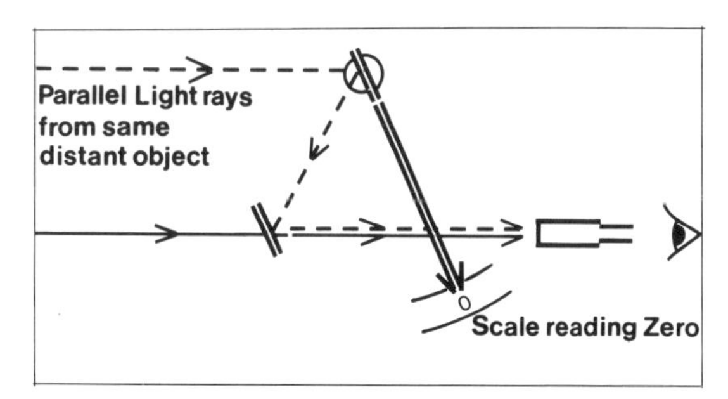

Fig 56
The principle of the sextant – index arm set at 0°

two mirrors are exactly parallel and the observer sees both the direct and reflected images of the one object. The two appear to be superimposed. This is really the principle on which the sextant works. As soon as the index bar is moved the mirrors are at an angle to one another. This angle between the two mirrors is a measure of the altitude, and it happens that a change of angle of 1 degree between them is equal to a change of 2 degrees in altitude. So even though the arc is only a sixth of a circle, or 60 degrees, the altitude scale can be doubled, which is why the sextant reads to 120 degrees.

Care of the sextant

It follows that the mirrors are the most important features on the sextant and that any slight misalignment between them will give a slightly false altitude. Even so, the sextant is basically a robust instrument; a good model well looked after will last for fifty years or more.

The sextant should be kept stowed in its box with any securing clamp in place when not in use. Even in fine weather a film of salt forms over the telescope lens and the mirrors, and this should be washed off with fresh water and drying should be done carefully with a lens tissue or soft clean cloth. In heavy weather the salt may have to be removed every time the sextant is used. The back of the arc should be kept clean with a small brush (usually supplied in the box) and the micrometer wheel and index arm pivot should be brushed lightly with light oil. No sextant should be left in the sun, especially a plastic one, which will warp.

Choice of sextant

The conventional sextant is made from metal or alloy, usually brass or aluminium, and over recent years moulded plastic sextants of polycarbonate or polystyrene have come onto the market. The former are expensive, high precision instruments. The latter are lightweight and much cheaper with some minor loss in accuracy. The advantages of the plastic type are considered by many to far outweigh any slight error in altitude.

The difficulty in using any sextant from the pitching deck of a small boat tends to negate the theoretically more precise altitude found with the conventional type. There are other considerations, however. The scale and micrometer wheel on the plastic sextants are rather smaller and more difficult to read, especially in poor light, than on the larger models. The latter are fitted with much larger mirrors and therefore have a greater reflecting area. This is important in high altitude sights, making it a good deal easier to hold the reflected image in any seaway, particularly in yachts.

This disadvantage would not apply to any plastic sextant now on sale which has the larger mirrors. In high winds the sheer lightness of the plastic type can become a positive disadvantage in that the sextant can act like a sail, adding to the difficulty of centring the sun on the horizon. Some navigators prefer the extra weight of the conventional sextant, which sits solid as a rock in any wind.

In the end the choice probably comes down to one of finance. Either sort will do the job, but you get what you pay for.

Some sextants, both conventional and plastic, dispense with the micrometer wheel, and the reading is taken against a straight Vernier scale engraved on the index arm. In my experience these are rather more difficult to read than the more modern micrometer type.

USING THE SEXTANT

There is a bit of a knack in using the instrument, so don't despair if the first few tries result in failure. The first attempts should be made on good steady land, such as the front lawn. Use the top of a lamp post as the sun and call the top of the fence the horizon; you will be measuring the angle between the top of the post and the fence. Try this procedure.

1 Set the index arm at 0 degrees.

2 Close the left eye and look at the object (post or sun) through the telescope and the clear glass of the horizon mirror.

3 Turn the micrometer wheel slightly with the left hand. Turn the sextant – *not* your head – a few millimetres left and right. You should see the object alternately through the clear glass and then the reflected image in the mirror, and one will be slightly higher than the other. The reflected image, the right-hand one, is the important one. Once the instrument is mastered, this step is not necessary.

4 Release the clamp. Keep the reflected image in the mirror and slowly bring it down towards the fence (or horizon) by a combination of the left hand moving the index arm to keep the object in view, and the right hand to pull the frame of the sextant back. This is where things will go wrong. The natural tendency is to push the left hand right forward, and the object will disappear.

Try this experiment. Hold your sextant at chest level with it set on zero. Slowly push the index arm forward until the reading is about 90 degrees, watching the index mirror all the time. As the arm goes forward, the mirror will point ever higher. With the reading at 90 degrees, it will be pointing high in the air. This is exactly what happens when the left hand is

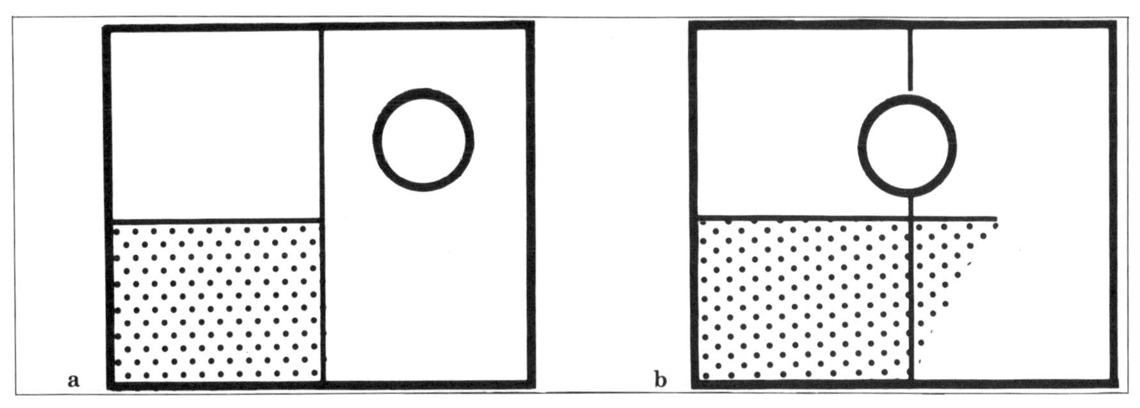

Fig 58**a**
Fig 58**b** *Centring the sun*

pushed forward too far. The object is lost to view and all you are seeing in the mirror is the empty sky above.

5 Bring the object slowly down until the fence (or horizon) comes into view through the clear glass of the horizon mirror. When the object is almost touching the fence, release the clamp and use the micrometer wheel to make the final adjustments to bring it right on.

6 The reading on the scale is the sextant altitude.

Caution. Before looking at the sun the first time put a horizon shade and a dark index mirror shade into place.

For the first few times the sextant is used, it may be helpful to leave the telescope off. The sun will look much smaller, but it is easier to find and bring down if the telescope is not used. Once the reader gains confidence and is bringing an object down with a smooth continuous motion, instead of the first jerky efforts, the same procedure should be tried from a beach or headland using the visible horizon.

At sea, of course, the boat moves around. This makes it more difficult, firstly to find the sun and secondly to hold the reflected image in the mirror while bringing it down to the horizon. It can be utterly infuriating until you learn this second skill.

The top and bottom of the sun are called the upper and lower limbs respectively. In general the lower limb is used and fine adjustments made with the micrometer wheel so that it just touches the horizon when finding the sun's altitude.

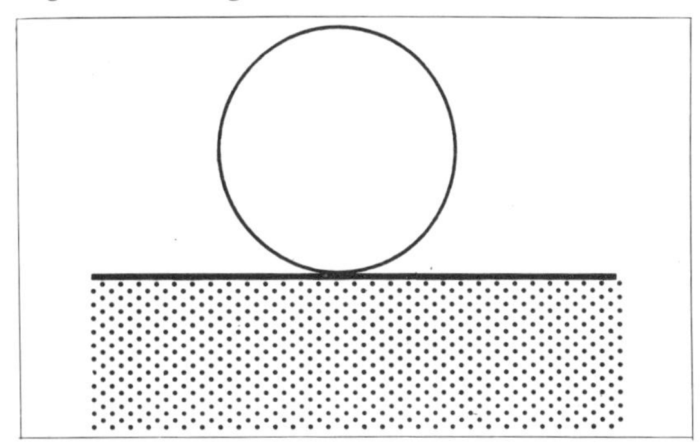

Fig 57
Lower limb

Centring the sun

Based on the explanation thus far, it would appear that with the sun on the horizon the navigator will see the reflected image in the mirrored right hand half of the horizon mirror and the horizon through the left hand clear half, as in Fig 58a. In fact it is both possible and necessary to centre the sun as shown in Fig 58b.

Rocking the sextant

The altitude is measured from the sun to the point directly below it on the horizon, which means that the sextant must be exactly vertical. If the sextant is cocked over one way or the other, the slanted angle measured will be slightly too big. The problem is overcome by gently rocking the sextant (*not* your head) from left to right. The sun will appear to describe a gentle arc as shown in Fig 59. The reading is taken when it is just touching the horizon at the bottom of the arc, because at that moment, the sextant is vertical.

Horizontal sextant angles

Altitudes are taken with the sextant upright or vertical. To find the angle between two shore fixing marks, the instrument is turned through 90 degrees so that the frame is parallel to the ground. When taking a HSA fix, the right hand object of the pair is viewed in the horizon mirror and its reflected image is moved left towards the left hand object. When it comes into view through the clear glass of the horizon mirror, the clamp is released and the two objects superimposed using the micrometer wheel (See Fig 60). The reading on the scale is the angle between the two objects.

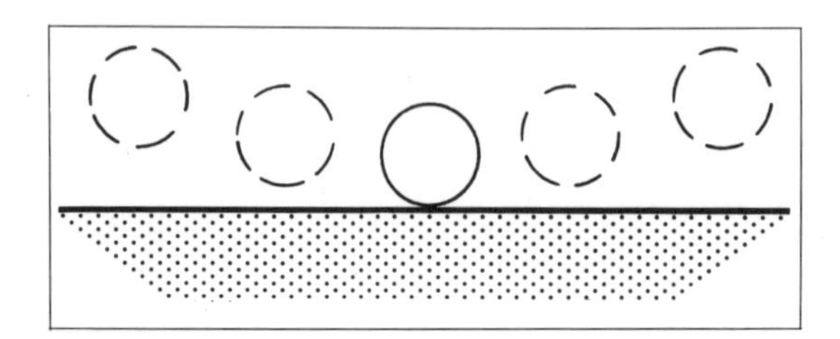

Fig 59
Rocking the sextant

Fig 60
Taking a horizontal sextant angle

SEXTANT ERRORS

Most new sextants come with instructions on their use and an explanation of how to find any errors which may be present. The initial setting up should be done by an expert. Any small basic error in the instrument should be marked by the manufacturer on the lid of the box and is generally small enough to be ignored.

Side error

Occasionally at sea the navigator may notice that with the sextant set at 0 degrees for the start of a sight, the direct and reflected images of the sun are not superimposed, but that one is slightly to the side of the other. This is called side error. It can be checked by choosing a distant object, such as a flagstaff or lighthouse, and with the sextant set on zero slowly rotating the micrometer wheel back and forth. The reflected image should pass through the direct image. Again, if it is slightly out to one side, side error is present. It is caused if the horizon mirror is not perpendicular to the plane of the sextant. It is corrected by using the screw in the centre of the frame of the horizon mirror, farthest from the frame of the instrument.

There are other errors and, although they can be corrected, that is a job best left to an expert. The errors are interrelated, and correcting one may induce another. Even when adjusted correctly, the sextant may have a residual error which is allowed for, rather than taken out.

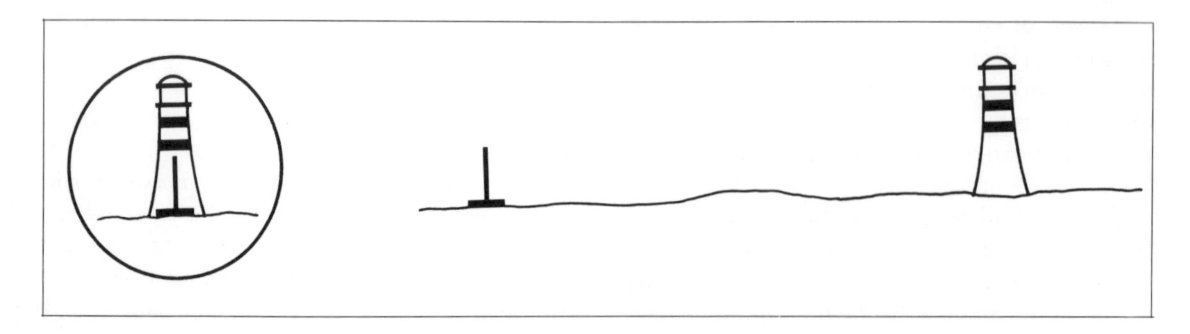

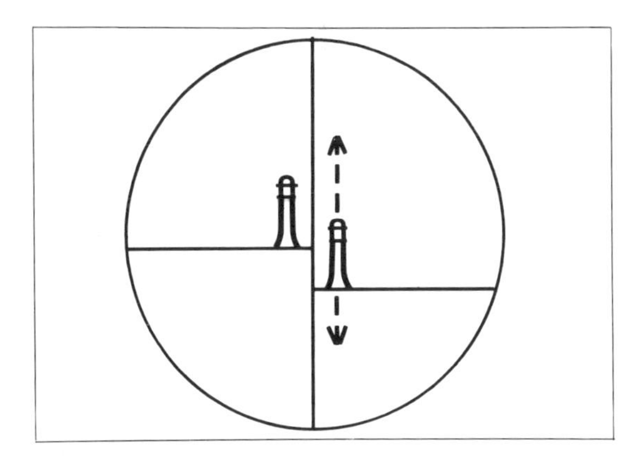

Fig 61
Side error

Index error

It has been explained that the sextant works on the principle of measuring the angle between the index and horizon mirrors to give altitude. The zero point of the instrument is when there is no angle between the two, i.e. when the mirrors are parallel to each other. If they are not parallel when the index arm is set to 0 degrees, that reading is not correct and any altitude taken with the sextant will have a small but consistent error. As this is concerned with the scale reading, it is called index error and is allowed for.

To find index error the sextant is set at 0 degrees and pointed at the horizon. If the direct and reflected images of the horizon form one straight line, there is no index error. If not, index error is present.

Fig 62
a *No index error*
b *Index error*

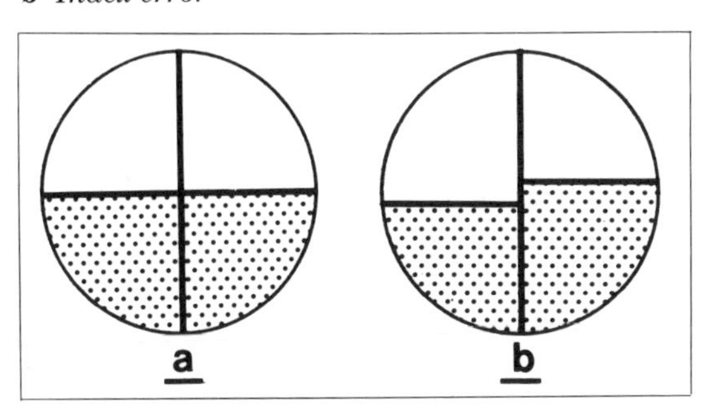

To find the amount of error, turn the micrometer wheel until the horizons are exactly in line, and take the reading. At this point the mirrors are parallel. Depending on which way the micrometer wheel has been turned, one of two types of reading will result. The main scale is to the left of 0 degrees as you look at the sextant, and a small scale is to the right. If the wheel turn is moving the index arm on to the main scale, the reading is said to be 'on' the arc. If the other way, the reading is 'off', e.g., if the reading is 02′.0 the index error is 2′ on the arc. The reading may appear to be say 58′.0. Look more carefully. You have in fact wound the wheel the other way and moved just 2′ off the arc.

Any reading on the arc is subtracted from the sextant altitude. Readings off the arc are added to the sextant altitude. This apparently self-contradictory phrase may help the reader to remember which is which:
If it's 'on', it's 'off' (subtract) and if it's 'off', it's 'on' (add).

The index error can change with differences in temperature or humidity, or if the sextant is given a slight knock. As the method of finding the error is simple and quick, it should be checked at least once a day at sea.

If index error exceeds 3′ of arc, the sextant should be adjusted by an expert. However, if this happens in the middle of an ocean cruise, don't panic. The sextant will see you through that particular voyage.

OCEAN NAVIGATION USING THE SEXTANT

Two observers in exactly the same place, but at different heights, see different visible horizons. Each would get a slightly different sextant altitude if they took simultaneous sunsights. True altitude is the angle of the sun above the sensible horizon through the observer at sea level, thus the observer's height of eye must be allowed for. This is called the dip correction and can be found from a table in the front of the *Nautical*

DIP				
Ht. of Eye	Corrⁿ	Ht. of Eye	Ht. of Eye	Corrⁿ
m	′	ft.	m	′
2·4		8·0	1·0	— 1·8
	—2·8			
2·6		8·6	1·5	— 2·2
	—2·9			
2·8		9·2	2·0	— 2·5
	—3·0			
3·0		9·8	2·5	— 2·8
	—3·1			
3·2		10·5	3·0	— 3·0
	—3·2			
3·4		11·2	See table	
	—3·3		←	
3·6		11·9		
	—3·4		m	′
3·8		12·6		
	—3·5			
4·0		13·3	20	— 7·9
	—3·6			
4·3		14·1	22	— 8·3
	—3·7			
4·5		14·9	24	— 8·6
	—3·8			
4·7		15·7	26	— 9·0
	—3·9			
5·0		16·5	28	— 9·3
	—4·0			
5·2		17·4		
	—4·1			

Fig 63
Extract from the 1978 Nautical Almanac, *page A2, showing dip correction*

Almanac shown in Fig 63. The height of eye in a yacht is about 3 metres, which gives a correction of –3′.0, but the exact height of eye should be used to find an accurate correction. If you look at the table in Fig 63, you will see that a correction of –3′.1 applies to both a height of eye of 3.1m and 3.2m, a correction of –3′.2 is for heights of eye of 3.3m and 3.4m, and so on down the table. The dip correction is always minus.

Finding height of eye

There are many ways of doing this. One is to select the best place for using a sextant while alongside or at anchor. Then stand on a box or something similar to get at the same level if the vantage point is above deck, and lower a weighted line over the side from eye level until it just touches the water, and measure the line. Simple and accurate.

Once the dip correction is found, it will stay the same throughout a voyage, unless height of eye is changed. Although index error may alter slightly, it can stay the same for days on end. Because of this, and as the two corrections are small, they are usually combined before applying them to the sextant altitude. An example is given at the bottom of this page.

Sun's altitude correction

The lower or upper limbs of the sun are used to measure sextant altitude because the most accurate reading can be obtained with their sharply defined edges. The data given in the *Nautical Almanac* are actually for the centre of the sun, and the true altitude must also be for the centre. So a correction must be made for the radius of the sun. This table is shown at the front of the *Almanac*, and also in Fig 64.

The size of the sun's disc alters through the year and corrections are given for October to March and for April to September.

Sextant altitude	36° 16′	Index error (IE)	–1′
IE and dip	4′–	Dip	–3′
Apparent altitude	36° 12′	Total	–4′

The apparent altitude is the sextant altitude corrected for dip and any index error.

Sextant altitude	23° 59′	Index error	+2′.5
IE and dip	0′.5–	Dip	–3′.0
Apparent altitude	23°58′.5	Total	–0′.5

If the height of eye is 3.7m, and the index error is 3′ on the arc, the total correction is –6.4.

ALTITUDE CORRECTION

OCT.—MAR.	SUN		APR.—SEPT.		
App. Alt.	Lower Limb	Upper Limb	App. Alt.	Lower Limb	Upper Limb
° ′	′	′	° ′	′	′
9 34			9 39		
	+10·8	−21·5		+10·6	−21·2
9 45			9 51		
	+10·9	−21·4		+10·7	−21·1
9 56			10 03		
	+11·0	−21·3		+10·8	−21·0
10 08			10 15		
	+11·1	−21·2		+10·9	−20·9
10 21			10 27		
	+11·2	−21·1		+11·0	−20·8
10 34			10 40		
	+11·3	−21·0		+11·1	−20·7
10 47			10 54		
	+11·4	−20·9		+11·2	−20·6
11 01			11 08		
	+11·5	−20·8		+11·3	−20·5
11 15			11 23		
	+11·6	−20·7		+11·4	−20·4
11 30			11 38		
	+11·7	−20·6		+11·5	−20·3
11 46			11 54		
	+11·8	−20·5		+11·6	−20·2
12 02			12 10		
	+11·9	−20·4		+11·7	−20·1
12 19			12 28		
	+12·0	−20·3		+11·8	−20·0
12 37			12 46		
	+12·1	−20·2		+11·9	−19·9
12 55			13 05		
	+12·2	−20·1		+12·0	−19·8
13 14			13 24		
	+12·3	−20·0		+12·1	−19·7
13 35			13 45		
	+12·4	−19·9		+12·2	−19·6
13 56			14 07		
	+12·5	−19·8		+12·3	−19·5
14 18			14 30		
	+12·6	−19·7		+12·4	−19·4
14 42			14 54		
	+12·7	−19·6		+12·5	−19·3
15 06			15 19		
	+12·8	−19·5		+12·6	−19·2
15 32			15 46		
	+12·9	−19·4		+12·7	−19·1
15 59			16 14		
	+13·0	−19·3		+12·8	−19·0
16 28			16 44		
	+13·1	−19·2		+12·9	−18·9
16 59			17 15		
	+13·2	−19·1		+13·0	−18·8
17 32			17 48		
	+13·3	−19·0		+13·1	−18·7
18 06			18 24		
	+13·4	−18·9		+13·2	−18·6
18 42			19 01		
	+13·5	−18·8		+13·3	−18·5
19 21			19 42		
	+13·6	−18·7		+13·4	−18·4
20 03			20 25		
	+13·7	−18·6		+13·5	−18·3
20 48			21 11		
	+13·8	−18·5		+13·6	−18·2
21 35			22 00		
	+13·9	−18·4		+13·7	−18·1
22 26			22 54		
	+14·0	−18·3		+13·8	−18·0
23 22			23 51		
	+14·1	−18·2		+13·9	−17·9
24 21			24 53		
	+14·2	−18·1		+14·0	−17·8
25 26			26 00		
	+14·3	−18·0		+14·1	−17·7
26 36			27 13		
	+14·4	−17·9		+14·2	−17·6
27 52			28 33		
	+14·5	−17·8		+14·3	−17·5
29 15			30 00		
	+14·6	−17·7		+14·4	−17·4
30 46			31 35		
	+14·7	−17·6		+14·5	−17·3
32 26			33 20		
	+14·8	−17·5		+14·6	−17·2
34 17			35 17		
	+14·9	−17·4		+14·7	−17·1
36 20			37 26		
	+15·0	−17·3		+14·8	−17·0
38 36			39 50		
	+15·1	−17·2		+14·9	−16·9
41 08			42 31		
	+15·2	−17·1		+15·0	−16·8
43 59			45 31		
	+15·3	−17·0		+15·1	−16·7
47 10			48 55		
	+15·4	−16·9		+15·2	−16·6
50 46			52 44		
	+15·5	−16·8		+15·3	−16·5
54 49			57 02		
	+15·6	−16·7		+15·4	−16·4
59 23			61 51		
	+15·7	−16·6		+15·5	−16·3
64 30			67 17		
	+15·8	−16·5		+15·6	−16·2
70 12			73 16		
	+15·9	−16·4		+15·7	−16·1
76 26			79 43		
	+16·0	−16·3		+15·8	−16·0
83 05			86 32		
	+16·1	−16·2		+15·9	−15·9
90 00			90 00		

Fig 64
The sun's altitude correction table. From the 1978 Nautical Almanac, *page A2*

Refraction

Refraction is the bending of the light rays from the sun or stars as they pass through the earth's atmosphere. This effect can be seen if a pencil or stick is placed in a half-empty glass of water. The pencil appears to be bent. Fishermen know this effect well, because if you stab where the fish appears to be under the water, a miss is guaranteed. Refraction of the sun's rays is maximum near the horizon and at low altitudes, decreasing to zero when the sun is directly overhead, and is always a minus correction. There used to be a separate table for the refraction correction, but as it is dependent on altitude it was combined in the altitude correction table.

It can also vary with alterations in temperature and barometric pressure, but these effects are small except at very low altitudes. To guard against the possibility of unknown errors from these effects, the yacht navigator should not use altitudes below 15 degrees.

True altitude

Once dip and index error have been allowed for, the apparent altitude is used to enter the table, under the right month, and the correction will give true altitude. All corrections for the lower limb are plus and for the upper limb, minus.

For example, if the month is December and the apparent altitude (App Alt in the table) is 22°30′, the lower limb correction is +14′.0.

Apparent altitude	22° 30′.0
Correction	14′.0+
True altitude	22° 44′.0

Follow the next example through, using the extracts from the *Nautical Almanac.*

Sextant altitude	37° 28′.4
Index error	−1′.6
Dip	−3′.0

The month is May.

Sextant altitude	37° 28′.4	Index	
Index error		error	−1′.6
and dip	−4′.6	Dip	−3′.0
Apparent altitude	37° 23′.8	Total	−4′.6
Altitude			
correction	+14′.7		
True altitude	37° 38′.5		

Now try these:

Sextant altitude	20° 48′.0
Index error	+1′.0
Dip	−4′.0

The month is March.
Using the method of calculation shown above, the true altitude is 20° 58′.7

Sextant altitude	49° 20′.0	
IE +0′.6	Dip −3′.4	December
Answer:		
True altitude	49° 32′.6	

Sextant altitude	42° 51′.6	
IE 2′.0 on the arc		
Height of eye	2.8m	June
Answer:		
Dip	2.9−	
True altitude	43° 01′.7	

Chapter Five

Time and the *Nautical Almanac*

Minute: sixtieth part of hour.
Hour: twenty-fourth part of day.

Concise Oxford Dictionary

The measurement of time is based on the sun. A day is the interval between two successive transits of the sun across the meridian of longitude through a place. This interval is called an apparent solar day. Due to several factors, the main one being that the earth does not move at a constant speed along its orbit around the sun, this interval is not quite a fixed length. As the day based on the true sun varies in length, so too do the hours and minutes in each of those days.

Mean time

To overcome the confusion of having a day of variable length, an artificial unit of constant length called the 'mean' day is used. This is the mean or average length of all the apparent solar days over a period of years. Thus one twenty-fourth part of a mean day gives an hour of fixed length, and so on down to seconds. These are all units of mean or average solar time.

All clocks are regulated to measure mean time. The wristwatch or clock on the wall are designed to measure the fixed intervals of time called mean solar minutes, mean solar hours and mean solar days.

A year is the time taken for the earth to complete one revolution around the sun, and for convenience it is taken as being 365 days in duration. Measured in the fixed length units of mean time, a year is actually 365 days 5 hours 48 minutes and 46 seconds. If uncorrected, the calendar would eventually become out of step with the seasons. So a leap year is introduced every fourth year in which an extra day, 29 February, is added to the calendar. This slightly overcorrects, so three leap years are left out in every four centuries. The last year of a century is only made a leap year if exactly divisible by 400. Thus 1900 was not a leap year, but the year 2000 will be.

Greenwich Mean Time

In Chapter One we saw that, although different places keep different times, they are all said to be so many hours ahead or behind GMT. The time at any one longitude can be compared with the time kept at any other longitude by reference back to the time kept on the universally recognised prime meridian of Greenwich. For the same reason any events to do with navigation, such as the change in declination or Greenwich hour angle of the sun or any other heavenly body, are chronicled against the one standard unchanging time – GMT.

Because of its international acceptance it has been agreed that the name is to be changed to 'Universal Time' or UT. If the reader comes across this name or abbreviation, it is the same as GMT.

Noon

Local noon at any place occurs when the sun is over the meridian of longitude which runs through the place. Fig 65 shows the sun and therefore the GP on longitude M. Two yachts marked A and B are on the same meridian, and therefore it is noon at exactly the same moment for both boats. The big difference is that to yacht A the true azimuth of the sun is due south, while to yacht B the sun's true bearing is due north. It is also noon at the same moment of time to any other observer on that meridian.

It is sometimes said that the sun is overhead at noon; the only point on *any* meridian at which the sun is overhead is at the GP.

THE *NAUTICAL ALMANAC*

The *Nautical Almanac* is produced jointly by HM Nautical Almanac Office, Royal Greenwich Observatory and the Nautical Almanac Office, United States Naval Observatory. It is used in most English-speaking countries. The data are also released for use in the almanacs for other non-English-speaking nations. The *Almanac* is issued annually and contains all the information needed by the navigator for celestial navigation. In particular it gives, for any moment of time, the Greenwich hour angle and declination of the sun and other navigational bodies.

Each page opening of the main part of the almanac gives data for three consecutive days. The information relating to stars and planets is on the left-hand page and for the sun and moon is on the right. The year, month and three dates and days of the week are listed at the top of each page.

Any data taken from the tables is said to be 'tabulated', e.g. it is the tabulated GHA of the sun. This is shortened to Tab GHA.

N.B. Greenwich Mean Time must be used when finding Greenwich hour angle or declination from the Almanac.

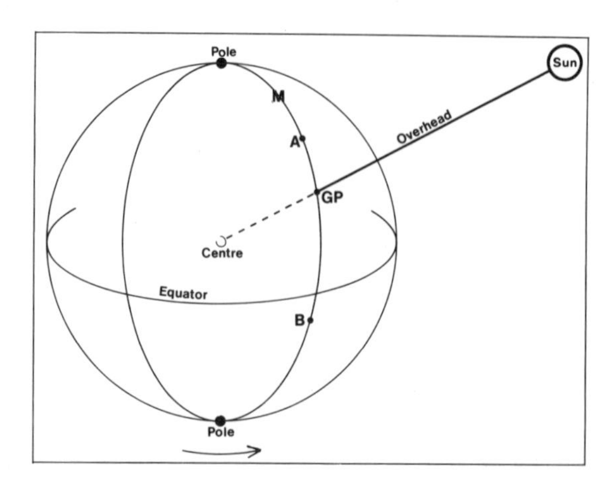

Fig 65
Noon

The GHA and Dec are tabulated for each hour every day, from 00 hours to 23 hours GMT. See Fig 66 for Monday 24 April. The Tab GHA and Tab Dec for 08 hours and 09 hours GMT are:

GMT	GHA	Dec
08	300° 27′.4	N12° 46′.8
09	315° 27′.5	N12° 47′.6

This means that at 08 hours GMT the sun's Geographical Position (GP) is:
Latitude 12° 46′.8 North
Longitude 300° 27′.4 West from Greenwich

Of course to plot this position on a chart the west longitude would have to be subtracted from 360° to give the more familiar 0° to 180° E or W units, i.e. (360° – 300° 27′.4) is equivalent to longitude 59° 32′.6 East.

Finding Greenwich hour angle

To find the GHA for any moment other than the exact hour, the increment for the additional minutes and seconds of time is found from the tinted pages at the back of the

Fig 66
Extract from the 1978 Nautical Almanac, *page 85, showing tabulated GHA and declination.*

G.M.T. d h	SUN G.H.A. ° ′	SUN Dec. ° ′	MOON G.H.A. ° ′	v ′	MOON Dec. ° ′	d ′	H.P. ′
22 00	180 20.6	N12 00.0	14 16.4	10.5	S 5 32.4	10.3	58.2
01	195 20.7	00.8	28 45.9	10.4	5 42.7	10.2	58.2
02	210 20.8	01.7	43 15.3	10.4	5 52.9	10.3	58.3
03	225 21.0	·· 02.5	57 44.7	10.3	6 03.2	10.2	58.3
04	240 21.1	03.4	72 14.0	10.3	6 13.4	10.2	58.3
05	255 21.2	04.2	86 43.3	10.2	6 23.6	10.1	58.3
06	270 21.3	N12 05.0	101 12.5	10.2	S 6 33.7	10.1	58.4
07	285 21.5	05.9	115 41.7	10.1	6 43.8	10.2	58.4
S 08	300 21.6	06.7	130 10.8	10.0	6 54.0	10.0	58.4
A 09	315 21.7	·· 07.6	144 39.8	10.0	7 04.0	10.1	58.5
T 10	330 21.8	08.4	159 08.8	9.9	7 14.1	10.0	58.5
U 11	345 22.0	09.3	173 37.7	9.9	7 24.1	10.0	58.5
R 12	0 22.1	N12 10.1	188 06.6	9.8	S 7 34.1	9.9	58.5
D 13	15 22.2	10.9	202 35.4	9.8	7 44.0	9.9	58.6
A 14	30 22.3	11.8	217 04.2	9.7	7 53.9	9.9	58.6
Y 15	45 22.5	·· 12.6	231 32.9	9.6	8 03.8	9.9	58.6
16	60 22.6	13.5	246 01.5	9.6	8 13.7	9.8	58.7
17	75 22.7	14.3	260 30.1	9.5	8 23.5	9.8	58.7
18	90 22.8	N12 15.1	274 58.6	9.4	S 8 33.3	9.7	58.7
19	105 23.0	16.0	289 27.0	9.4	8 43.0	9.7	58.7
20	120 23.1	16.8	303 55.4	9.4	8 52.7	9.6	58.8
21	135 23.2	·· 17.7	318 23.8	9.2	9 02.3	9.6	58.8
22	150 23.3	18.5	332 52.0	9.2	9 11.9	9.6	58.8
23	165 23.4	19.3	347 20.2	9.2	9 21.5	9.5	58.8
23 00	180 23.6	N12 20.2	1 48.4	9.1	S 9 31.0	9.4	58.9
01	195 23.7	21.0	16 16.5	9.0	9 40.4	9.5	58.9
02	210 23.8	21.8	30 44.5	9.0	9 49.9	9.3	58.9
03	225 23.9	·· 22.7	45 12.5	8.9	9 59.2	9.3	58.9
04	240 24.1	23.5	59 40.4	8.8	10 08.5	9.3	59.0
05	255 24.2	24.3	74 08.2	8.8	10 17.8	9.2	59.0
06	270 24.3	N12 25.2	88 36.0	8.7	S10 27.0	9.1	59.0
07	285 24.4	26.0	103 03.7	8.7	10 36.1	9.1	59.0
08	300 24.5	26.8	117 31.4	8.6	10 45.2	9.1	59.1
S 09	315 24.7	·· 27.7	131 59.0	8.5	10 54.3	9.0	59.1
U 10	330 24.8	28.5	146 26.5	8.5	11 03.3	8.9	59.1
N 11	345 24.9	29.4	160 54.0	8.4	11 12.2	8.8	59.1
D 12	0 25.0	N12 30.2	175 21.4	8.3	S11 21.0	8.8	59.2
A 13	15 25.1	31.0	189 48.7	8.3	11 29.8	8.8	59.2
Y 14	30 25.3	31.8	204 16.0	8.2	11 38.6	8.6	59.2
15	45 25.4	·· 32.7	218 43.2	8.2	11 47.2	8.6	59.2
16	60 25.5	33.5	233 10.4	8.1	11 55.8	8.6	59.2
17	75 25.6	34.3	247 37.5	8.0	12 04.4	8.4	59.3
18	90 25.7	N12 35.2	262 04.5	8.0	S12 12.8	8.4	59.3
19	105 25.8	36.0	276 31.5	7.9	12 21.2	8.3	59.3
20	120 26.0	36.8	290 58.4	7.9	12 29.5	8.3	59.3
21	135 26.1	·· 37.7	305 25.3	7.8	12 37.8	8.2	59.3
22	150 26.2	38.5	319 52.1	7.7	12 46.0	8.1	59.4
23	165 26.3	39.3	334 18.8	7.7	12 54.1	8.0	59.4
24 00	180 26.4	N12 40.2	348 45.5	7.6	S13 02.1	8.0	59.4
01	195 26.6	41.0	3 12.1	7.5	13 10.1	7.8	59.4
02	210 26.7	41.8	17 38.6	7.5	13 17.9	7.8	59.4
03	225 26.8	·· 42.6	32 05.1	7.5	13 25.7	7.7	59.5
04	240 26.9	43.5	46 31.6	7.3	13 33.4	7.7	59.5
05	255 27.0	44.3	60 57.9	7.3	13 41.1	7.5	59.5
06	270 27.1	N12 45.1	75 24.2	7.3	S13 48.6	7.5	59.5
07	285 27.3	45.9	89 50.5	7.2	13 56.1	7.4	59.5
08	300 27.4	46.8	104 16.7	7.2	14 03.5	7.2	59.5
M 09	315 27.5	·· 47.6	118 42.9	7.0	14 10.7	7.2	59.6
O 10	330 27.6	48.4	133 08.9	7.1	14 17.9	7.2	59.6
N 11	345 27.7	49.2	147 35.0	7.0	14 25.1	7.0	59.6
D 12	0 27.8	N12 50.1	162 01.0	6.9	S14 32.1	6.9	59.6
A 13	15 27.9	50.9	176 26.9	6.8	14 39.0	6.9	59.6
Y 14	30 28.1	51.7	190 52.7	6.9	14 45.9	6.7	59.6
15	45 28.2	·· 52.5	205 18.6	6.7	14 52.6	6.7	59.6
16	60 28.3	53.4	219 44.3	6.7	14 59.3	6.5	59.7
17	75 28.4	54.2	234 10.0	6.7	15 05.8	6.5	59.7
18	90 28.5	N12 55.0	248 35.7	6.6	S15 12.3	6.4	59.7
19	105 28.6	55.8	263 01.3	6.6	15 18.7	6.2	59.7
20	120 28.7	56.6	277 26.9	6.5	15 24.9	6.2	59.7
21	135 28.9	·· 57.5	291 52.4	6.4	15 31.1	6.1	59.7
22	150 29.0	58.3	306 17.8	6.4	15 37.2	5.9	59.7
23	165 29.1	59.1	320 43.2	6.4	15 43.1	5.9	59.7
	S.D. 15.9	d 0.8	S.D. 16.0		16.1		16.2

Lat. °	Twilight Naut. h m	Twilight Civil h m	Sunrise h m	Moonrise 22 h m	Moonrise 23 h m	Moonrise 24 h m	Moonrise 25 h m
N 72	////	////	02 53	19 40	21 39	23 45	26 14
N 70	////	01 34	03 17	19 25	21 14	23 03	24 45
68	////	02 15	03 36	19 14	20 55	22 35	24 06
66	////	02 42	03 50	19 05	20 40	22 13	23 39
64	01 22	03 03	04 02	18 57	20 27	21 56	23 18
62	01 59	03 19	04 13	18 50	20 17	21 42	23 01
60	02 24	03 33	04 21	18 44	20 08	21 31	22 47
N 58	02 43	03 44	04 29	18 39	20 00	21 20	22 35
56	02 59	03 54	04 36	18 34	19 54	21 12	22 25
54	03 12	04 02	04 42	18 30	19 48	21 04	22 16
52	03 23	04 10	04 47	18 27	19 42	20 57	22 08
50	03 33	04 17	04 52	18 23	19 37	20 50	22 00
45	03 53	04 31	05 03	18 16	19 27	20 37	21 45
N 40	04 08	04 43	05 11	18 10	19 18	20 26	21 32
35	04 21	04 52	05 19	18 05	19 10	20 16	21 21
30	04 31	05 00	05 25	18 01	19 04	20 08	21 12
20	04 47	05 14	05 36	17 53	18 53	19 54	20 55
N 10	04 59	05 24	05 46	17 46	18 43	19 41	20 41
0	05 09	05 34	05 55	17 40	18 34	19 30	20 28
S 10	05 18	05 42	06 04	17 34	18 24	19 18	20 15
20	05 25	05 51	06 13	17 27	18 15	19 06	20 01
30	05 31	05 59	06 24	17 20	18 04	18 52	19 45
35	05 34	06 04	06 30	17 15	17 58	18 44	19 35
40	05 37	06 09	06 36	17 11	17 50	18 35	19 25
45	05 40	06 14	06 44	17 05	17 42	18 24	19 13
S 50	05 43	06 20	06 54	16 58	17 32	18 11	18 58
52	05 44	06 23	06 58	16 55	17 28	18 05	18 51
54	05 45	06 26	07 03	16 52	17 23	17 59	18 43
56	05 46	06 29	07 08	16 48	17 17	17 52	18 34
58	05 47	06 33	07 14	16 44	17 11	17 43	18 24
S 60	05 48	06 37	07 21	16 40	17 04	17 34	18 13

Lat. °	Sunset h m	Twilight Civil h m	Twilight Naut. h m	Moonset 22 h m	Moonset 23 h m	Moonset 24 h m	Moonset 25 h m
N 72	21 08	////	////	03 51	03 45	03 39	03 31
N 70	20 43	22 32	////	04 00	04 02	04 05	04 14
68	20 24	21 47	////	04 07	04 14	04 25	04 43
66	20 09	21 19	////	04 13	04 25	04 41	05 05
64	19 56	20 57	22 43	04 18	04 34	04 55	05 23
62	19 46	20 40	22 03	04 23	04 42	05 06	05 37
60	19 37	20 26	21 36	04 27	04 49	05 15	05 49
N 58	19 29	20 15	21 16	04 30	04 55	05 24	06 00
56	19 22	20 05	21 00	04 33	05 00	05 31	06 09
54	19 16	19 56	20 47	04 36	05 05	05 38	06 17
52	19 11	19 48	20 35	04 39	05 09	05 44	06 25
50	19 06	19 41	20 25	04 41	05 13	05 49	06 31
45	18 55	19 26	20 05	04 46	05 21	06 01	06 46
N 40	18 46	19 15	19 49	04 51	05 28	06 10	06 57
35	18 39	19 05	19 37	04 54	05 34	06 19	07 07
30	18 32	18 57	19 26	04 58	05 40	06 26	07 16
20	18 21	18 43	19 10	05 03	05 49	06 38	07 31
N 10	18 11	18 32	18 58	05 08	05 57	06 50	07 45
0	18 02	18 23	18 47	05 13	06 05	07 00	07 57
S 10	17 53	18 14	18 39	05 18	06 13	07 10	08 10
20	17 43	18 06	18 32	05 23	06 21	07 22	08 23
30	17 33	17 57	18 25	05 28	06 31	07 34	08 38
35	17 27	17 52	18 22	05 32	06 36	07 42	08 47
40	17 20	17 47	18 19	05 36	06 42	07 50	08 57
45	17 12	17 42	18 16	05 40	06 50	08 00	09 09
S 50	17 02	17 35	18 13	05 45	06 58	08 12	09 24
52	16 58	17 33	18 12	05 47	07 02	08 17	09 30
54	16 53	17 30	18 11	05 50	07 07	08 24	09 38
56	16 48	17 26	18 10	05 53	07 12	08 30	09 46
58	16 42	17 23	18 09	05 56	07 17	08 38	09 56
S 60	16 35	17 19	18 07	06 00	07 23	08 47	10 07

Day	SUN Eqn. of Time 00ʰ m s	SUN Eqn. of Time 12ʰ m s	SUN Mer. Pass. h m	MOON Mer. Pass. Upper h m	MOON Mer. Pass. Lower h m	MOON Age d	MOON Phase
22	01 22	01 28	11 59	23 53	11 26	15	○
23	01 34	01 40	11 58	24 47	12 19	16	
24	01 46	01 51	11 58	00 47	13 15	17	

30m	SUN PLANETS	ARIES	MOON	v or d	Corrn	v or d	Corrn	v or d	Corrn
s	° ′	° ′	° ′	′	′	′	′	′	′
00	7 30·0	7 31·2	7 09·5	0·0	0·0	6·0	3·1	12·0	6·1
01	7 30·3	7 31·5	7 09·7	0·1	0·1	6·1	3·1	12·1	6·2
02	7 30·5	7 31·7	7 10·0	0·2	0·1	6·2	3·2	12·2	6·2
03	7 30·8	7 32·0	7 10·2	0·3	0·2	6·3	3·2	12·3	6·3
04	7 31·0	7 32·2	7 10·5	0·4	0·2	6·4	3·3	12·4	6·3
05	7 31·3	7 32·5	7 10·7	0·5	0·3	6·5	3·3	12·5	6·4
06	7 31·5	7 32·7	7 10·9	0·6	0·3	6·6	3·4	12·6	6·4
07	7 31·8	7 33·0	7 11·2	0·7	0·4	6·7	3·4	12·7	6·5
08	7 32·0	7 33·2	7 11·4	0·8	0·4	6·8	3·5	12·8	6·5
09	7 32·3	7 33·5	7 11·6	0·9	0·5	6·9	3·5	12·9	6·6
10	7 32·5	7 33·7	7 11·9	1·0	0·5	7·0	3·6	13·0	6·6
11	7 32·8	7 34·0	7 12·1	1·1	0·6	7·1	3·6	13·1	6·7
12	7 33·0	7 34·2	7 12·4	1·2	0·6	7·2	3·7	13·2	6·7
13	7 33·3	7 34·5	7 12·6	1·3	0·7	7·3	3·7	13·3	6·8
14	7 33·5	7 34·7	7 12·8	1·4	0·7	7·4	3·8	13·4	6·8
15	7 33·8	7 35·0	7 13·1	1·5	0·8	7·5	3·8	13·5	6·9
16	7 34·0	7 35·2	7 13·3	1·6	0·8	7·6	3·9	13·6	6·9
17	7 34·3	7 35·5	7 13·6	1·7	0·9	7·7	3·9	13·7	7·0
18	7 34·5	7 35·7	7 13·8	1·8	0·9	7·8	4·0	13·8	7·0
19	7 34·8	7 36·0	7 14·0	1·9	1·0	7·9	4·0	13·9	7·1
20	7 35·0	7 36·2	7 14·3	2·0	1·0	8·0	4·1	14·0	7·1
[illegible]	7 35·3	7 36·5	7 14·5	2·1	1·1	8·1	4·1	[illegible]	[illegible]
[illegible]	[illegible]	7 36·7	7 14·7	2·2	[illegible]	[illegible]	[illegible]	[illegible]	[illegible]
47	[illegible]	[illegible]	[illegible]	[illegible]	[illegible]	[illegible]	[illegible]	16·7	8·5
48	7 42·0	[illegible]	[illegible]	[illegible]	2·4	10·8	5·5	16·8	8·5
49	7 42·3	7 43·5	7 21·2	4·9	2·5	10·9	5·5	16·9	8·6
50	7 42·5	7 43·8	7 21·4	5·0	2·5	11·0	5·6	17·0	8·6
51	7 42·8	7 44·0	7 21·7	5·1	2·6	11·1	5·6	17·1	8·7
52	7 43·0	7 44·3	7 21·9	5·2	2·6	11·2	5·7	17·2	8·7
53	7 43·3	7 44·5	7 22·1	5·3	2·7	11·3	5·7	17·3	8·8
54	7 43·5	7 44·8	7 22·4	5·4	2·7	11·4	5·8	17·4	8·8
55	7 43·8	7 45·0	7 22·6	5·5	2·8	11·5	5·8	17·5	8·9
56	7 44·0	7 45·3	7 22·9	5·6	2·8	11·6	5·9	17·6	8·9
57	7 44·3	7 45·5	7 23·1	5·7	2·9	11·7	5·9	17·7	9·0
58	7 44·5	7 45·8	7 23·3	5·8	2·9	11·8	6·0	17·8	9·0
59	7 44·8	7 46·0	7 23·6	5·9	3·0	11·9	6·0	17·9	9·1
60	7 45·0	7 46·3	7 23·8	6·0	3·1	12·0	6·1	18·0	9·2

31m	SUN PLANETS	ARIES	MOON	v or d	Corrn	v or d	Corrn	v or d	Corrn
s	° ′	° ′	° ′	′	′	′	′	′	′
00	7 45·0	7 46·3	7 23·8	0·0	0·0	6·0	3·2	12·0	6·3
01	7 45·3	7 46·5	7 24·1	0·1	0·1	6·1	3·2	12·1	6·4
02	7 45·5	7 46·8	7 24·3	0·2	0·1	6·2	3·3	12·2	6·4
03	7 45·8	7 47·0	7 24·5	0·3	0·2	6·3	3·3	12·3	6·5
04	7 46·0	7 47·3	7 24·8	0·4	0·2	6·4	3·4	12·4	6·5
05	7 46·3	7 47·5	7 25·0	0·5	0·3	6·5	3·4	12·5	6·6
06	7 46·5	7 47·8	7 25·2	0·6	0·3	6·6	3·5	12·6	6·6
07	7 46·8	7 48·0	7 25·5	0·7	0·4	6·7	3·5	12·7	6·7
08	7 47·0	7 48·3	7 25·7	0·8	0·4	6·8	3·6	12·8	6·7
09	7 47·3	7 48·5	7 26·0	0·9	0·5	6·9	3·6	12·9	6·8
10	7 47·5	7 48·8	7 26·2	1·0	0·5	7·0	3·7	13·0	6·8
11	7 47·8	7 49·0	7 26·4	1·1	0·6	7·1	3·7	13·1	6·9
12	7 48·0	7 49·3	7 26·7	1·2	0·6	7·2	3·8	13·2	6·9
13	7 48·3	7 49·5	7 26·9	1·3	0·7	7·3	3·8	13·3	7·0
14	7 48·5	7 49·8	7 27·2	1·4	0·7	7·4	3·9	13·4	7·0
15	7 48·8	7 50·0	7 27·4	1·5	0·8	7·5	3·9	13·5	7·1
16	7 49·0	7 50·3	7 27·6	1·6	0·8	7·6	4·0	13·6	7·1
17	7 49·3	7 50·5	7 27·9	1·7	0·9	7·7	4·0	13·7	7·2
18	7 49·5	7 50·8	[illegible]	[illegible]	[illegible]	[illegible]	4·1	13·8	7·2
19	[illegible]	[illegible]	[illegible]	[illegible]	[illegible]	[illegible]	[illegible]	[illegible]	7·3
[illegible]	[illegible]	[illegible]	[illegible]	[illegible]	[illegible]	[illegible]	[illegible]	[illegible]	[illegible]
[illegible]	[illegible]	7 57·3	7 34·3	4·4	2·3	10·4	5·5	16·4	[illegible]
[illegible]	7 56·3	7 57·6	7 34·6	4·5	2·4	10·5	5·5	16·5	8·7
46	7 56·5	7 57·8	7 34·8	4·6	2·4	10·6	5·6	16·6	8·7
47	7 56·8	7 58·1	7 35·0	4·7	2·5	10·7	5·6	16·7	8·8
48	7 57·0	7 58·3	7 35·3	4·8	2·5	10·8	5·7	16·8	8·8
49	7 57·3	7 58·6	7 35·5	4·9	2·6	10·9	5·7	16·9	8·9
50	7 57·5	7 58·8	7 35·7	5·0	2·6	11·0	5·8	17·0	8·9
51	7 57·8	7 59·1	7 36·0	5·1	2·7	11·1	5·8	17·1	9·0
52	7 58·0	7 59·3	7 36·2	5·2	2·7	11·2	5·9	17·2	9·0
53	7 58·3	7 59·6	7 36·5	5·3	2·8	11·3	5·9	17·3	9·1
54	7 58·5	7 59·8	7 36·7	5·4	2·8	11·4	6·0	17·4	9·1
55	7 58·8	8 00·1	7 36·9	5·5	2·9	11·5	6·0	17·5	9·2
56	7 59·0	8 00·3	7 37·2	5·6	2·9	11·6	6·1	17·6	9·2
57	7 59·3	8 00·6	7 37·4	5·7	3·0	11·7	6·1	17·7	9·3
58	7 59·5	8 00·8	7 37·7	5·8	3·0	11·8	6·2	17·8	9·3
59	7 59·8	8 01·1	7 37·9	5·9	3·1	11·9	6·2	17·9	9·4
60	8 00·0	8 01·3	7 38·1	6·0	3·2	12·0	6·3	18·0	9·5

Fig 67
Extract from the 1978 Nautical Almanac, *tinted page xvii, showing increments and corrections for the GHA*

Almanac. These give the increase in GHA for every minute and part minute over one hour.

The sun's GHA increases exactly 15 degrees per hour. Thus in half an hour the change should be 7° 30′. Fig 67 shows the increment page for 30 minutes and 31 minutes. In the left hand column headed 'Sun', and opposite 30 mins 00 secs, the correction is 7° 30′, as expected. Look opposite the line for 30 mins 53 secs where the increment is 7° 43′.3. The increment for 31 mins 08 secs is 7° 47′.0.

To find the GHA of the sun at 08 hours, 23 mins and 59 secs GMT on 24 April 1978, the Tab GHA for 08 hours is found from the *Almanac*, and the increment for the minutes and seconds added, e.g.:

Tab GHA for 08h GMT	300° 27′.4
Increment for 23m 59s	5° 59′.8 +
GHA at 08h 23m 59s GMT	306° 27′.2

Finding the sun's declination

Unlike the GHA, the sun's declination changes quite slowly hour by hour. Using the figures above, it can be seen that the declination has changed from N 12° 46′.8 to N 12° 47′.6 between 08 and 09 hours GMT, an increase of 0′.8. In fact the *Almanac* saves the navigator the trouble of working out the small change in the value of declination in one hour by giving it at the foot of the sun's declination column as shown in Fig 66. In this case the Dec would change 0′.4 in half an hour. Again the tinted pages at the back of the *Almanac* can be used to find the change in Dec for each minute during an hour.

The tabulated value of d (0.8) is found in the column headed v or d, and the correction is alongside it to the right. In many cases the correction needed can be found by mental arithmetic. The correction is plus or minus, depending on whether the declination is increasing or decreasing during the day.

Using the same time and date in the GHA example above:

Tab Dec for 08h GMT	N12° 46′.8	d=0.8
d correction for 23m 59s	0′.3+	(increasing)
Sun's declination at 08h 23m 59s	N12° 47′.1	

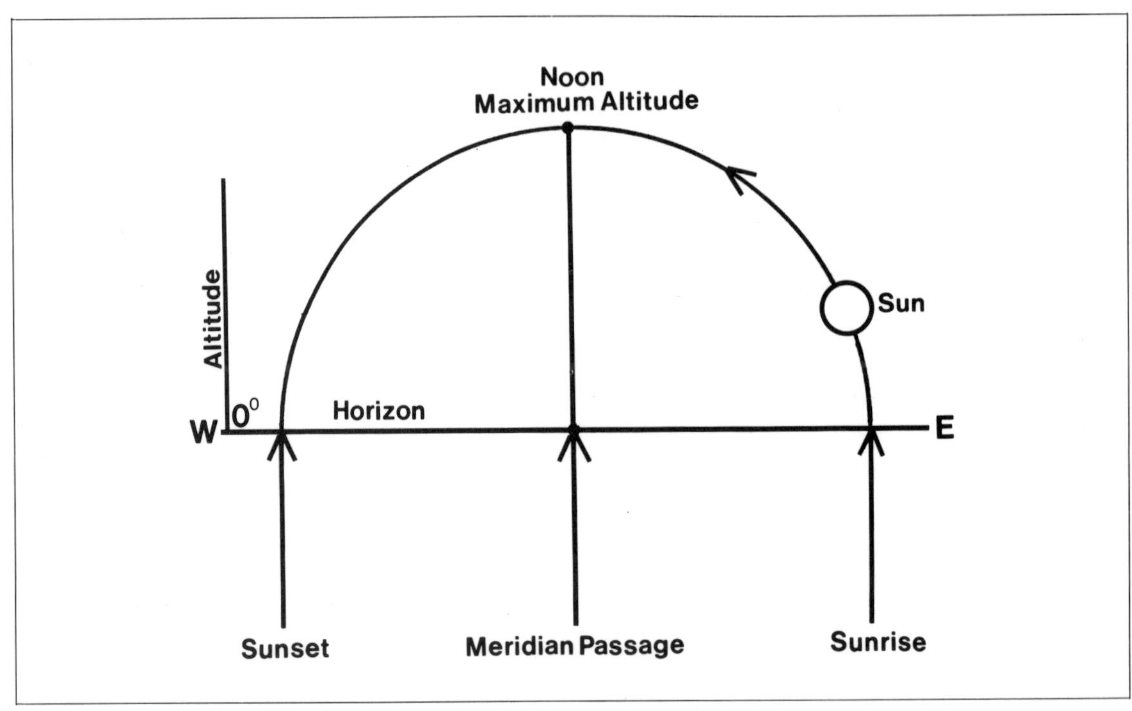

Fig 68
A plot of the sun's altitude against the time of day

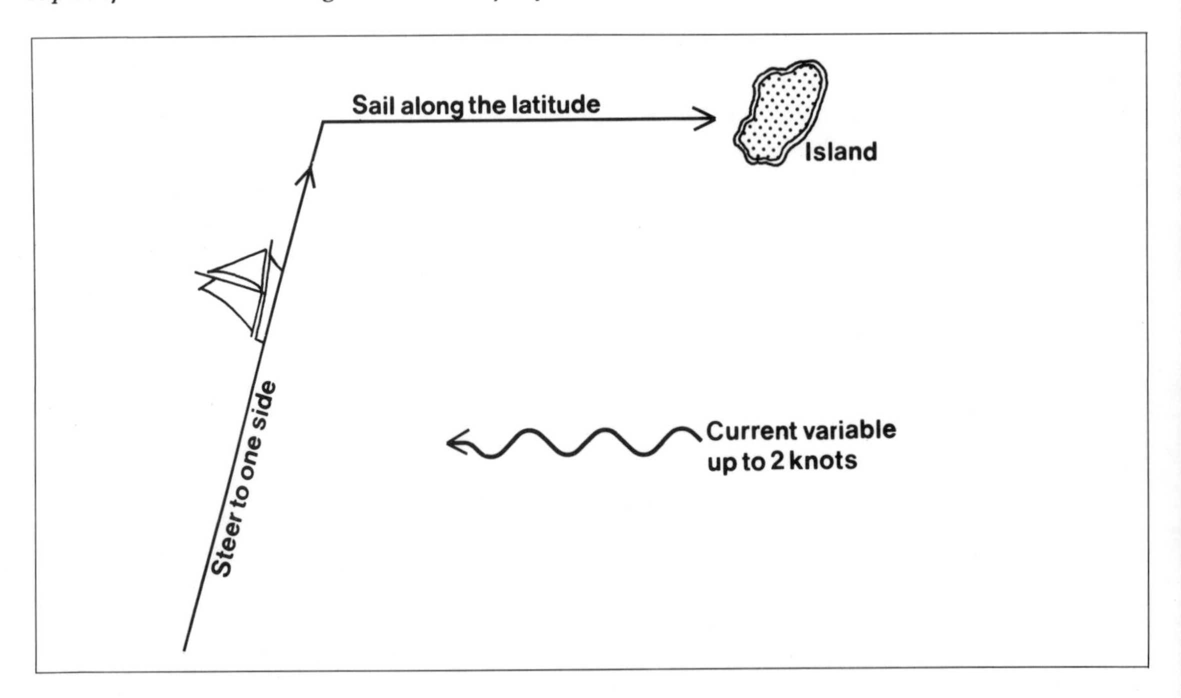

Fig 69
Offset sailing

Chapter Six

The Noon Latitude

An observer can find his distance from the sun's GP by subtracting the true altitude from 90 degrees, as shown in Fig 47. So at sunrise and sunset each day when the altitude is least the GP is at its maximum distance. (90° – 0° altitude = 90°, distance = 90° x 60 = 5 400 nautical miles.) After rising in the east, the GP gets closer as the sun climbs higher in the sky. When the sun reaches its highest altitude each day, the GP is at its closest point to the observer. This is at midday, which means exactly what it says – halfway between sunrise and sunset. The sun is on the same meridian of longitude as the observer, and the true azimuth is either due north or due south. In the afternoon, as the GP moves further away to the west, the altitude falls again.

At its maximum altitude the sun is moving across the observer's longitude from east to west, and this is called the meridian passage of the sun. Although this is midday or noon, it may not be exactly 1200 local time. For example, noon on the Greenwich meridian varies between 1144 and 1214 GMT during the year. The time of the sun's meridian passage is discussed further on page 71.

Fig 68 shows a curve of the sun's altitude increasing from 0 degrees at sunrise to the maximum altitude at meridian passage, and decreasing again until the sun sets. The curve flattens out immediately either side of the highest point, and in practice the sun's altitude hardly changes for a few minutes before and after the time of meridian passage. The navigator has perhaps up to seven or eight minutes in which to bring the sun accurately on to the horizon. In addition, should the sun be clouded over at the exact time of noon, the altitude at meridian passage can still be found.

Latitude from meridian altitude

Finding the altitude of the sun at the time of daily meridian passage is one of the oldest ways of finding latitude and is certainly the quickest. As the celestial position line is always at right angles to the true bearing, and as the sun is either due north or due south at noon, the resulting position line runs east-west, i.e. it is a parallel of latitude.

Before the introduction of the chronometer in the late eighteenth century, mariners were unable to find longitude at sea without using very lengthy calculations. The sextant was not invented until 1757 and accurate measurement was difficult at sea using its forerunners, such as the quadrant, when the sun's altitude was changing rapidly. However, such disadvantages did not affect the noon sight, and the early navigators were able to establish their latitude with some precision.

It is thought that long ocean voyages were often undertaken by deliberately steering well to one side or other of the destination. The mariner then sailed until his vessel reached the same latitude as the destination, and then turned east or west as appropriate. Thus even though the longitude by dead reckoning might be grossly in error, so long as the ship sailed along the correct parallel of latitude, checked by the daily latitude sight at noon, the port of destination had to be somewhere ahead.

Even now, a yachtsman heading for a small isolated island with perhaps an unknown or variable current setting him off track can use this method as shown in Fig 69.

Fig 70 shows the situation at meridian passage where the observer is in south latitudes and the sun's declination is also south. As the sun and the observer are both on the same longitude, it can be seen that a combination of the declination and the observer's distance from the GP is equal to the latitude of the observer. In every case at noon, if the sun's declination and zenith distance are known (and the distance of the sun from the zenith = the distance of the GP from the observer's position) the navigator can find his latitude, i.e. he must lie somewhere on that particular parallel of latitude. The advantages of the meridian passage sight are that an accurate time is not required, the navigator has several minutes in which to find the altitude when the sun is steady, and no tables are needed other than the *Nautical Almanac* for finding declination. The calculations are also quite short, as shown below.

In the situation shown in Fig 70, the sun's true altitude at noon was found to be 70° 00′ and the sun's declination was 10° 00′ S. Latitude at noon by dead reckoning: 30° 04′ S.

Zenith distance =	(90° minus true altitude)
	90° 00′
True altitude	70° 00′ –
Zenith distance	20° 00′
Sun's declination (*Nautical Almanac*)	S10° 00′ +
Observer's latitude (at the time of noon)	30° 00′ S

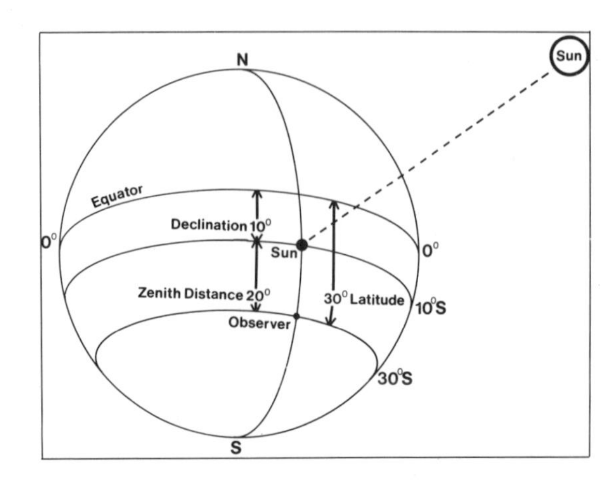

Fig 70
Meridian passage when the observer is in south latitudes and the sun's declination is also south

Finding the time of noon

A rather time-consuming method of finding the sun's highest altitude would be to take a sextant on deck late in the morning and continually check the altitude. It would increase steadily but the rate of increase would slow as the time of meridian passage grew closer. Finally the altitude would remain the same for a few minutes and then start to decrease.

It would be more useful to work out the time of noon in advance, and the *Nautical Almanac* contains the necessary information. If the navigator goes on deck shortly before then, he needs only spend a few minutes with the sextant before finding the sun's noon altitude.

In Fig 72, in the table headed 'Sun., Mer. Pass.', the time of noon is tabulated for each of the three consecutive dates on each page opening in the *Nautical Almanac*. In fact, this is the GMT of noon on the Greenwich meridian.

To anyone exactly 15 degrees longitude to the east of Greenwich, the sun would reach its highest point in the sky exactly one hour before noon at Greenwich. To find the time of noon anywhere on the earth, allowance must be made for the navigator's longitude.

CONVERSION OF ARC TO TIME

0°–59°		60°–119°		120°–179°		180°–239°		240°–299°		300°–359°		
°	h m	°	h m	°	h m	°	h m	°	h m	°	h m	
0	0 00	60	4 00	120	8 00	180	12 00	240	16 00	300	20 00	
1	0 04	61	4 04	121	8 04	181	12 04	241	16 04	301	20 04	
2	0 08	62	4 08	122	8 08	182	12 08	242	16 08	302	20 08	
3	0 12	63	4 12	123	8 12	183	12 12	243	16 12	303	20 12	
4	0 16	64	4 16	124	8 16	184	12 16	244	16 16	304	20 16	
5	0 20	65	4 20	125	8 20	185	12 20	245	16 20	305	20 20	
6	0 24	66	4 24	126	8 24	186	12 24	246	16 24	306	20 24	
7	0 28	67	4 28	127	8 28	187	12 28	247	16 28	307	20 28	
8	0 32	68	4 32	128	8 32	188	12 32	248	16 32	308	20 32	
9	0 36	69	4 36	129	8 36	189	12 36	249	16 36	309	20 36	
10	0 40	70	4 40	130	8 40	190	12 40	250	16 40	310	20 40	10
11	0 44	71	4 44	131	8 44	191	12 44	251	16 44	311	20 44	11
12	0 48	72	4 48	132	8 48	192	12 48	252	16 48	312	20 48	12
13	0 52	73	4 52	133	8 52	193	12 52	253	16 52	313	20 52	13
14	0 56	74	4 56	134	8 56	194	12 56	254	16 56	314	20 56	14
15	1 00	75	5 00	135	9 00	195	13 00	255	17 00	315	21 00	15
16	1 04	76	5 04	136	9 04	196	13 04	256	17 04	316	21 04	16
17	1 08	77	5 08	137	9 08	197	13 08	257	17 08	317	21 08	
18	1 12	78	5 12	138	9 12	198	13 12	258	17 12	318	21 12	
19	1 16	79	5 16	139	9 16	199	13 16	259	17 16	319	21 16	
20	1 20	80	5 20	140	9 20	200	13 20	260	17 20	320	21 20	
21	1 24	81	5 24	141	9 24	201	13 24	261	17 24	321	21 24	
22	1 28	82	5 28	142	9 28	202	13 28	262	17 28	322	21 28	
23	1 32	83	5 32	143	9 32	203	13 32	263	17 32	323	21 32	
24	1 36	84	5 36	144	9 36	204	13 36	264	17 36	324	21 36	
25	1 40	85	5 40	145	9 40	205	13 40	265	17 40	325	21 40	
26	1 44	86	5 44	146	9 44	206	13 44	266	17 44	326	21 44	
27	1 48	87	5 48	147	9 48	207	13 48	267	17 48	327	21 48	
28	1 52	88	5 52	148	9 52	208	13 52	268	17 52	328	21 52	
29	1 56	89	5 56	149	9 56	209	13 56	269	17 56	329	21 56	
30	2 00	90	6 00	150	10 00	210	14 00	270	18 00	330	22 00	30
31	2 04	91	6 04	151	10 04	211	14 04	271	18 04	331	22 04	31
32	2 08	92	6 08	152	10 08	212	14 08	272	18 08	332	22 08	32
33	2 12	93	6 12	153	10 12	213	14 12	273	18 12	333	22 12	33
34	2 16	94	6 16	154	10 16	214	14 16	274	18 16	334	22 16	34

Fig 71
Conversion of arc, or longitude, to time. From the 1978 Nautical Almanac, *tinted page i*

The first of the tinted pages in the *Nautical Almanac* (Fig 71) is a table called 'Conversion of Arc to Time'. For the purpose of most calculations needed by the navigator, this could be read as 'Conversion of Longitude to Time'. For example, a longitude of 90 degrees converts to exactly 6h 00m of time. As each degree of longitude equals 4 minutes of time, 91 degrees of longitude becomes 6h 04m.

The method of finding the time of meridian passage in longitude 3°00′E on 7 May 1978 is as follows:

Time of Mer Pass on 7 May (*Nautical Almanac*)	11h 57m
Longitude 3°E converted to time	00h 12m–
GMT of noon at 3°E	11h 45m

17	75 54.3		23.3						54.5
18	90 54.3	N17	24.0	60 09.3	11.9	N17	59.0	1.9	54.5
19	105 54.4		24.7	74 40.2	11.9	18	00.9	1.7	54.5
20	120 54.4		25.3	89 11.1	11.9	18	02.6	1.7	54.5
21	135 54.4	··	26.0	103 42.0	11.8	18	04.3	1.6	54.5
22	150 54.4		26.6	118 12.8	11.9	18	05.9	1.5	54.5
23	165 54.5		27.3	132 43.7	11.9	18	07.4	1.4	54.4
	S.D. 15.9	*d*	0.7	S.D.	15.1		15.0		14.9

S 60	15 56	16 43	17 34	16 34	17 04	17 41	18 26
	SUN			MOON			
Day	Eqn. of Time 00ʰ	12ʰ	Mer. Pass.	Mer. Pass. Upper	Lower	Age	Phase
	m s	m s	h m	h m	h m	d	
7	03 28	03 30	11 57	12 15	24 39	00	●
→8	03 32	03 33	11 56	13 03	00 39	01	
9	03 35	03 37	11 56	13 51	01 27	02	

Fig 72
Time of meridian passage. From the 1978 Nautical Almanac, *page 95*

The rhyme which was given earlier in the text for remembering how to apply magnetic variation to change a magnetic to a true course can be adapted for use in celestial navigation, i.e.:
'Longitude east, Greenwich least,
Longitude west, Greenwich best.'

From the example above it can be seen that the easterly longitude has been subtracted to give a GMT which is less (i.e. earlier) than the time of noon at Greenwich.

The same procedure is used for any longitude. For example, to find the time of noon at dead reckoning longitude 136°E on 8 May 1978:

Time of Mer. Pass. on 8th May	11h 56m
Longitude 136°E	09h 40m (E – W +)
GMT of noon at longitude 136°E	02h 52m

Although this gives the actual time in GMT, the navigator has a practical interest in the local time of noon, i.e. the time on his wristwatch.

The zone time at longitude 136°E is 9 hours ahead of GMT. To find the local time of noon, the calculation must be completed by allowing for the difference in hours between GMT and zone time being kept on board.

GMT of noon at 136° E	02h 52m
Zone time 9 hours ahead of GMT	9h +
Local time of noon	11h 52m

Choosing the noon longitude

In the examples given, I have stated that the vessel is at a given longitude. In practice the navigator at sea must provide this information himself, supposedly the dead reckoning longitude at noon. At first sight it may seem that the answer, i.e. the local time of noon, must be known before the requisite longitude used in an earlier step in the calculation can be provided. In fact there is little problem. If in harbour or stopped at sea, the longitude does not change. Similarly on a north or south course at sea, the longitude is constant. A yacht, by and large, does not travel at any great speed, so that even on an east or west course the longitude changes quite slowly. A sufficiently accurate time of noon for the navigator's purpose can be worked out by using the longitude by dead reckoning at 1200 local time.

One of the advantages of the noon sight is that the sun remains at its maximum altitude for several minutes. Even if the dead reckoning longitude used were wrong by one whole degree, the time of noon would only be in error by four minutes of time. Any doubt in the navigator's mind about the accuracy of a longitude he may have used can be overcome by giving a margin for error, i.e. he should start taking the sun's altitude a quarter of an hour before the time worked out, instead of the usual five minutes or so beforehand.

Taking the meridian passage sight

The navigator should go on deck some minutes prior to the time of meridian passage and bring the lower limb of the sun onto the horizon. Adjust the altitude every half minute or so; the sextant can become very heavy if it is kept glued to the eye for 5 or 10 minutes.

As the time of meridian passage approaches, the sun will cease to climb. At this point read off and jot down the altitude. There may be another minor adjustment needed as the sun appears to 'stand', but then the altitude will decrease as the sun starts to fall. The noon altitude is either the one jotted down or the slightly higher one if an adjustment has been made.

Find the declination of the sun for the GMT of meridian passage from the *Nautical Almanac*. This can be done earlier in the day when working out the time of noon, because GMT is found anyway in the calculation. Correct the sextant altitude to give true altitude.

Latitude

Subtract the true altitude from 90 degrees, calling the remainder the zenith distance.
2 (a) In south latitudes:
If the sun's declination is south and its true bearing at meridian passage is 000 degrees, add zenith distance and declination. If the sun's declination is south and its true bearing at meridian passage is 180 degrees, subtract zenith distance from declination.
If the sun's declination is north, subtract declination from zenith distance.

(b) In north latitudes:
If the sun's declination is south and its true bearing at meridian passage is 180 degrees, subtract declination from zenith distance.
If the sun's declination is north and its true bearing at meridian passage is 180 degrees, add declination to zenith distance. If the sun's declination is north and its true bearing at meridian passage is 000 degrees, subtract zenith distance from declination.

For example, at meridian passage of the sun on 6 August 1978 the true altitude was found to be 74° 25′.2. Position by dead reckoning was 32° 10′N, 47° 04′W. The sun's true bearing was south (180 degrees). Local time on board was three hours behind GMT.

Time of noon:

Meridian passage on 6 August (*Nautical Almanac*)	12	06(E–,W+)
Longitude 47° 04′W converted to time	03	08+
GMT of noon at 47° 04′W	15	14
Local time 3 hours behind GMT (subtract)	–3	
Local time of noon	12	14

Latitude at noon	90° 00′
True altitude	74° 25′.2–
Zenith distance	15° 34′.8
Sun's declination (*Nautical Almanac* for the GMT of noon)	N16° 41′.1+
Latitude (at the time of local noon, i.e. 1214)	34° 15′.9N

Although the rules for deciding how zenith distance and declination should be combined to find latitude are given above, the navigator can generally see by inspection what has to be done. In the example given, the two were added. The only other combination would have been to subtract the smaller from the larger (16° 41.2 – 15° 34′.8) which would give a latitude of just over 1 degree. This is over 1 800 nautical miles from the dead reckoning position. In most cases the latitude by dead reckoning will be fairly close to the actual latitude, and if the calculation is inadvertently done incorrectly, the error is immediately obvious.

Unless sailing in or very near the tropics, the true bearing of the sun at meridian passage can be found by a quick check of the compass or use of a hand bearing compass to decide if the sun is passing to the north or south of the boat. In temperate climates the northern hemisphere reader will know that the sun is to the south at noon, and the southern hemisphere reader that the sun passes north. However in the tropics, the sun is always overhead at some point throughout the year. If the navigator's latitude and the sun's declination are almost the same, the sun will pass almost directly overhead at meridian passage, and there can be some difficulty in deciding the bearing.

There can also be a practical problem in using the sextant. Normally the point of the horizon directly below the sun is quite obvious. If the altitude is high up in the 80 degree to 90 degree range, it is not obvious at all. The trick here is to find the point on the horizon that is due north or south, as appropriate, using a compass. Then bring the sun down to that point. In these circumstances the boat should be manoeuvred so that the navigator gets a clear view. This only happens very occasionally, but forewarned is forearmed.

To any beginner who strikes this situation, I would say two things; firstly, it has happened to us all at one time or another. Secondly, I would not wish on any reader my state of panic when it first happened to me! It may help to add that in about ten years of criss-crossing the tropics in warships and yachts I can only recall four occasions when I was faced with this particular problem.

Plotting latitude

Once the latitude is found at noon, it should be plotted on the chart or plotting sheet. The latter is used to do all the fiddly work, thus keeping the ocean chart free of too much detail so that only fixes and an uncluttered dead reckoning track need be shown. There are several types of plotting sheet on sale, and each can be used many times, as can a chart. The noon latitude is an east-west position running along the particular latitude.

In Fig 73 the vessel is on true course 040°, speed 6 knots. The dead reckoning track from 0600 to 1200 is shown. Time of noon was 1206. At this time the latitude was found to be 32° 40′N. The position line is plotted by aligning the parallel rulers along a parallel of latitude and moving one edge so that it goes through the noon latitude, and the line drawn in. The time is noted alongside.

It is clear from the diagram that if the boat lies somewhere on the latitude line, then it is not at the 1206 dead reckoning position. Although we have yet to get a fix, the dead reckoning track is restarted from the noon latitude. The point where the perpendicular from the DR meets the latitude is taken as being the boat's position at 1206. The track is now plotted from this point as shown.

Latitude by meridian passage of the sun is independent of any error in the dead reckoning position or need to know an accurate time. The only disadvantage, if it could be called that, is the requirement to wait until noon to find the latitude. Earlier mariners were utterly frustrated by this inflexibility. No matter that the sun shone brightly in a cloudless sky for the rest of the day, they were quite unable to use it to find their position. The thinking navigators of the time were desperate for a means of using the sun to find their latitude and longitude at any time of the day.

The problem in finding a longitude at sea is that accurate time is needed. A Board of Longitude was set up in England in 1714 and authorised by the British Government to pay up to £20 000 to anyone who could come forward with a method of finding an accurate longitude. A Yorkshire carpenter turned clockmaker, John Harrison, invented a sufficiently accurate timepiece in 1735. He made four models, and a copy of the last one was delivered in 1769 and used by Captain James Cook during his second and third voyages. Although his first timepiece met the required standard of accuracy Harrison was not paid the whole of his £20 000 until 1772.

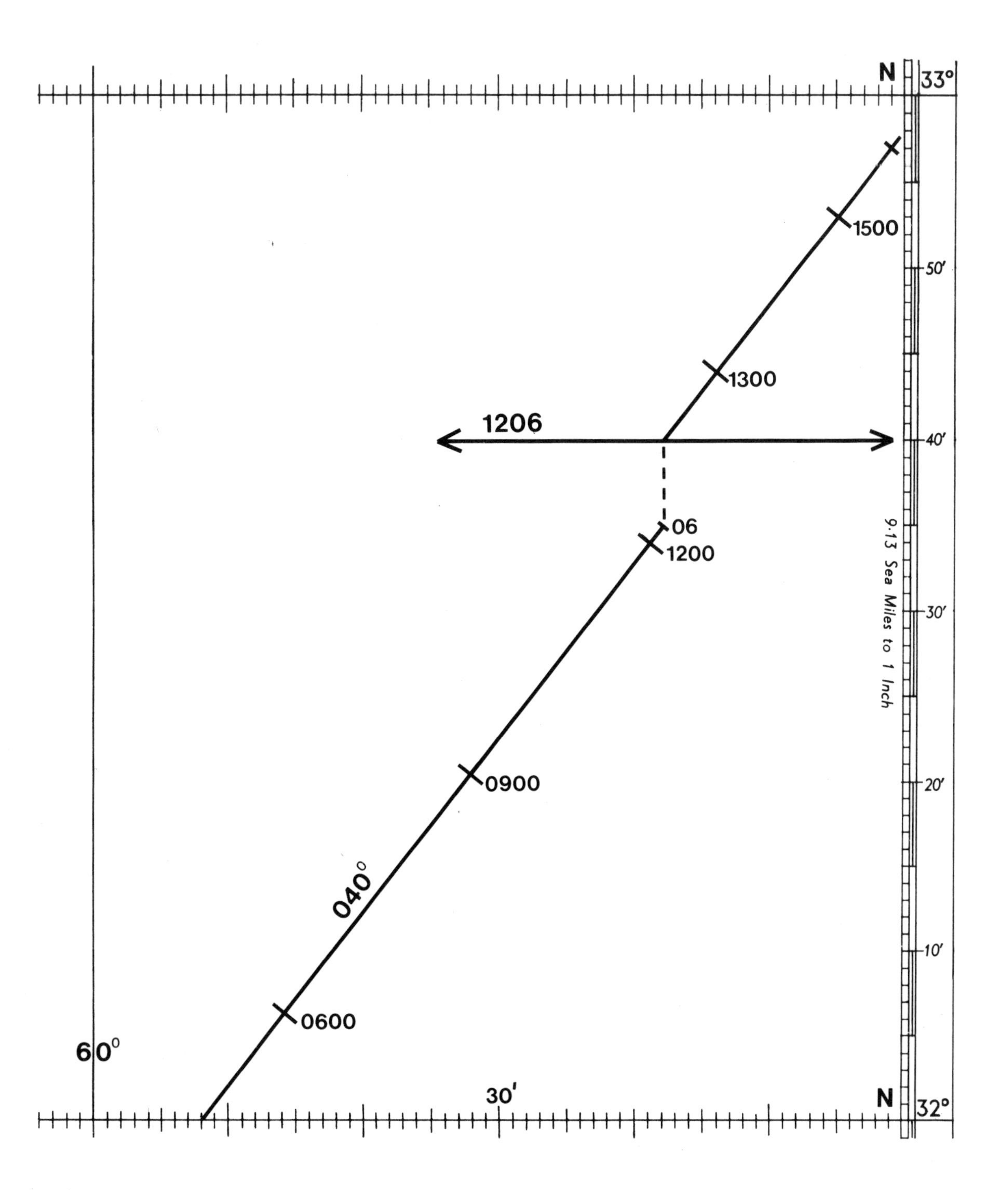

Fig 73
Plotting the noon latitude

Local hour angle

Before going on to the method of finding position from the sun at any time of day, there is one other term the reader should understand – local hour angle.

First, to clear up a point which might be slightly puzzling. Greenwich hour angle is equivalent to the westerly longitude of the sun's GP. Local hour angle is also in effect a longitude, so why the use of the word 'hour' in their names? A fine shade of difference is given in the textbooks, but the term was more familiar in an older era of celestial navigation when the standard practice was to use what were called 'time sights'.

We have seen that longitude and time are equivalent, for all practical purposes, so to say that the sun is one hour west of Greenwich is the same as saying that its GHA is 15 degrees. Similarly, one hour after meridian passage at any place, the earlier navigator spoke of the sun as being 'one hour west of him'. Note here that the navigator was describing the position of the sun with reference to himself.

Local hour angle (LHA) is the difference between the longitude of a place and the longitude (GHA) of the sun, measured west from the meridian of longitude through the observer or place. Thus at noon, in all but the polar regions, when the sun is on an observer's meridian the GHA is equal to the observer's longitude and the LHA equals 0 degrees. The time of noon is seldom exactly 1200, so one hour after noon is seldom exactly 1300 hours. Nevertheless, one hour after noon at any given point, the LHA of the sun would be 15 degrees. Six hours after noon, the LHA would be 6 x 15 degrees or 90 degrees, and so on. Twenty-three hours after meridian passage the LHA is 345°.

Local hour angle is found by adding or subtracting longitude and GHA. Fig 74a and 74b shows part of the earth viewed from above the North Pole. The observer is on longitude 40°W. GHA of the sun is 100°. The LHA in this case is
100° (GHA) – 40° (longitude) = 60°.

In Fig. 74b it is clear that the LHA is made up of the easterly longitude and the GHA, i.e. LHA equals 130° (GHA) +100° (longitude) = 230°.

Finding local hour angle

The Greenwich hour angle for any moment can be found from the *Nautical Almanac*. To find the local hour angle (LHA) for any given moment of time and longitude, the local time must first be converted to GMT. Then:

$$\text{LHA} = \text{GHA} \quad \left.\begin{matrix} - \\ + \end{matrix}\right\} \begin{matrix} \text{west} \\ \text{east} \end{matrix} \text{ longitude}$$

For example, to find the sun's LHA in longitude 80° E at 04h 00m GMT on 12 November 1978:

Tab GHA for 04 hours GMT (*Nautical Almanac*)	243° 58′.3
Longitude	80° 00′ East +
Local hour angle	323° 58′.3

Here again the rhyme given on page 00 can be used as an aid to memory:

Longitude east, Greenwich (hour angle) least,

Longitude west, Greenwich (hour angle) best.

To find the sun's LHA at longitude 18° E at 1400 local time on 22 February 1978 – the zone is 1 hour ahead of GMT:

Local Time	14h 00m
Zone	1h –
GMT	13h 00m

The time of sun's meridian passage at longitude 18° E on this date was 12h 02m. As the LHA at noon is 0 degrees and as almost

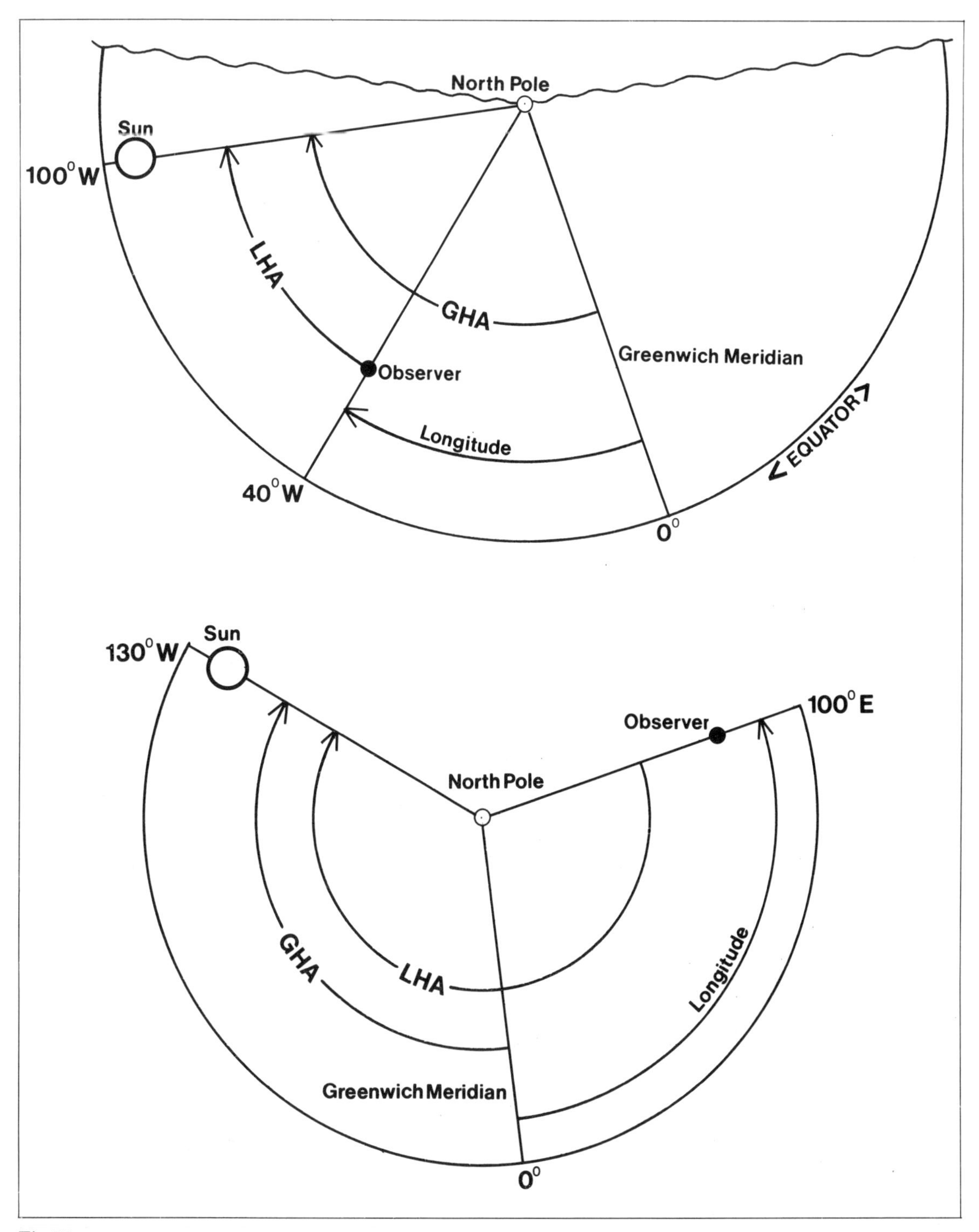

Fig 74
Local hour angle

exactly two hours have gone by since the time of noon, then the LHA at 14h 00m should be very close to 30 degrees.

Tab GHA for 13h GMT	11° 36′.7
Longitude	18° 00′ E +
LHA	29° 36′.7

There is no black magic here. The sun's LHA is 30 degrees two hours after noon at any given place or longitude every day. The navigator can predict, within limits, the value of LHA for any time of the day. This means that there is a ready check available on the accuracy of a LHA calculation before the detailed working is actually done. The *Nautical Almanac* enables the navigator to find an accurate LHA.

The reader should remember that:

1 In the afternoon the sun's LHA increases from 0 degrees at the local time of noon at exactly 15 degrees per hour. If the sun sets at about 1700, the LHA would have increased to about 75 degrees with sunset. If sunset is two hours later, at 1900, LHA is approximately 100-110 degrees. The point here is that if the navigator inadvertently added longitude when it should have been subtracted, or vice versa, the error should immediately be apparent. Certainly there is no way the sun's LHA can be in the 200-300 degree range in the afternoon.

2 In the morning, the LHA has increased to about 300 degrees at 0800 (i.e. four hours before noon). Again, it is impossible for the sun's LHA to be, say, 140° at 0900.

To sum up: In the afternoon the sun's LHA is relatively small. In the morning, the LHA is always large, rising to 360° at noon.

The following calculation is to find the LHA of the sun in longitude 43° 16′W at 10h 03m local time on 16 September 1978. As this is about two hours before noon, the answer should be, very approximately, 360° minus 30°, or 330°. Local time is 3 hours behind GMT.

Local time	10h 03m 16s
Zone	3h +
GMT	13h 03m 16s

Tab GHA for 13h GMT	16° 16′.0
Increment for 03m 16s	0° 49′.0
GHA at 13h 03m 16s GMT	17° 05′.0
	360° +
GHA	377° 05′.0
Longitude	43 16′.0 W −
LHA	333° 49′.0

If the longitude is larger than the GHA, 360° must be added so that the subtraction can be done.

Chapter Seven
Sunsights

You will recall that the position line found from the sun is a range circle in which the radius is the observer's distance from the sun's GP. The closer the observer is to the GP, the higher the altitude of the sun. The actual distance can be found by subtracting the altitude from 90 degrees and multiplying this by 60 to give nautical miles. If the boat is only a relatively short distance away, say up to 200 miles, the range circle can be drawn in directly on the chart with a pair of compasses using the GP as the centre. In most cases the distance is much greater. For example if the sun's altitude were 40 degrees, the distance would be given by $90° - 40° = 50° \times 60 =$ 3 000 nautical miles.

To draw such a circle on a chart presents several practical difficulties. The centre of the circle, the GP, may not even lie within the area bounded by the chart. More significantly, due to the distortion of the latitude scale on a Mercator chart, a circle with a large radius actually appears as an ellipse. This is why the direct drawing of a range circle on a chart is restricted to 200 miles, because up to this distance there is no major loss in accuracy. However, the full circle is not needed because the boat's position is at only one point on the circumference. The problem is overcome by a change in reasoning. The navigator assumes that he is at a given position, chosen so as to simplify the calculations needed in a celestial sight. The rules for choosing this position are given below.

Intercept and chosen position

The altitude of the sun is a measure of the navigator's distance from the GP. The various sets of navigation tables are used to calculate the altitude that the sun would be at the chosen position (CP) at exactly the same moment that the navigator used his sextant. As this calculated altitude is a measure of the distance between the chosen position and the GP, a comparison of the two altitudes gives the difference in the two distances. The difference in minutes of altitude or arc is equal to the difference in nautical miles. This difference between the true and calculated altitudes is called the intercept.

Fig 75 shows the range or position circles through an observer and a chosen position. The line from the chosen position to the GP is the azimuth or true bearing of the sun from the CP. This true bearing is found from the same set of tables that gives the calculated altitude. The intercept is shown.

In geometry it is a fact that any straight line going from the circumference of a circle to the centre crosses the circumference at right angles. Both the circles through the CP and the observer have the GP as a common centre. So the bearing line from the CP to the sun crosses the observer's circle of position at right

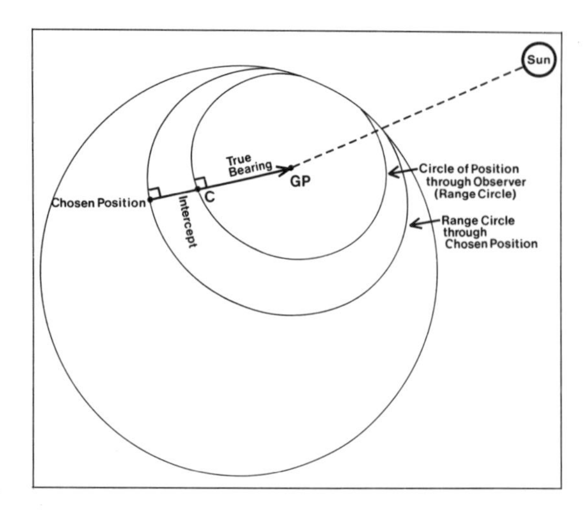

Fig 75
Range circles through an observer and chosen position

angles. (Point C). If it were possible to plot point C on a chart, a line through C drawn at right angles to the true bearing would be part of the observer's circle of position, i.e. a position line. Although it is part of a circle, the radius is so large and the curvature of the circumference so slight that the position line is a straight line. These celestial range arcs can be some thousands of miles in radius (refer back to Fig 42).

I'll say that again, using Fig 76, which is a magnification of part of the previous diagram. The chosen position is known, so this can be plotted on a chart. The intercept is found by comparing the true altitude deduced from the sextant with the calculated altitude found from a set of tables. The same set of tables gives the true bearing of the sun's GP from the chosen position.

If the bearing is laid off on the chart from the chosen position, the intercept distance can be measured along the bearing line. In this example it gives point C. C is one point on the circumference of the position circle through the boat. A straight line drawn at right angles to the bearing through C is part of the position circle, i.e. a position line.

C is *not* the boat's position. Before a fix can be plotted, a second position line must be obtained, and where the two position lines cut is the boat's position.

The result has been that the relevant section of the position circle has been found, not by trying to draw a range arc of a thousand or more miles radius, but by merely measuring a few miles along the bearing of the sun from the chosen position and then drawing in a straight line through the point found.

In Fig 76, the observer is closer to the sun's GP than is the chosen position. This is not always the case, i.e. the observer might be further away from the sun than the chosen position. The principle is exactly the same, but look at Fig 77.

The first observer (0.1.) is clearly closer to the sun's GP than is the chosen position, and the second observer (0.2.) is further away. the true altitude at 0.1. is greater than the calculated altitude, and the true altitude at 0.2. is less. The comparison of true and calculated altitudes not only gives the intercept, but also shows whether the observer is closer to or further away from the sun than the particular chosen position.

The chosen or assumed position has to be as close as possible to the boat's position by dead reckoning at the time of taking the sunsight.

Latitude The whole degree latitude closest to the dead reckoning latitude is used, e.g.:

DR latitude	36° 02′ N	40° 58′ S	16° 30′ N
Chosen latitude	36° N	41° S	16° N or 17° N

Longitude In the process of working out the local hour angle of the sun relative to the chosen position, the dead reckoning longitude is adjusted so that the resulting LHA is a whole degree, e.g.:

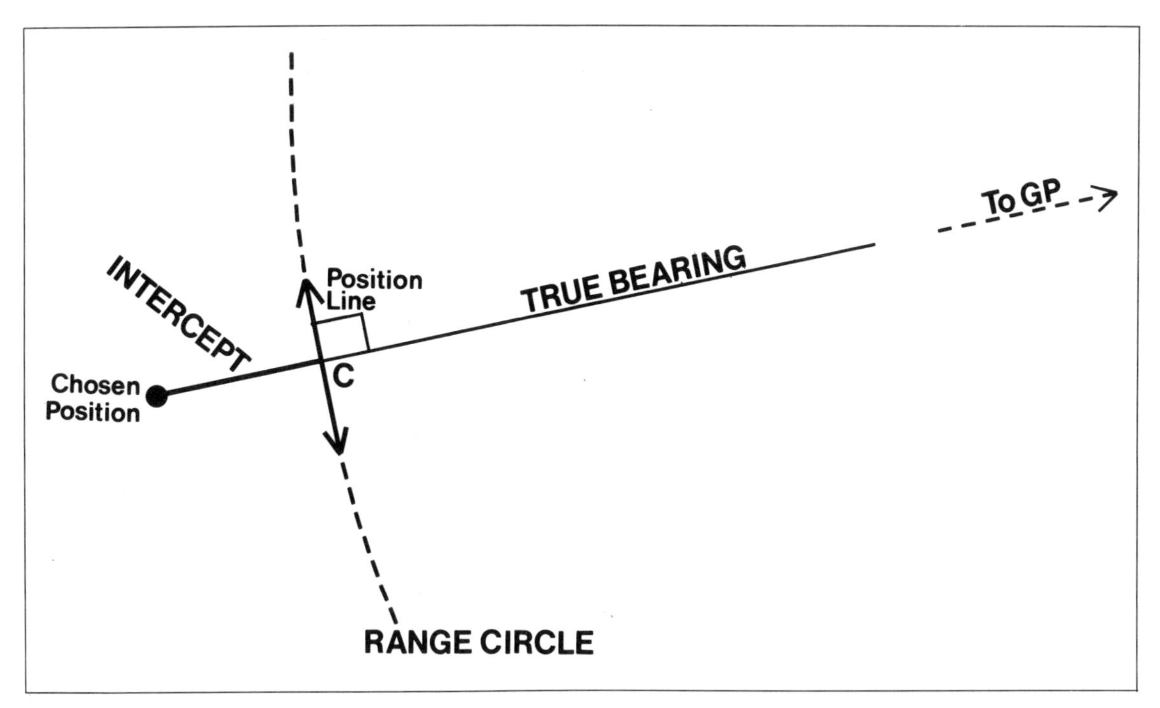

Fig 76
Finding the position line

Fig 77
Comparison of true and calculated altitude to find the intercept

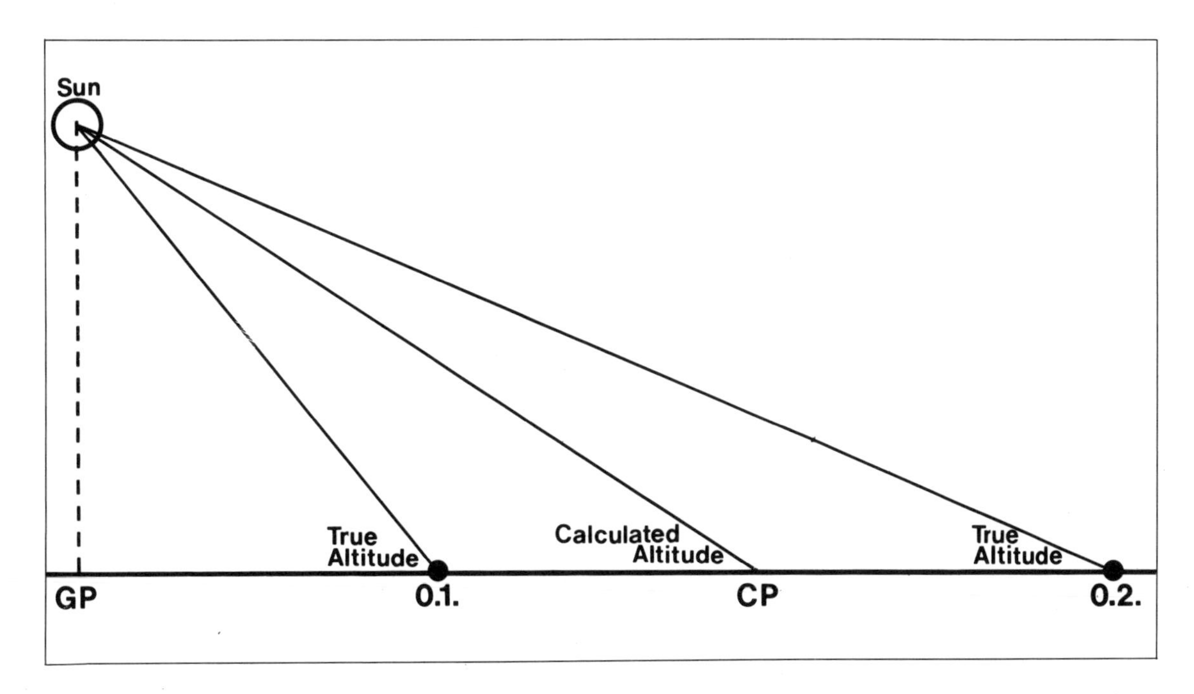

Position by DR: 22° 11′.5 N 40° 10′.6 W
(LHA = GHA – W longitude)

GHA	140° 16′.0
Chosen longitude	40° 16′.0 –
LHA	100°

Chosen position: 22° N 40° 16′ W

Position by DR: 29° 41′.6 S 174° 38′.0 E
(LHA = GHA + E longitude)

GHA	136° 14′.0
Chosen longitude	174° 46′.0 +
LHA	311°

Chosen position: 30° S 174° 46′ E

The minutes of the chosen longitude must be found before the degrees are written in. If the GHA had been 140° 58′ in the first example above, the working would have been:

GHA	140° 58′.0
Chosen longitude (minutes)	58′.0 –
Chosen longitude	39° 58′.0 –
LHA	101°

39° 58′ W is *closer* to the DR longitude than 40° 58′ W, so that is the one that should be used.

Examples: Work out the chosen position and the LHA.

Position by DR	*GHA*	
1 40° 32′ N 60° 38′ W	343° 52′	Early morning
2 35° 29′ N 16° 02′ E	28° 52′.7	Afternoon
3 23° 30′ S 178° 24′ E	151° 18′.0	Morning
4 15° 45′ S 106° 53′ E	269° 50′.0	Early afternoon

Answers:

Chosen latitude	*Chosen longitude*	*LHA*
1 41° N	60° 52′.0 W	283°
2 35° N	16° 07′.3 E	45°
3 23° S or 24° S	178° 42′.0E	330°
4 16° S	*107*° 10′.0 E	17°

Chapter Eight
Finding Position at Sea

THE PZX TRIANGLE

The following abbreviations are commonly used in celestial navigation:

P: The North or South Poles.

Z: The zenith. This is used in the sense of the point directly overhead, or the observer's position on the earth.

X: The sun or the sun's GP.

Fig 78 shows the meridians of longitude through an observer (Z) and the sun's GP (X).

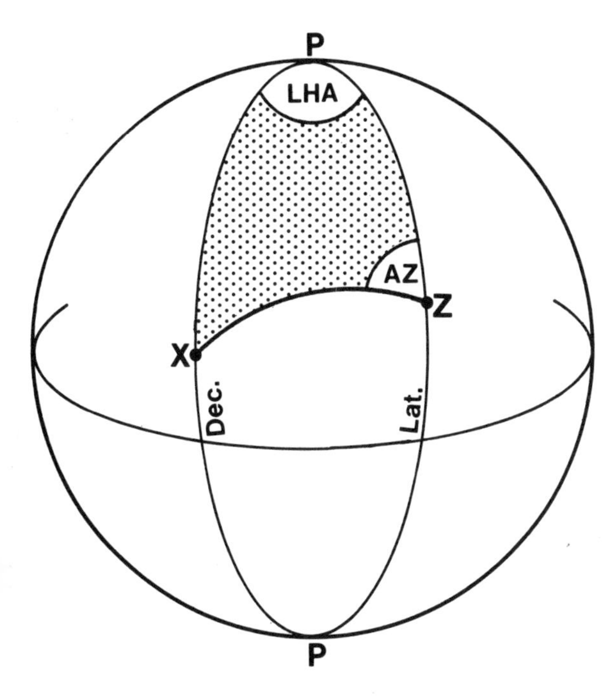

Fig 78
The PZX triangle

The Pole, the observer and the sun form a triangle, commonly known as the PZX triangle. As the earth is a sphere, the triangle PZX is a spherical triangle. In plane geometry if two sides of a triangle are known and so is the included angle, the length of the third side and the other two angles can be found. The same is true of a spherical triangle, but it must be solved by spherical trigonometry.

The declination of the sun can be found from the *Nautical Almanac*, therefore in Fig 78 PX = 90° – Dec. If the latitude of the observer is known, PZ = 90° – Lat.

The angle at the Pole is the difference in longitude between the observer and the sun, i.e. the local hour angle. Therefore the length of the third side ZX and the other two angles can be calculated. ZX is the distance between the observer and the sun's GP. The angle at X is not used in navigation. Z is called the azimuth angle, and once this is known the true bearing of the sun can be found quite simply.

In former days the navigator had to do these calculations himself. They were fairly tedious but the professional who used them day in and day out at sea became quite fast.

NAVIGATION TABLES

The first breakthrough came in 1837 when the principle of the position line was discovered by an American shipmaster, Captain Thomas H. Sumner, and in the United States it is known to this day as the Sumner line. The method of plotting the position line using an intercept is credited to Commander Marc St Hilaire of the French Navy, who put the concept forward in 1875.

For the next 60 years, nevigators the world over solved PZX triangles using various logarithmic tables, which were extremely accurate. The positions or fixes obtained using these tables appeared equally accurate. These traditional methods of solving the PZX triangle were in quite general use up to a decade ago, and are still used.

However, in the early 1930s a new factor emerged. The growing air forces of the world were demanding faster aircraft and the air navigators simply did not have the time to find their position by celestial sights involving lengthy calculations. At about this time the United States Navy was preparing a volume of computed altitudes and azimuths (H.O. 214). This was in effect a ready reckoner which contained the solutions to several hundred thousand PZX triangles. In fact the complements of the angles are used instead of the angles themselves, which means they give the altitude of the sun at the chosen position, not the side ZX. This is more convenient, as the intercept can be found by comparing the true and calculated altitudes.

Instead of the navigator doing the calculations himself he merely identified the triangle he wanted solved and took the answer from the book. The first published volume of these tables was made available in 1936.

The tables for air navigation were first prepared in the United States in about 1935. The British Empire edition of the same tables was being compiled by the summer of 1936. The first edition of the *Sight Reduction Tables for Air Navigation* (H.O. 249) as we know them today was published in the United States in 1947. With minor modifications for Royal Air Force usage, very similar tables (A.P. 3270) were published in Great Britain shortly afterwards. In 1952 the British Admiralty published marine navigation tables (HD 486) based on the United States Hydrographic Office tables (H.O. 214). These were used as the standard method for solving celestial sights in the Royal Navy and in most of the Commonwealth navies for over two decades, although Volume I of the *Air Tables* was being accepted as a complementary method of solving sights by 1958.

A new edition of the *Marine Tables* (NP 401/HD 605) has recently gone on sale to the public. Its theoretical accuracy has been improved from 0′.5 to 0′.1, which means the tables can be used in a large ship which gives a relatively stable platform for the navigator taking the sight. They come in six volumes, each covering 16 degrees of latitude, and the interpolation needed for declination is rather more complicated than in the older HD 486.

On the other hand the *Air Tables* (AP 3270) are in three volumes covering latitudes 0-89 degrees. These are permanent, although Volume I, for stars, changes only every 5 years. The yacht navigator is much like the air navigator, in that he can become quite fatigued by the closing stages of a rough voyage. A simpler method such as used in AP 3270 offers less opportunity for error.

The only question left is one of accuracy. In the speeding-up process, the tables are rounded off so that the theoretical accuracy is about a mile. This was done for a reason. Earlier I said that in the older methods extremely accurate logarithmic tables were used, which gave an apparently equally accurate answer. The fallacy was that the final answer can only be as accurate as all the input data.

One very important bit of input is the true altitude, which is found from the sextant altitude. By and large the yachtsman will not be able to find this to better than half a minute in any sea conditions. The earlier custom of working a sight to a precision not justified by some of the input data could create a false sense of security, apart from the extra calculations involved.

I have been using the *Air Tables*, at sea, in

both professional and private capacities for some 20 years, and have therefore proved their accuracy.

In the United Kingdom, the Royal Yachting Association is now the authority for the award of Certificates of Competence to yachtsmen. In particular, the RYA sets the examination for the award of the Yachtmaster Ocean Certificate. The syllabus specifically provides for the use of air navigation tables for working out both sun and star sights.

CALCULATORS

The latest aid in the speeding-up process of solving celestial navigation problems is the electronic calculator. There are some versatile but expensive models available using pre-recorded programme cards, which will solve any calculation the navigator is likely to need. The appropriate card or other type of insert for the particular navigation problem is placed in the calculator and certain data, such as dead reckoning latitude and longitude, are keyed in.

In the most complex models, some sets of programmes are designed so that they follow each other in a particular order, passing data from programme to programme through the data registers. For example, in solving a sunsight, the calculator itself may be able to provide Greenwich hour angle and declination. The instrument may even give a most probable position, in latitude and longitude, based on a single sunsight. If data for three stars are keyed in, the final programme in the series can compute the latitude and longitude of the fix based on these observations.

Rather less expensive are the programmable scientific calculators. Instructions are provided on how to key in the programme needed to solve the more common navigation problems, including solving the PZX triangle. Once the instrument is programmed, fuller information must be provided, such as chosen latitude, declination and local hour angle. Note here that the navigator must still extract the data from the *Nautical Almanac* himself, and work out local hour angle. In a celestial sight the answer given will either be a calculated altitude or an intercept and bearing, if the calculator can accept sextant altitude or true altitude. Other types of problem that can be solved include dead reckoning, rhumb line navigation and great circle courses and distance. The most useful models accept and display angular notations in the familiar degrees, minutes and tenths of a minute.

Any scientific calculator can be used to solve navigation problems, as long as the owner is competent in using the instrument and it can accept the normal trigonometric functions including $\text{Sin}^{-1}X$, $\text{Cos}^{-1}X$, decimal degrees and logarithms. For these readers who are proficient in using a scientific calculator, the equations for computing altitude and azimuth are commonly given in the form:

Hc (calculated altitude)

$$Hc = \sin^{-1}(\cos dec \times \cos lat \times \cos LHA \pm \sin dec \times \sin lat)$$

i.e. plus when latitude and declination have the same name and minus if opposite names.

$$Z = \sin^{-1}\left(\frac{\sin LHA \times \cos dec}{\cos Hc}\right)$$

Despite the apparent advantages listed above, a calculator has certain limitations, and the reader should be quite clear as to what a calculator does. It replaces the manual navigation tables in the same way as an ordinary calculator replaces the ready reckoner. By freeing the navigator from much of the detailed working, it can mean there is less chance of error and more time for ensuring the safety of the craft.

Use of a calculator does not mean that the navigator will get a better or more accurate answer. If inaccurate data are keyed in, there is no way the instrument can correct the data, therefore the answer displayed will be slightly in error.

Advances in calculator design are so rapid that within a few years there may be inexpensive models available which can be used to solve any navigation problem. Clearly the calculator will eventually replace the manual tables, but it will never eliminate the need to learn the other facets of the navigation art.

In the meantime, it is interesting to note that several manufacturers of calculators display a prominent caution in the front of the handbook for their particular model. In essence these all say that the user should also carry the normal navigation equipment and tables on board in case of calculator failure or battery discharge. The corollary to that, of course, is if the navigator still carries the manual tables, he must also know how to use them.

USE OF THE *AIR TABLES*

The function of the *Air Tables* is to enable the navigator to find the calculated altitude and the true bearing of the sun at the chosen position.

The following abbreviations are used in the tables and the reader may need to refer back to this list from time to time.

LAT	Latitude
LHA	Local hour angle
Hc	Height (calculated) i.e. the calculated altitude
Ho	Height (observed) i.e. the true altitude
Z	the azimuth angle i.e. the angle at Z in the PZX triangle
Zn	the azimuth based on north, i.e. the true bearing

Entering the tables

Three values are needed to find the right page to use. They are the chosen latitude, the declination and the local hour angle.

Fig 79 shows that each page is for an exact latitude. This extract is for latitude 37 degrees north *or* south, and any declination between 0 degrees and 14 degrees. If declination and latitude are both north or both south, they have the same names. If one is north and the other south, they have contrary names.

There are 15 columns on each page, each headed with a whole degree declination, e.g. the third column from the left in Fig 80 is for declination 2° same name as latitude. In each column the calculated or tabulated altitude is listed under the heading Hc and the azimuth angle under Z. On every page in the tables the extreme left and right hand columns are headed LHA. Local hour angles from 0 degrees to 180 degrees are on the left and from 180 degrees to 360 degrees on the right.

For example, in the extract from the tables below, with chosen latitude 37°, declination 16° (same) and LHA 10°, we find that:

Hc = 67° 13′ Z = 155°

If:

Latitude = 37°
Declination = 17° (same)
and LHA = 15°

The Hc and Z are 66° 01′ and 143°.

If:

Chosen latitude 37°
Declination 15° (same) and
LHA 66°

Hc and Z are 28° 00′ and 92°.

True bearing

Z has to be converted to a true bearing. The rules to do this are given on *every* page of the *Air Tables*. If the chosen latitude is N, the rules are given at the top of the page and if S at the bottom of the page, as in Fig 81.

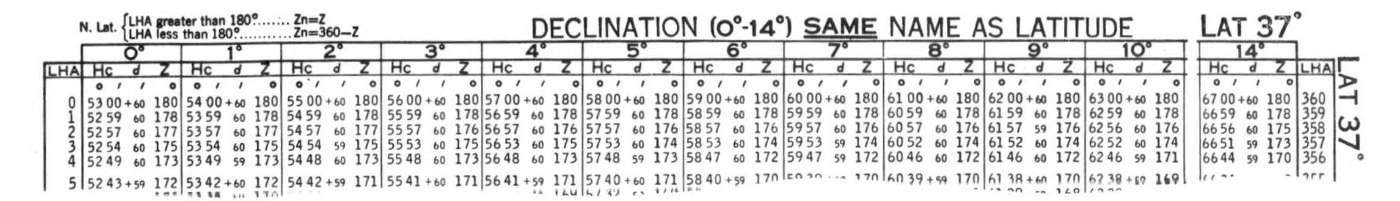

N. Lat. {LHA greater than 180°....... Zn=Z; LHA less than 180°........... Zn=360−Z}

DECLINATION (0°-14°) SAME NAME AS LATITUDE — LAT 37°

LHA	0° Hc	d	Z	1° Hc	d	Z	2° Hc	d	Z	3° Hc	d	Z	4° Hc	d	Z	5° Hc	d	Z	6° Hc	d	Z	7° Hc	d	Z	8° Hc	d	Z	9° Hc	d	Z	10° Hc	d	Z	14° Hc	d	Z	LHA
	° ′	′	°	° ′	′	°	° ′	′	°	° ′	′	°	° ′	′	°	° ′	′	°	° ′	′	°	° ′	′	°	° ′	′	°	° ′	′	°	° ′	′	°	° ′	′	°	
0	53 00	+60	180	54 00	+60	180	55 00	+60	180	56 00	+60	180	57 00	+60	180	58 00	+60	180	59 00	+60	180	60 00	+60	180	61 00	+60	180	62 00	+60	180	63 00	+60	180	67 00	+60	180	360
1	52 59	60	178	53 59	60	178	54 59	60	178	55 59	60	178	56 59	60	178	57 59	60	178	58 59	60	178	59 59	60	178	60 59	60	178	61 59	60	178	62 59	60	178	66 59	60	178	359
2	52 57	60	177	53 57	60	177	54 57	60	177	55 57	60	176	56 57	60	176	57 57	60	176	58 57	60	176	59 57	60	176	60 57	60	176	61 57	59	176	62 56	60	176	66 56	60	175	358
3	52 54	60	175	53 54	60	175	54 54	59	175	55 53	60	175	56 53	60	175	57 53	60	174	58 53	60	174	59 53	59	174	60 52	60	174	61 52	60	174	62 52	60	174	66 51	59	173	357
4	52 49	60	173	53 49	59	173	54 48	60	173	55 48	60	173	56 48	60	173	57 48	59	173	58 47	60	172	59 47	59	172	60 46	60	172	61 46	60	172	62 46	59	171	66 44	59	170	356
5	52 43	+59	172	53 42	+60	172	54 42	+59	171	55 41	+60	171	56 41	+59	171	57 40	+60	171	58 40	+59	170	[illegible]	[illegible]	170	60 39	+59	170	61 38	+60	170	62 38	+60	169	[illegible]	[illegible]	[illegible]	[illegible]

Fig 79 (above)
Extract from the Sight Reduction Tables for Air Navigation (Air Tables)*, Vol II, page 222*

Fig 80 (right)
Declination 15°-29°, same name as latitude. Extract from the Air Tables *Vol II, page 225*

Fig 81 (below)
True bearing conversion rules from the Air Tables

N. Lat. {LHA greater than 180°....... Zn=Z; LHA less than 180°........... Zn=360−Z}

LHA	15° Hc	d	Z	16° Hc	d	Z	17° Hc	d	Z	18° Hc	d	Z
	° ′	′	°	° ′	′	°	° ′	′	°	° ′	′	°
69	06 56	40	115	[illegible]					[illegible]	04 57	40	117
1	[illegible]			[illegible]	60	179	36 00	60	179	35 00	[illegible]	[illegible]
0	38 00	−60	180	37 00	−60	180	36 00	−60	180	35 00	−60	180
	15°			16°			17°			18°		

S. Lat. {LHA greater than 180°....... Zn=180−Z; LHA less than 180°........... Zn=180+Z}

For example, if latitude is 37° N, LHA is 10° and Z is 155°. From Fig 81, in north latitudes when the LHA is *less* than 180°:

Zn	= 360° − Z
	= 360° − 155°
True bearing	= 205°

If the latitude was 37° S in south latitudes when the LHA is *less* than 180°:

Zn	= 180° + Z
	= 180° + 155°
True bearing	= 335°

Let's put this step in a practical context. Although the navigator is not actually at the chosen position, he will not be far away. The true bearing of the sun from the CP and from the navigator will be almost the same. By using a hand bearing compass, or even a rough

LAT 37°

LHA	15° Hc	d	Z	16° Hc	d	Z	17° Hc	d	Z	18° Hc	d	Z	(cut)
	° ′	′	°	° ′	′	°	° ′	′	°	° ′	′	°	
0	68 00	+60	180	69 00	+60	180	70 00	+60	180	71 00	+60	180	7
1	67 59	60	177	68 59	60	177	69 59	60	177	70 59	60	177	71
2	67 56	60	175	68 56	59	175	69 55	60	174	70 55	60	174	71
3	67 50	60	172	68 50	60	172	69 50	59	172	70 49	60	171	71
4	67 43	59	170	68 42	59	169	69 41	60	169	70 41	59	168	71 4
5	67 33	+59	167	68 32	+59	167	69 31	+59	166	70 30	+59	166	71 2
6	67 22	58	165	68 20	59	164	69 19	58	164	70 17	58	163	71 1
7	67 08	58	162	68 06	58	162	69 04	58	161	70 02	57	160	70 5
8	66 53	57	[illegible]							[illegible] 44	57	158	70 41
9	66 35	57									56	155	70 21
10	[illegible]			67 13	+55	155	68 08	+56	154		55	153	69 5
11	65 56	55									54	150	69 3
12	65 33	55	[illegible]							[illegible] 16	53	148	69 0
13	65 09	54	149	66 03	54	148	66 57	53	147	67 50	52	146	68 4
14	64 44	53	147	65 37	53	146	66 30	52	145	67 22	51	143	68
15	64 17	+52	145	65 09	+52	144	66 01	+51	143	66 52	+51	141	67
16	63 48	52	143	64 40	51	142	65 31	51	141	66 22	50	139	67
17	63 19	51	141	64 10	50	140	65 00	50	139	65 50	49	137	6
18	62 48	50	139	63 38	50	138	64 28	49	137	65 17	48	135	6
19	62 16	50	138	63 06	48	136	63 54	48	135	64 42	48	134	
20	61 43	+49	136	62 32	+48	135	63 20	+47	133	64 07	+47	132	
21	61 09	48	134	61 57	48	133	62 45	46	132	63 31	46	130	
22	60 35	47	133	61 22	46	131	62 08	46	130	62 54	45	129	
23	59 59	46	131	60 45	46	130	61 31	45	128	62 16	44	127	
24	59 22	46	130	60 08	45	128	60 53	45	127	61 38	43	[illegible]	
50	40 40	+35	103	[illegible]			[illegible]			[illegible] 24	+33	99	4
51	39 53	35	102	40 28	34	101	41 02	34	100	41 36	33	99	4
52	39 06	35	101	39 41	34	100	40 15	34	99	40 49	33	98	41
53	38 19	35	101	38 54	34	100	39 28	33	98	40 01	33	97	40
54	37 32	34	100	38 06	34	99	38 40	34	98	39 14	33	97	39 4
55	36 45	+34	99	37 19	+34	98	37 53	+33	97	38 26	+33	96	38 5
56	35 57	35	98	36 32	33	97	37 05	33	96	37 38	33	95	38 11
57	35 10	34	98	35 44	34	97	36 18	33	96	36 51	32	95	37 23
58	34 22	34	97	34 56	34	96	35 30	33	95	36 03	32	94	36 35
59	33 35	34	96	34 09	33	95	34 42	33	94	35 15	33	93	35 48
60	32 47	+34	96	33 21	+33	95	33 54	+33	94	34 27	+33	93	35 00
61	31 59	34	95	32 33	34	94	33 07	32	93	33 39	33	92	34 12
62	31 12	33	94	31 45	34	94	32 19	33	93	32 52	32	92	33 24
63	30 24	34	94	30 58	33	93	31 31	33	92	32 04	32	91	32 36
64	29 36	34	93	30 10	33	92	30 43	33	91	31 16	32	90	31 48
65	28 48	+34	93	29 22	+33	92	29 55	+33	91	30 28	+32	90	31 00
66	28 00	34	92	28 34	33	91	29 07	33	90	29 40	32	89	30 12
67	27 12	34	91	27 46	33	90	28 19	33	89	28 52	32	89	29 24
68	26 24	34	91	26 58	33	90	27 31	33	89	28 04	32	88	28 36
69	25 37	33	90	26 10	33	89	26 43	33	88	27 16	33	87	27 49
	15°			16°			17°			18°			

S. Lat. {LHA greater than 180°....... Zn=180−Z; LHA less than 180°........... Zn=180+Z}

DECLINATION (15°-29°) SAME NAME AS LATITUDE

line of sight across the steering compass, the true bearing of the sun can be found, accurate to a few degrees before the tables are even consulted.

If the answer is already known within a few degrees, the working becomes obvious.

For instance let us assume that local time is about 10 am, Latitude 37° S, LHA 336° and Z 137°. A check of the sun with the compass had shown that its true bearing is about 040°. Look again at Fig 81. In south latitudes there are only two choices. Zn either equals 180° − Z or it equals 180° + Z. Let's try both.

	180°	180°
Z	137° +	137° −
Zn	317°	043°

As the approximate bearing was 040°, 043° has to be the correct answer.

Now for the clincher. In this example it is 10 o'clock in the morning (1000). The sun is always in the eastern part of the sky in the morning all over the world. 043° is an easterly direction, the other is not. 317° is a westerly direction and would be the answer to an afternoon sunsight, as the sun is always in the western part of the sky in the afternoon.

In north latitudes in the morning, Zn = Z, so no calculation is required, and in the afternoon Zn = 360° − Z.

Use the rules for this next example, then check it using the practical instructions just outlined.

Latitude S, LHA 304°, Z 119°. Morning sunsight. What is the true bearing of the sun (Zn)? Answer: 061°T.

It has already been explained that Zn is known to the navigator within limits, prior to using the tables. Hc is also known approximately. The intercept is the difference between the true and calculated altitudes. The sextant altitude is taken before any calculations are carried out. It is difficult to lay down any average length for the intercept, but anything from 1 to 30 miles is quite normal. It is unlikely to exceed 60 miles, which means that Ho and Hc should be within a degree of one another, e.g.:

Hc	43° 22′	32° 10′	27° 54′
Ho	43° 02′	31° 32′	27° 56′
Intercept:	20′	38′	2′

If the sextant altitude, even if not corrected, is say 42° and the uncorrected Hc from the *Air Tables* is 65°, you can stop right there, because a mistake has been made. As it is difficult to read the sextant altitude with that sort of inaccuracy, the first thing to check is the calculations. Half the time the navigator will have used the wrong page in the *Air Tables*. The most likely error here is that he has used a Declination (same) page when he should have used a Declination (contrary) page. One trap here is that some pages in the *Air Tables* look like the one in Fig 82.

The gap is put there intentionally to draw attention to the fact that the declination name has changed, i.e. it may be same at the top, but contrary after the gap.

If these checks don't show the mistake, then before going through the detail of the GHA, LHA and Dec, the *Nautical Almanac* should be looked at again because there are two common errors here:

1 The wrong date was used.

2 In his haste, the navigator used the left hand column of the left hand page instead of the left hand column of the right hand page. The former is headed Aries, giving dreadful results if used for the Sun.

The intercept

Three examples were given earlier in comparing Hc and Ho to find the intercept. One more step ends the calculations. Look back to Fig 77. The observer may be either closer to the sun than is the chosen position, or further away from it. Depending on which, the intercept distance is named 'to' or 'from'. If Ho is greater than Hc, the intercept is towards, if Ho is less than Hc the intercept is from. For example:

Hc	54° 16′	38° 02′
Ho	54° 20′ (greater)	37° 46′ (less)
Int:	4 M towards	Int: 16 M from

These rules are given in the front of the *Air Tables* under the heading 'explanation', which also contains some examples of finding Hc.

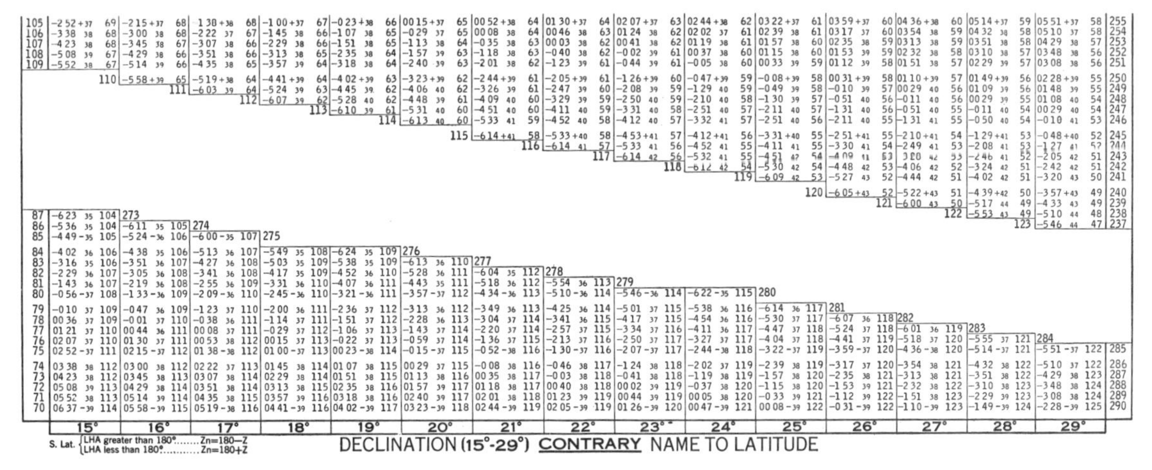

LHA	15°	16°	17°	18°	19°	20°	21°	22°	23°	24°	25°	26°	27°	28°	29°	LHA
105	−2 52 +37 69	−2 15 +37 68	−1 38 +38 68	−1 00 +37 67	−0 23 +38 66	00 15 +37 65	00 52 +38 64	01 30 +37 64	02 07 +37 63	02 44 +38 62	03 22 +37 61	03 59 +37 60	04 36 +38 60	05 14 +37 59	05 51 +37 58	255
106	−3 38 38 68	−3 00 38 68	−2 22 37 67	−1 45 38 66	−1 07 38 65	−0 29 37 65	00 08 38 64	00 46 38 63	01 24 38 62	02 02 37 61	02 39 38 61	03 17 37 60	03 54 38 59	04 32 38 58	05 10 37 58	254
107	−4 23 38 68	−3 45 38 67	−3 07 38 66	−2 29 38 66	−1 51 38 65	−1 13 38 64	−0 35 38 63	00 03 38 62	00 41 38 62	01 19 38 61	01 57 38 60	02 35 38 59	03 13 38 59	03 51 38 58	04 29 38 57	253
108	−5 08 39 67	−4 29 38 66	−3 51 38 66	−3 13 38 65	−2 35 38 64	−1 57 39 63	−1 18 38 63	−0 40 38 62	−0 02 39 61	00 37 38 60	01 15 38 60	01 53 39 59	02 32 38 58	03 10 38 57	03 48 38 56	252
109	−5 52 38 67	−5 14 39 66	−4 35 38 65	−3 57 39 64	−3 18 38 64	−2 40 39 63	−2 01 38 62	−1 23 39 61	−0 44 39 61	−0 05 38 60	00 33 39 59	01 12 39 58	01 51 38 57	02 29 39 57	03 08 38 56	251
110		−5 58 +39 65	−5 19 +38 64	−4 41 +39 64	−4 02 +39 63	−3 23 +39 62	−2 44 +39 61	−2 05 +39 61	−1 26 +39 60	−0 47 +39 59	−0 08 +39 58	00 31 +39 58	01 10 +39 57	01 49 +39 56	02 28 +39 55	250
111			−6 03 39 64	−5 24 39 63	−4 45 39 62	−4 06 40 62	−3 26 39 61	−2 47 39 60	−2 08 39 59	−1 29 40 59	−0 49 39 58	−0 10 39 57	00 29 40 56	01 09 39 56	01 48 39 55	249
112				−6 07 39 62	−5 28 40 62	−4 48 39 61	−4 09 40 60	−3 29 39 59	−2 50 40 59	−2 10 40 58	−1 30 39 57	−0 51 40 56	−0 11 40 56	00 29 39 55	01 08 40 54	248
113					−6 10 39 61	−5 31 40 60	−4 51 40 60	−4 11 40 59	−3 31 40 58	−2 51 40 57	−2 11 40 57	−1 31 40 56	−0 51 40 55	−0 11 40 54	00 29 40 54	247
114						−6 13 40 60	−5 33 41 59	−4 52 40 58	−4 12 40 57	−3 32 41 57	−2 51 40 56	−2 11 40 55	−1 31 41 55	−0 50 40 54	−0 10 41 53	246
115							−6 14 +41 58	−5 33 +40 58	−4 53 +41 57	−4 12 +41 56	−3 31 +40 55	−2 51 +41 55	−2 10 +41 54	−1 29 +41 53	−0 48 +40 52	245
116								−6 14 41 57	−5 33 41 56	−4 52 41 55	−4 11 41 55	−3 30 41 54	−2 49 41 53	−2 08 41 53	−1 27 41 52	244
117									−6 14 42 56	−5 32 41 55	−4 51 42 54	−4 09 41 53	−3 20 42 53	−2 46 41 52	−2 05 42 51	243
118										−6 12 42 54	−5 30 42 54	−4 48 42 53	−4 06 42 52	−3 24 42 51	−2 42 42 51	242
119											−6 09 42 53	−5 27 43 52	−4 44 42 51	−4 02 42 51	−3 20 43 50	241
120												−6 05 +43 52	−5 22 +43 51	−4 39 +42 50	−3 57 +43 49	240
121													−6 00 43 50	−5 17 44 49	−4 33 43 49	239
122														−5 53 43 49	−5 10 44 48	238
123															−5 46 44 47	237
87	−6 23 35 104															273
86	−5 36 35 104	−6 11 35 105														274
85	−4 49 −35 105	−5 24 −36 106	−6 00 −35 107													275
84	−4 02 36 106	−4 38 35 106	−5 13 36 107	−5 49 35 108	−6 24 35 109											276
83	−3 16 35 106	−3 51 36 107	−4 27 36 108	−5 03 35 109	−5 38 35 109	−6 13 36 110										277
82	−2 29 36 107	−3 05 36 108	−3 41 36 108	−4 17 35 109	−4 52 36 110	−5 28 36 111	−6 04 35 112									278
81	−1 43 36 107	−2 19 36 108	−2 55 36 109	−3 31 36 110	−4 07 36 111	−4 43 35 111	−5 18 36 112	−5 54 36 113								279
80	−0 56 −37 108	−1 33 −36 109	−2 09 −36 110	−2 45 −36 110	−3 21 −36 111	−3 57 −37 112	−4 34 −36 113	−5 10 −36 114	−5 46 −36 114	−6 22 −35 115						280
79	−0 10 37 109	−0 47 36 109	−1 23 37 110	−2 00 36 111	−2 36 37 112	−3 13 36 112	−3 49 36 113	−4 25 36 114	−5 01 37 115	−5 38 36 116	−6 14 36 117					281
78	00 36 37 109	−0 01 37 110	−0 38 36 111	−1 14 37 111	−1 51 37 112	−2 28 36 113	−3 04 37 114	−3 41 36 115	−4 17 37 115	−4 54 36 116	−5 30 37 117	−6 07 36 118				282
77	01 21 37 110	00 44 36 111	00 08 37 111	−0 29 37 112	−1 06 37 113	−1 43 37 114	−2 20 37 114	−2 57 37 115	−3 34 37 116	−4 11 36 117	−4 47 37 118	−5 24 37 118	−6 01 36 119			283
76	02 07 37 110	01 30 37 111	00 53 38 112	00 15 37 113	−0 22 37 113	−0 59 37 114	−1 36 37 115	−2 13 37 116	−2 50 37 117	−3 27 37 117	−4 04 37 118	−4 41 37 119	−5 18 37 120	−5 55 37 121		284
75	02 52 −37 111	02 15 −37 112	01 38 −38 112	01 00 −37 113	00 23 −38 114	−0 15 −37 115	−0 52 −38 116	−1 30 −37 116	−2 07 −37 117	−2 44 −38 118	−3 22 −37 119	−3 59 −37 120	−4 36 −38 120	−5 14 −37 121	−5 51 −37 122	285
74	03 38 38 112	03 00 38 112	02 22 37 113	01 45 38 114	01 07 38 115	00 29 37 115	−0 08 38 116	−0 46 38 117	−1 24 38 118	−2 02 37 119	−2 39 38 119	−3 17 37 120	−3 54 38 121	−4 32 38 122	−5 10 37 122	286
73	04 23 38 112	03 45 38 113	03 07 38 114	02 29 38 114	01 51 38 115	01 13 38 116	00 35 38 117	−0 03 38 118	−0 41 38 118	−1 19 38 119	−1 57 38 120	−2 35 38 121	−3 13 38 121	−3 51 38 122	−4 29 38 123	287
72	05 08 39 113	04 29 38 114	03 51 38 114	03 13 38 115	02 35 38 116	01 57 39 117	01 18 38 117	00 40 38 118	00 02 39 119	−0 37 38 120	−1 15 38 120	−1 53 39 121	−2 32 38 122	−3 10 38 123	−3 48 38 124	288
71	05 52 38 113	05 14 39 114	04 35 38 115	03 57 39 116	03 18 38 116	02 40 39 117	02 01 38 118	01 23 39 119	00 44 39 119	00 05 38 120	−0 33 39 121	−1 12 39 122	−1 51 38 123	−2 29 39 123	−3 08 38 124	289
70	06 37 −39 114	05 58 −39 115	05 19 −38 116	04 41 −39 116	04 02 −39 117	03 23 −39 118	02 44 −39 119	02 05 −39 119	01 26 −39 120	00 47 −39 121	00 08 −39 122	−0 31 −39 122	−1 10 −39 123	−1 49 −39 124	−2 28 −39 125	290
	15°	16°	17°	18°	19°	20°	21°	22°	23°	24°	25°	26°	27°	28°	29°	

S. Lat. {LHA greater than 180°........Zn=180−Z; LHA less than 180°..........Zn=180+Z}

DECLINATION (15°-29°) CONTRARY NAME TO LATITUDE

Fig 82
Gap in the Air Tables *(from Vol II) showing that the declination changes from same name to contrary name.*

Corrections to the tabulated altitude

We have seen that latitude declination and local hour angle are needed to enter the tables. The chosen latitude is always an exact degree, which is what is given in the tables, so that is catered for. The LHA columns in the tables are also whole degrees. The chosen longitude is selected so that LHA becomes a whole degree. However, if the reader checks back to the examples on finding the sun's declination, the answer is rarely an exact degree. If declination was 16° 23′.1, the tables only give Hc (same) and Z for a declination of exactly 16 degrees. So a correction has to be made for the additional minutes of declination, in this case the 23′.1.

In Fig 83 a and b sandwiched between Hc and Z at the head of each column is d. This is the difference in minutes of arc (altitude) between the values of Hc given for one declination and those given in the column immediately to the right, i.e. the next degree higher declination. Either a plus or a minus sign is shown to indicate whether the altitude has decreased or increased. Opposite LHA 30° and Dec 16° (same) Hc = 56° 10′, d = +42′. LHA 30° and Dec 17° (same) Hc = 56° 52′, i.e.:

Dec 17°	Hc 56° 52′
Dec 16°	Hc 56° 10′
	42′ difference

If the sun's declination were 16° 30′, then the required Hc would be halfway between the two values, i.e. 56° 10′ plus half 42′:

Hc	56° 10′
d correction	21′ +
Hc	56° 31′

Thus the tables give us Hc for the degrees of declination, the total change in Hc between one declination and the next, and whether it is increasing or decreasing. Minutes of declination are allowed for by using a proportion of this total change and adding or subtracting this correction in accordance with the sign (plus or minus) in the tables. Note here that even if the declination in the above example had been 16° 59′, the Hc is taken from the 16° column and the correction for 59′ used.

Fortunately there is a card included the *Air Tables* for use in finding the correction quickly and this is called TABLE 5 – Correction to Tabulated Altitude for Minutes of Declination.

The value of d is written along the top, with minutes of declination down each side. To use the table, the declination is rounded off to the

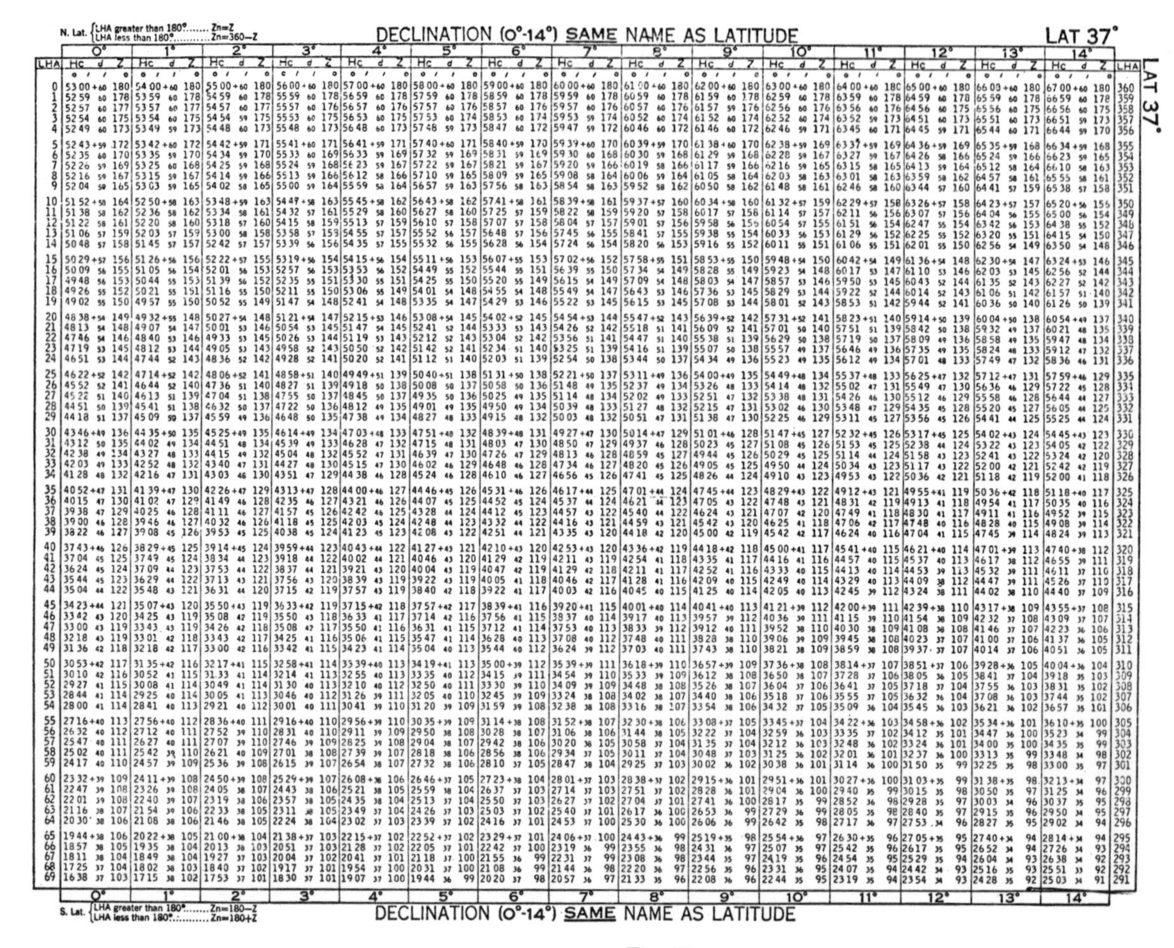

Fig 83
From Air Tables *Vol II, page 222 and page 225*

nearest whole minute.

To find the correction for 23′.1 and d = 42+, use 23′ exactly. The correction from the table is 16 minutes.

Finding the corrected Hc takes just three lines and one look at Table 5, e.g.:

Hc *(Air Tables)*	56°10′ (d + 42)
d correction (Table 5)	16′ +
Hc	56°26′

Instead of using a ruler to lay along the correct line when taking Hc, d and Z from the *Tables,* why not use the Table 5 card? Then it is already at hand for the next step.

Combining these steps, the complete working from the *Air Tables* looks like this:

Latitude 37° S, Dec 16° 23′.1 (same). LHA 30°. Afternoon sunsight:

Hc	56°10′	d + 42	Z = 120°
d corr	16′ +		Zn = 180° + 120°
Hc	56°26′		= 300°

Latitude 37° N. Dec 22° 49′ .3 (same). LHA 354° Morning sunsight:

Hc	74°08′	d +57	Z = 159°
d corr	47′+		Zn = Z
Hc	74°55′		= 159°

Plotting the position line

Once the intercept and true bearing of the sun have been found, the position line is

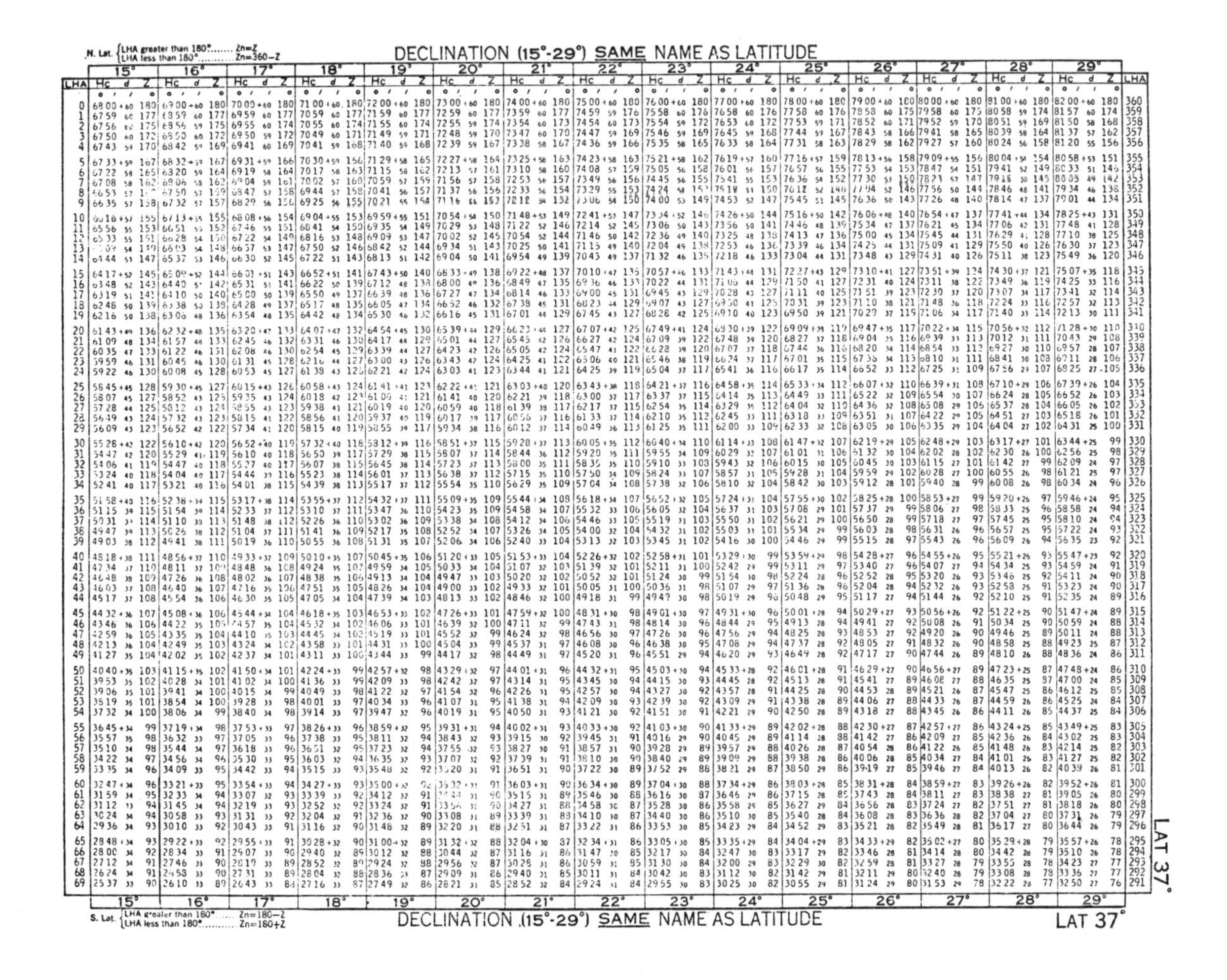

plotted. Although this can be done directly on the chart in use, it is more common for navigators to do the more detailed work on a separate plotting sheet. The procedure is shown in Fig 85, and has been broken down into five steps. In the example the intercept is 16 miles towards 046 degrees at 0930 local time.

Step 1 Plot the chosen position, i.e. the chosen latitude and chosen longitude.

Step 2 Draw in the true bearing of the sun through the chosen position.

Step 3 Measure off the 16 miles along the line which gives point P on the intercept.

Step 4 P is one point on the position line. Through P draw a line at right angles to the sun's bearing. This is the position line required.

Step 5 The chosen position and intercept have now enabled the navigator to find the position line. They are of no further use and should be erased. The celestial position line is often identified by an arrow-head at each end, as shown in Fig 85. Finally the local time at which the sight was taken is entered at any convenient point along the line.

Fig 86 shows the plotted position line if the intercept had been 16 miles away *from* a sun's true bearing of 046°.

It should be noted that one sunsight does not give a fix. At this stage the navigator has found a position line, not a position. He knows he is somewhere on the line, but not where he is along the line. Two position lines from the sun are needed to get a fix. This can be done during the morning, certainly in the summer

TABLE 5.—Correction to Tabulated Altitude for Minutes of Declination

d / ′	1	2	3	4	5	6	7	8	9	10	11	12	13	14	15	16	17	18	19	20	21	22	23	24	25	26	27	28	29	30
0	0	0	0	0	0	0	0	0	0	0	0	0	0	0	0	0	0	0	0	0	0	0	0	0	0	0	0	0	0	0
1	0	0	0	0	0	0	0	0	0	0	0	0	0	0	0	0	0	0	0	0	0	0	0	0	0	0	0	0	0	0
2	0	0	0	0	0	0	0	0	0	0	0	0	0	0	0	1	1	1	1	1	1	1	1	1	1	1	1	1	1	1
3	0	0	0	0	0	0	0	0	0	0	1	1	1	1	1	1	1	1	1	1	1	1	1	1	1	1	1	1	1	2
4	0	0	0	0	0	0	0	1	1	1	1	1	1	1	1	1	1	1	1	1	1	1	2	2	2	2	2	2	2	2
5	0	0	0	0	0	0	1	1	1	1	1	1	1	1	1	1	1	2	2	2	2	2	2	2	2	2	2	2	2	2
6	0	0	0	0	0	1	1	1	1	1	1	1	1	1	2	2	2	2	2	2	2	2	2	2	2	3	3	3	3	3
7	0	0	0	0	1	1	1	1	1	1	1	1	2	2	2	2	2	2	2	2	2	3	3	3	3	3	3	3	3	4
8	0	0	0	1	1	1	1	1	1	1	1	2	2	2	2	2	2	2	3	3	3	3	3	3	3	3	4	4	4	4
9	0	0	0	1	1	1	1	1	1	2	2	2	2	2	2	2	3	3	3	3	3	3	3	4	4	4	4	4	4	4
10	0	0	0	1	1	1	1	1	2	2	2	2	2	2	2	3	3	3	3	3	4	4	4	4	4	4	4	5	5	5
11	0	0	1	1	1	1	1	1	2	2	2	2	2	3	3	3	3	3	3	4	4	4	4	4	5	5	5	5	5	6
12	0	0	1	1	1	1	1	2	2	2	2	2	3	3	3	3	3	4	4	4	4	4	5	5	5	5	5	6	6	6
13	0	0	1	1	1	1	2	2	2	2	2	3	3	3	3	3	4	4	4	4	5	5	5	5	5	6	6	6	6	6
14	0	0	1	1	1	1	2	2	2	2	3	3	3	3	4	4	4	4	4	5	5	5	5	6	6	6	6	7	7	7
15	0	0	1	1	1	2	2	2	2	2	3	3	3	4	4	4	4	4	5	5	5	6	6	6	6	6	7	7	7	8
16	0	1	1	1	1	2	2	2	2	3	3	3	3	4	4	4	5	5	5	5	6	6	6	6	7	7	7	7	8	8
17	0	1	1	1	1	2	2	2	3	3	3	3	4	4	4	5	5	5	5	6	6	6	7	7	7	7	8	8	8	8
18	0	1	1	1	2	2	2	2	3	3	3	4	4	4	4	5	5	5	6	6	6	7	7	7	8	8	8	8	9	9
19	0	1	1	1	2	2	2	3	3	3	3	4	4	4	5	5	5	6	6	6	7	7	7	8	8	8	9	9	9	10
20	0	1	1	1	2	2	2	3	3	3	4	4	4	5	5	5	6	6	6	7	7	7	8	8	8	9	9	9	10	10
21	0	1	1	1	2	2	2	3	3	4	4	4	5	5	5	6	6	6	7	7	7	8	8	8	9	9	9	10	10	10
22	0	1	1	1	2	2	3	3	3	4	4	4	5	5	6	6	6	7	7	7	8	8	8	9	9	10	10	10	11	11
23	0	1	1	2	2	2	3	3	3	4	4	5	5	5	6	6	7	7	7	8	8	8	9	9	10	10	10	11	11	12
24	0	1	1	2	2	2	3	3	4	4	4	5	5	6	6	6	7	7	8	8	8	9	9	10	10	10	11	11	12	12
25	0	1	1	2	2	2	3	3	4	4	5	5	5	6	6	7	7	8	8	8	9	9	10	10	10	11	11	12	12	12
26	0	1	1	2	2	3	3	3	4	4	5	5	6	6	6	7	7	8	8	9	9	10	10	10	11	11	12	12	13	13
27	0	1	1	2	2	3	3	4	4	4	5	5	6	6	7	7	8	8	9	9	9	10	10	11	11	12	12	13	13	14
28	0	1	1	2	2	3	3	4	4	5	5	6	6	7	7	7	8	8	9	9	10	10	11	11	12	12	13	13	14	14
29	0	1	1	2	2	3	3	4	4	5	5	6	6	7	7	8	8	9	9	10	10	11	11	12	12	13	13	14	14	15
30	0	1	2	2	2	3	4	4	4	5	6	6	6	7	8	8	8	9	10	10	10	11	12	12	12	13	14	14	14	15
31	1	1	2	2	3	3	4	4	5	5	6	6	7	7	8	8	9	9	10	10	11	11	12	12	13	13	14	14	15	16
32	1	1	2	2	3	3	4	4	5	5	6	6	7	7	8	9	9	10	10	11	11	12	12	13	13	14	14	15	15	16
33	1	1	2	2	3	3	4	4	5	6	6	7	7	8	8	9	9	10	10	11	12	12	13	13	14	14	15	15	16	16
34	1	1	2	2	3	3	4	5	5	6	6	7	7	8	8	9	10	10	11	11	12	12	13	14	14	15	15	16	16	17
35	1	1	2	2	3	4	4	5	5	6	6	7	8	8	9	9	10	10	11	12	12	13	13	14	15	15	16	16	17	18
36	1	1	2	2	3	4	4	5	5	6	7	7	8	8	9	10	10	11	11	12	13	13	14	14	15	16	16	17	17	18
37	1	1	2	2	3	4	4	5	6	6	7	7	8	9	9	10	10	11	12	12	13	14	14	15	15	16	17	17	18	18
38	1	1	2	3	3	4	4	5	6	6	7	8	8	9	10	10	11	11	12	13	13	14	15	15	16	16	17	18	18	19
39	1	1	2	3	3	4	5	5	6	6	7	8	8	9	10	10	11	12	12	13	14	14	15	16	16	17	18	18	19	20
40	1	1	2	3	3	4	5	5	6	7	7	8	9	9	10	11	11	12	13	13	14	15	15	16	17	17	18	19	19	20
41	1	1	2	3	3	4	5	5	6	7	8	8	9	10	10	11	12	12	13	14	14	15	16	16	17	18	18	19	20	20
42	1	1	2	3	4	4	5	6	6	7	8	8	9	10	10	11	12	13	13	14	15	15	16	17	18	18	19	20	20	21
43	1	1	2	3	4	4	5	6	6	7	8	9	9	10	11	11	12	13	14	14	15	16	16	17	18	19	19	20	21	22
44	1	1	2	3	4	4	5	6	7	7	8	9	10	10	11	12	12	13	14	15	15	16	17	18	18	19	20	21	21	22
45	1	2	2	3	4	4	5	6	7	8	8	9	10	10	11	12	13	14	14	15	16	16	17	18	19	20	20	21	22	22
46	1	2	2	3	4	5	5	6	7	8	8	9	10	11	12	12	13	14	15	15	16	17	18	18	19	20	21	21	22	23
47	1	2	2	3	4	5	5	6	7	8	9	9	10	11	12	13	13	14	15	16	16	17	18	19	20	20	21	22	23	24
48	1	2	2	3	4	5	6	6	7	8	9	10	10	11	12	13	14	14	15	16	17	18	18	19	20	21	22	22	23	24
49	1	2	2	3	4	5	6	7	7	8	9	10	11	11	12	13	14	15	16	16	17	18	19	20	20	21	22	23	24	24
50	1	2	2	3	4	5	6	7	8	8	9	10	11	12	12	13	14	15	16	17	18	18	19	20	21	22	22	23	24	25
51	1	2	3	3	4	5	6	7	8	8	9	10	11	12	13	14	14	15	16	17	18	19	20	20	21	22	23	24	25	26
52	1	2	3	3	4	5	6	7	8	9	10	10	11	12	13	14	15	16	16	17	18	19	20	21	22	23	23	24	25	26
53	1	2	3	4	4	5	6	7	8	9	10	11	11	12	13	14	15	16	17	18	19	19	20	21	22	23	24	25	26	26
54	1	2	3	4	4	5	6	7	8	9	10	11	12	13	14	14	15	16	17	18	19	20	21	22	22	23	24	25	26	27
55	1	2	3	4	5	6	6	7	8	9	10	11	12	13	14	15	16	16	17	18	19	20	21	22	23	24	25	26	27	28
56	1	2	3	4	5	6	7	7	8	9	10	11	12	13	14	15	16	17	18	19	20	21	21	22	23	24	25	26	27	28
57	1	2	3	4	5	6	7	8	9	10	10	11	12	13	14	15	16	17	18	19	20	21	22	23	24	25	26	27	28	28
58	1	2	3	4	5	6	7	8	9	10	11	12	13	14	14	15	16	17	18	19	20	21	22	23	24	25	26	27	28	29
59	1	2	3	4	5	6	7	8	9	10	11	12	13	14	15	16	17	18	19	20	21	22	23	24	25	26	27	28	29	30

d / ′	31	32	33	34	35	36	37	38	39	40	41	42	43	44	45	46	47	48	49	50	51	52	53	54	55	56	57	58	59	60	d / ′
0	0	0	0	0	0	0	0	0	0	0	0	0	0	0	0	0	0	0	0	0	0	0	0	0	0	0	0	0	0	0	0
1	1	1	1	1	1	1	1	1	1	1	1	1	1	1	1	1	1	1	1	1	1	1	1	1	1	1	1	1	1	1	1
2	1	1	1	1	1	1	1	1	1	1	1	1	1	1	2	2	2	2	2	2	2	2	2	2	2	2	2	2	2	2	2
3	2	2	2	2	2	2	2	2	2	2	2	2	2	2	2	2	2	2	2	2	3	3	3	3	3	3	3	3	3	3	3
4	2	2	2	2	2	2	2	3	3	3	3	3	3	3	3	3	3	3	3	3	3	3	4	4	4	4	4	4	4	4	4
5	3	3	3	3	3	3	3	3	3	3	3	4	4	4	4	4	4	4	4	4	4	4	4	4	5	5	5	5	5	5	5
6	3	3	3	3	4	4	4	4	4	4	4	4	4	4	4	5	5	5	5	5	5	5	5	5	6	6	6	6	6	6	6
7	4	4	4	4	4	4	4	4	5	5	5	5	5	5	5	5	5	6	6	6	6	6	6	6	6	7	7	7	7	7	7
8	4	4	4	5	5	5	5	5	5	5	5	6	6	6	6	6	6	6	7	7	7	7	7	7	7	7	8	8	8	8	8
9	5	5	5	5	5	5	6	6	6	6	6	6	6	7	7	7	7	7	7	8	8	8	8	8	8	8	9	9	9	9	9
10	5	5	6	6	6	6	6	6	6	7	7	7	7	7	8	8	8	8	8	8	8	9	9	9	9	9	10	10	10	10	10
11	6	6	6	6	6	7	7	7	7	7	8	8	8	8	8	8	9	9	9	9	9	10	10	10	10	10	10	11	11	11	11
12	6	6	7	7	7	7	7	8	8	8	8	8	9	9	9	9	9	10	10	10	10	10	11	11	11	11	11	12	12	12	12
13	7	7	7	7	8	8	8	8	8	9	9	9	9	10	10	10	10	10	11	11	11	11	11	12	12	12	12	13	13	13	13
14	7	7	8	8	8	8	9	9	9	9	10	10	10	10	10	11	11	11	11	12	12	12	12	13	13	13	13	14	14	14	14
15	8	8	8	8	9	9	9	10	10	10	10	10	11	11	11	12	12	12	12	12	13	13	13	14	14	14	14	14	15	15	15
16	8	9	9	9	9	10	10	10	10	11	11	11	11	12	12	12	13	13	13	13	14	14	14	14	15	15	15	15	16	16	16
17	9	9	9	10	10	10	10	11	11	11	12	12	12	12	13	13	13	14	14	14	14	15	15	15	16	16	16	16	17	17	17
18	9	10	10	10	10	11	11	11	12	12	12	13	13	13	14	14	14	14	15	15	15	16	16	16	16	17	17	17	18	18	18
19	10	10	10	11	11	11	12	12	12	13	13	13	14	14	14	15	15	15	16	16	16	16	17	17	17	18	18	18	19	19	19
20	10	11	11	11	12	12	12	13	13	13	14	14	14	15	15	15	16	16	16	17	17	17	18	18	18	19	19	19	20	20	20
21	11	11	12	12	12	13	13	13	14	14	14	15	15	15	16	16	16	17	17	18	18	18	19	19	19	20	20	20	21	21	21
22	11	12	12	12	13	13	14	14	14	15	15	15	16	16	16	17	17	18	18	18	19	19	19	20	20	21	21	21	22	22	22
23	12	12	13	13	13	14	14	15	15	15	16	16	16	17	17	18	18	18	19	19	20	20	20	21	21	21	22	22	23	23	23
24	12	13	13	14	14	14	15	15	16	16	16	17	17	18	18	18	19	19	20	20	20	21	21	22	22	22	23	23	24	24	24
25	13	13	14	14	15	15	15	16	16	17	17	18	18	18	19	19	20	20	20	21	21	22	22	22	23	23	24	24	25	25	25
26	13	14	14	15	15	16	16	16	17	17	18	18	19	19	20	20	20	21	21	22	22	23	23	23	24	24	25	25	26	26	26
27	14	14	15	15	16	16	17	17	18	18	18	19	19	20	20	21	21	22	22	22	23	23	24	24	25	25	26	26	27	27	27
28	14	15	15	16	16	17	17	18	18	19	19	20	20	21	21	21	22	22	23	23	24	24	25	25	26	26	27	27	28	28	28
29	15	15	16	16	17	17	18	18	19	19	20	20	21	21	22	22	23	23	24	24	25	25	26	26	27	27	28	28	29	29	29
30	16	16	16	17	18	18	18	19	20	20	20	21	22	22	22	23	24	24	24	25	26	26	26	27	28	28	28	29	30	30	30
31	16	17	17	18	18	19	19	20	20	21	21	22	22	23	23	24	24	25	25	26	26	27	27	28	28	29	29	30	30	31	31
32	17	17	18	18	19	19	20	20	21	21	22	22	23	23	24	25	25	26	26	27	27	28	28	29	29	30	30	31	31	32	32
33	17	18	18	19	19	20	20	21	21	22	23	23	24	24	25	25	26	26	27	28	28	29	29	30	30	31	31	32	32	33	33
34	18	18	19	19	20	20	21	22	22	23	23	24	24	25	26	26	27	27	28	28	29	29	30	31	31	32	32	33	33	34	34
35	18	19	19	20	20	21	22	22	23	23	24	24	25	26	26	27	27	28	29	29	30	30	31	32	32	33	33	34	34	35	35
36	19	19	20	20	21	22	22	23	23	24	25	25	26	26	27	28	28	29	29	30	31	31	32	32	33	34	34	35	35	36	36
37	19	20	20	21	22	22	23	23	24	25	25	26	27	27	28	28	29	30	30	31	31	32	33	33	34	35	35	36	36	37	37
38	20	20	21	22	22	23	23	24	25	25	26	27	27	28	28	29	30	30	31	32	32	33	34	34	35	35	36	37	37	38	38
39	20	21	21	22	23	23	24	25	25	26	27	27	28	29	29	30	31	31	32	32	33	34	34	35	36	36	37	38	38	39	39
40	21	21	22	23	23	24	25	25	26	27	27	28	29	29	30	31	31	32	33	33	34	35	35	36	37	37	38	39	39	40	40
41	21	22	23	23	24	25	25	26	27	27	28	29	29	30	31	31	32	33	33	34	35	36	36	37	38	38	39	40	40	41	41
42	22	22	23	24	24	25	26	27	27	28	29	29	30	31	32	32	33	34	34	35	36	36	37	38	38	39	40	41	41	42	42
43	22	23	24	24	25	26	27	27	28	29	29	30	31	32	32	33	34	34	35	36	37	37	38	39	39	40	41	42	42	43	43
44	23	23	24	25	26	26	27	28	29	29	30	31	32	32	33	34	34	35	36	37	37	38	39	40	40	41	42	43	43	44	44
45	23	24	25	26	26	27	28	28	29	30	31	32	32	33	34	34	35	36	37	38	38	39	40	40	41	42	43	44	44	45	45
46	24	25	25	26	27	28	28	29	30	31	31	32	33	34	34	35	36	37	38	38	39	40	41	41	42	43	44	44	45	46	46
47	24	25	26	27	27	28	29	30	31	31	32	33	34	34	35	36	37	38	38	39	40	41	42	42	43	44	45	45	46	47	47
48	25	26	26	27	28	29	30	30	31	32	33	34	34	35	36	37	38	38	39	40	41	42	42	43	44	45	46	46	47	48	48
49	25	26	27	28	29	29	30	31	32	33	33	34	35	36	37	38	38	39	40	41	42	42	43	44	45	46	47	47	48	49	49
50	26	27	28	28	29	30	31	32	32	33	34	35	36	37	38	38	39	40	41	42	42	43	44	45	46	47	48	48	49	50	50
51	26	27	28	29	30	31	31	32	33	34	35	36	37	37	38	39	40	41	42	42	43	44	45	46	47	48	48	49	50	51	51
52	27	28	29	29	30	31	32	33	34	35	36	36	37	38	39	40	41	42	42	43	44	45	46	47	48	49	49	50	51	52	52
53	27	28	29	30	31	32	33	34	34	35	36	37	38	39	40	41	42	42	43	44	45	46	47	48	49	49	50	51	52	53	53
54	28	29	30	31	32	32	33	34	35	36	37	38	39	40	40	41	42	43	44	45	46	47	48	49	50	50	51	52	53	54	54
55	28	29	30	31	32	33	34	35	36	37	38	38	39	40	41	42	43	44	45	46	47	48	49	50	50	51	52	53	54	55	55
56	29	30	31	32	33	34	35	35	36	37	38	39	40	41	42	43	44	45	46	47	48	49	49	50	51	52	53	54	55	56	56
57	29	30	31	32	33	34	35	36	37	38	39	40	41	42	43	44	45	46	47	48	48	49	50	51	52	53	54	55	56	57	57
58	30	31	32	33	34	35	36	37	38	39	40	41	42	43	44	44	45	46	47	48	49	50	51	52	53	54	55	56	57	58	58
59	30	31	32	33	34	35	36	37	38	39	40	41	42	43	44	45	46	47	48	49	50	51	52	53	54	55	56	57	58	59	59

Fig 84
From Air Tables, *Vol II, page 242*

months, by taking a second sextant shot of the sun when the true bearing has changed a minimum of 30 degrees. This is the minimum cut acceptable between the two position lines; any less and the resulting position would not be reliable. However, it is more common to wait until noon, when the navigator can find his latitude directly, as explained in Chapter Six, and the position is found by crossing the morning sun line with the noon latitude.

In either case the boat will have moved between the times of taking the two sights, and this movement has to be allowed for to find the correct position. It is in fact a running fix, and the first position line is transferred to the time of the second sight in the same manner that a bearing line is transferred for a running fix in coastal navigation. The boat's course is known. The log distance is noted as each sight is taken, and the difference in the two readings gives the distance the boat has moved between the time of each sight. Alternatively, the distance run can be worked out using log speed and the interval between the two times.

Plotting the boat's position

Continuing with the same example that was used in Fig 85 let us assume that noon on that day is 1230 local time. The course is 036 degrees true, speed 6 knots.

Step 1 See Fig 87 which shows the 0930 position line plotted in the previous example.

Step 2 Draw in the noon latitude.

Step 3 Between 0930 and 1230 the boat will have sailed 18 miles. From *any point* on the first position line lay off the course and mark

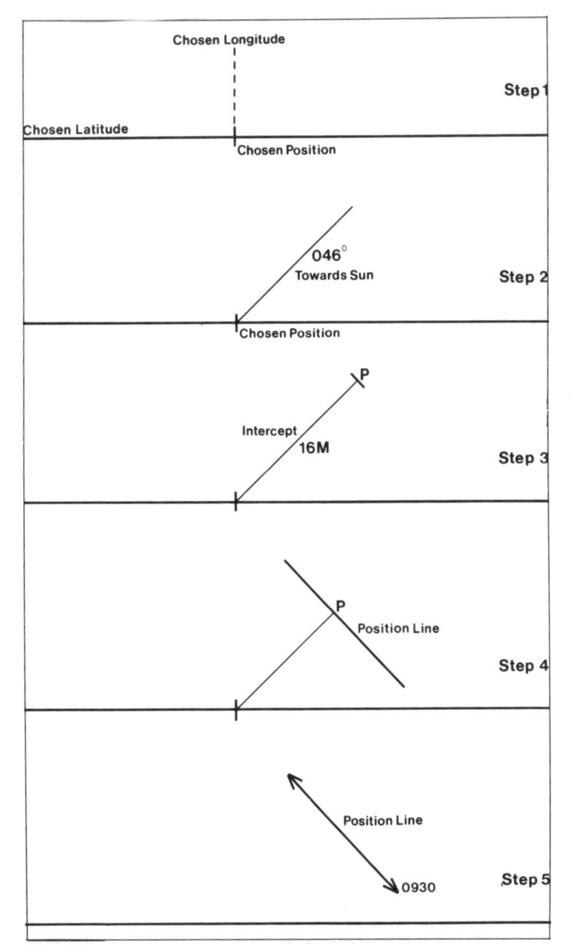

Fig 85
Plotting the position line

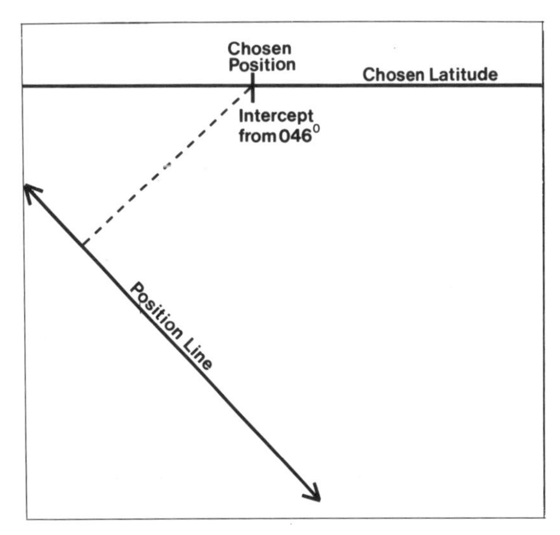

Fig 86
Plotting the position line if the intercept had been 16 miles away from the sun's true bearing of 046°.

this distance along it, point R in the diagram.
Step 4 Finally, using the parallel rulers, transfer the 0930 position line through the point R. The fix or boat's position at 1230 is where the noon latitude and transferred position line cut. A transferred position line is identified by double arrow-heads as shown.
Step 5 Dead reckoning ahead starts again from this fix.

A second position can be found in the mid or late afternoon by taking another sextant shot of the sun, but here the noon latitude is transferred to the time of the second sight. Fig 88 shows the plotted fix for a position line found at 1500. Here the second part of *Step 3* above is not needed as the dead reckoning track starting at the noon fix should already be on the chart or plotting sheet. So the noon latitude line can be transferred directly through the 1500 dead reckoning position giving the fix. Dead reckoning ahead is started again from this position.

If the plotting is done on a separate sheet, the fix is transferred by latitude and longitude to the ocean chart in use. It is unusual in practice to get a position line or fix from the sun on the exact hour or half hour, and the majority of fixes or position lines turn out to be at a time a few minutes one side or the other. It is inconvenient to transfer a position found at say 1428 or 1456 to the ocean chart. The position at exactly 1430 or exactly 1500 is preferable. To achieve this the latitude and longitude of the dead reckoning position at the exact hour or half hour based on the celestial fix should be used. Even in bad weather or with an unknown ocean current, the dead reckoning ahead over just a few minutes must be accurate enough for the navigator's purpose.

In Fig 89 the fix is at 1453 and the latitude and longitude of the 1500 position based on this fix is the position to transfer to the ocean chart.

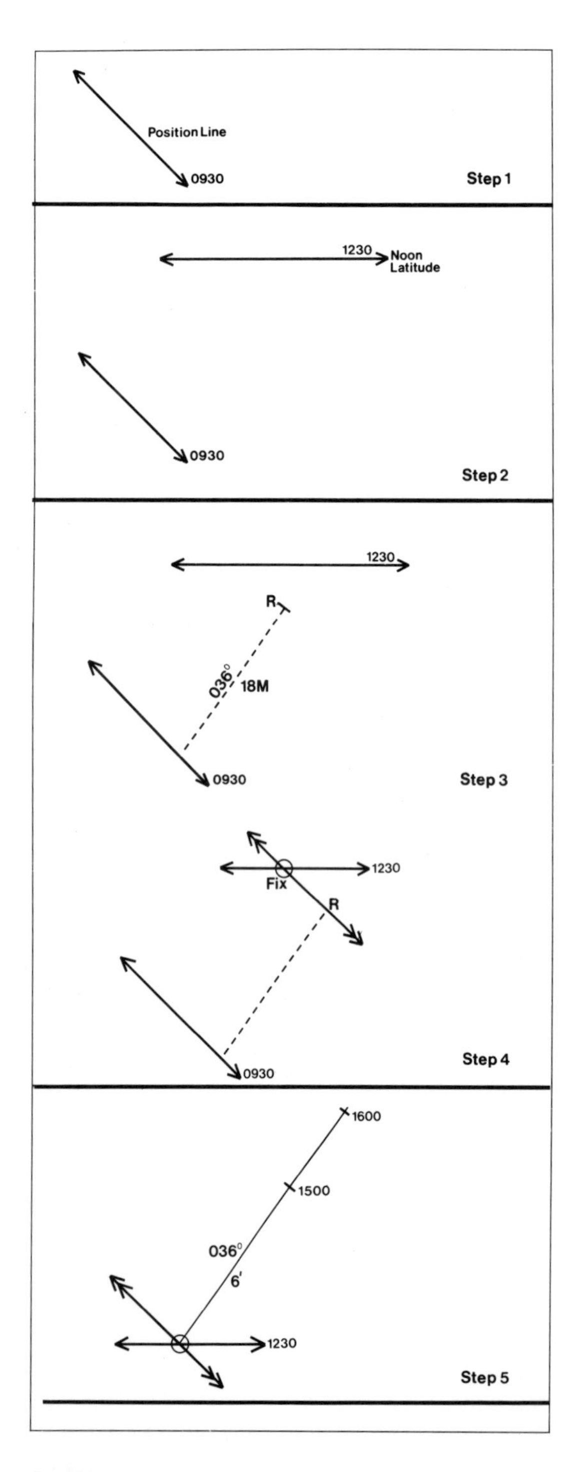

Fig 87
Plotting the position: morning position line and noon latitude

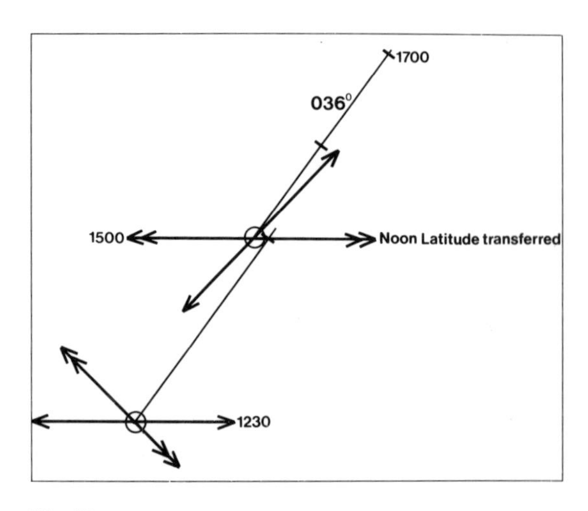

Fig 88
Afternoon fix

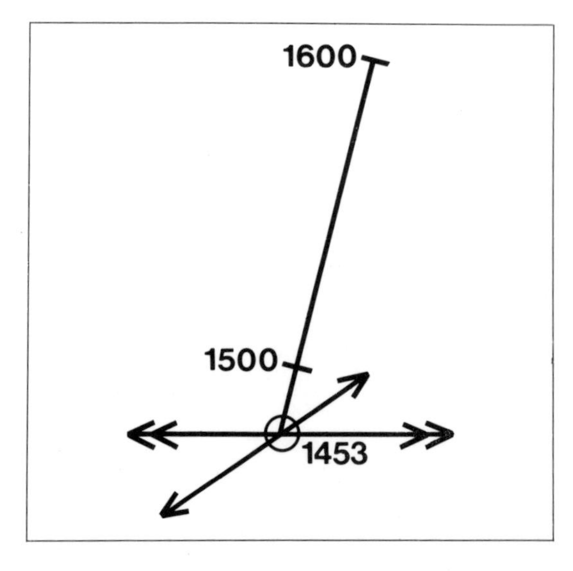

Fig 89
Transfer position marked at 1500 to the ocean chart. Course 015° (T), speed 7 knots. 1453 to 1500 (7 mins), distance run 0.8 M

Chapter Nine

Practical Ocean Navigation

In ocean navigation, the aim each day should be to take a minimum of three shots of the sun which will give two fixes. Traditionally the navigator tries for a morning sun line, a noon latitude and an afternoon sunsight. A position from the sun is a running fix and the morning line is run up to the noon latitude, which in turn is run to the afternoon sun line.

The tendency is to take the first sight as early as possible before noon to get the maximum angle of cut between the crossed position lines.

The fallacy here is that the navigator depends upon dead reckoning to find the run between sights. If the boat is in an unknown current or making rather more leeway in a strong wind than is allowed for, the fix will be in error. The longer the run, the greater the error. The interval between two successive sights should be kept as short as possible consistent with getting an acceptable angle of cut. 30 degrees is a minimum, 40 degrees is satisfactory, 50 degrees is good and any angle over this is only marginally more accurate than a 50-degree cut.

Weather conditions will always be the controlling factor and the sun moves through a greater range of bearings between sunrise and sunset in the summer than in the winter. However, the *Air Tables* can be used to find approximately how long before or after noon a sight should be taken to get the desired cut.

For example, to get a 50-degree cut, the azimuth angle (Z) in either the northern and southern hemisphere and for either a morning or afternoon sight needs to be 130 degrees, because in the northern hemisphere:

Zn	= Z or Zn	= 360° – Z
	= 130°	= 360° – 130°
		= 230°

Both 130° and 230° are 50 degrees either side of south which is generally the bearing of the sun at noon.

In the southern hemisphere:

Zn	= 180° – Z	or 180° + Z
	= 180° – 130°	or 180° + 130°
	= 050°	or 310°

These two bearings are also 50 degrees either side of north or the sun's noon bearing.

Enter the *Air Tables* at the latitude nearest to the DR latitude. Take the sun's declination from the *Nautical Almanac* and find the appropriate declination column. Look under Z for 130° or the closest angle listed. Look to the side to find the value of LHA. Using declination 15°, the LHA is 24° in Fig 90. Local hour angle changes at 15 degrees per hour. From the conversion of arc to time table, shown in Fig 71, 24° = 1h 36m. So at approximately one and a half hours either side of noon the sun will be on a bearing which will give a 50 degree cut with the latitude from the meridian passage. The time of noon has to be worked out anyway, so thre is no additional work here.

N. Lat. {LHA greater than 180°....... Zn=Z; LHA less than 180°........... Zn=360−Z}

LHA	15° Hc	d	Z	16° Hc	d	Z	17° Hc	d	Z
	° ′	′	°	° ′	′	°	° ′	′	°
0	68 00	+60	180	69 00	+60	180	70 00	+60	180
1	67 59	60	177	68 59	60	177	69 59	60	177
2	67 56	60	175	68 56	59	175	69 55	60	174
3	67 50	60	172	68 50	60	172	69 50	59	172
4	67 43	59	170	68 42	59	169	69 41	60	16[illegible]
5	67 33	+59	167	68 32	+59	167	69 31	+59	16[illegible]
6	67 22	58	165	68 20	59	164	69 19	58	16[illegible]
7	67 08	58	162	68 06	58	162	69 04	58	16[illegible]
8	66 53	57	160	67 50	57	159	68 47	57	15[illegible]
9	66 35	57	158	67 32	57	157	68 29	56	15[illegible]
10	66 16	+57	155	67 13	+55	155	68 08	+56	15[illegible]
11	65 56	55	153	66 51	55	152	67 46	55	151
12	65 33	55	151	66 28	54	150	67 22	54	149
13	65 09	54	149	66 03	54	148	66 57	53	147
14	64 44	53	147	65 37	53	146	66 30	52	145
15	64 17	+52	145	65 09	+52	144	66 01	+51	143
16	63 48	52	143	64 40	51	142	65 31	51	141
17	63 19	51	141	64 10	50	140	65 00	50	139
18	62 48	50	139	63 38	50	138	64 28	49	137
19	62 16	50	138	63 06	48	136	63 54	48	135
20	61 43	+49	136	62 32	+48	135	63 20	+47	133
21	61 09	48	134	61 57	48	133	62 45	46	132
22	60 35	47	133	61 22	46	131	62 08	46	130
23	59 59	46	131	60 45	46	130	61 31	45	128
24	59 22	46	130	60 08	45	128	60 53	45	127
25	58 45	+45	128	59 30	+45	127	60 15	+43	12[illegible]
26	58 07	45	127	58 52	43	125	59 35	43	12[illegible]

Fig 90
Declination and LHA from the Air Tables *Vol II, page 225*

What would be the answers for a 40 degree angle of cut if the declination was 16°? Using the extract above:
Z = 140° LHA = 17°, i.e. 1h 08m either side of the time of noon.

The examples given here would be in the summer months in each hemisphere. Closer to winter the interval each side of noon would be longer for the same angle of cut.

In practice a pattern shows itself in the first day or two of any ocean cruise. If the navigator gets a sight at about 0900 on the first day it should give a reasonable angle of cut with the noon latitude. It may be apparent from the first day's results that the morning shot could be delayed until 0930 or 1000 on subsequent days.

The foregoing has been an outline of the minimum day's work using the sun. There is no reason, apart from a little extra work, why the first fix should not be found much earlier than noon. During the summer months the sun should be high enough to find the first altitude by about 0800. A second sight at say 1030 should give an acceptable fix. Both these sights would have to be worked from the *Air Tables*, and some navigators might prefer to wait for the easier noon latitude.

Let's compromise. Take the early sight but don't work it out. Treat it as 'insurance'. Get the second sight at 1000 or 1030 and run this one up to the noon sight. If the sun clouds over prior to noon, the navigator has the data to work out and plot two position lines for a mid-morning fix.

There is one corollary here. If the dead reckoning position is rough because the navigator was unable to sight the sun the day before, the boat's position should be found as soon as possible.

Starsights

There is little doubt that a position found from the intersection of three or more star position lines taken only a few minutes apart is the most accurate method of finding position. There is no dead reckoning involved, which eliminates one potential source of error. Any slight mistake in each position line shows up as a cocked hat fix, and this can be interpreted to give a most probable position. Even so, the altitudes must be found over a relatively short period of time, and the navigator is unlikely to get more than one shot of each star. If the sea conditions are such that the horizon is largely lost to view, then the results will be poor. If the vessel is sailing in calm weather with good horizons, results from the sun will be perfectly satisfactory.

The constraint with starsights is that they can only be taken when both the stars and the horizon are visible. This is generally 20 to 30 minutes before sunrise and after sunset and is called the period of civil twilight. For the remainder of the night the horizon is too indistinct to use, even with a good moon. As a minimum of three stars is used, the calculations take longer than for a sunsight.

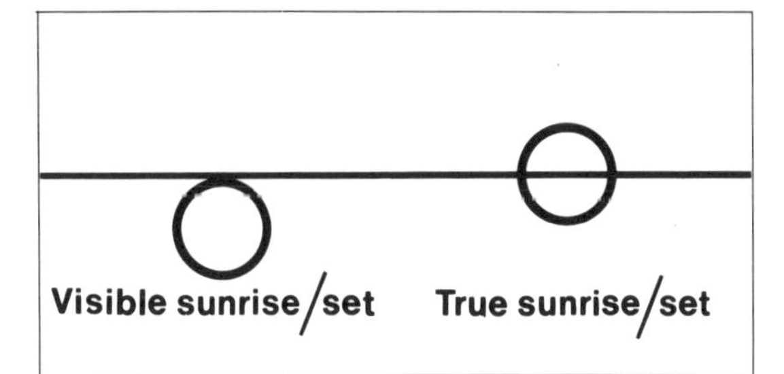

Fig 91
a *Visible sunrise/sunset*
b *True sunrise/sunset*

Fig 92
Visible sun at true sunrise/sunset

The reader is strongly recommended to gain proficiency with the sextant and achieve accurate results using the sun before turning to finding position by the stars. The working required for each star is slightly simpler than for the sun and is given in Appendix 1.

Checking the compass – amplitudes

The compass should be checked from time to time at sea. Apart from any other cause such as a knock, the deviation may change as any corrections that were carried out when the compass was swung are only fully effective in the latitude in which the boat was when the deviation card was made out. The simplest and quickest way to do this is by taking the bearing of the sun at sunrise or sunset.

The sun rarely rises bearing exactly due east or sets bearing due west. The difference in degrees between east and the actual bearing of the sun at sunrise, or west and the bearing at sunset is called a bearing amplitude, e.g:

East	090°	West	270°
Sunrise bearing	100°	Sunset bearing	254°
Bearing amplitude	10°	Amplitude	16°

If the declination is north the sun will rise (or set) north of east (or west) in any latitude.

If declination is south the sun will rise and set south of east and west respectively in any latitude.

Fig 93 is from a table of true amplitudes. The table is entered using the whole degree latitude nearest to the boat's latitude, and the declination of the sun rounded off to the nearest degree. The amplitude extracted from the table is then added or subtracted from 090° (or 270°) to give the true bearing of the sun at rising (or setting). The tables are made out for the centre of the sun at true sunrise or sunset. Visible sunrise (or sunset) is when the upper limb just appears above (or disappears below) the horizon. True sunrise and sunset

Fig 93
Extract from a table of true amplitudes. From Nories Nautical Tables, *page 430*

TRUE AMPLITUDES

Lat.	Declination							
	16°	17°	18°	19°	20°	20½°	21°	2
°	°	°	°	°	°	°	°	
2	16·0	17·0	18·0	19·0	20·0	20·5	21·0	2
4	16·0	17·1	18·1	19·1	20·1	20·6	21·1	2
6	16·1	17·1	18·1	19·1	20·1	20·6	21·1	2
8	16·2	17·2	18·2	19·2	20·2	20·7	21·2	2
10	16·3	17·3	18·3	19·3	20·3	20·8	21·4	2
12	16·4	17·4	18·4	19·4	20·5	21·0	21·5	
14	16·5	17·5	18·6	19·6	20·6	21·2	21·7	
16	16·7	17·7	18·8	19·8	20·9	21·4	21·9	
18	16·9	17·9	19·0	20·0	21·1	21·6	22·1	
20	17·1	18·1	19·2	20·3	21·4	21·9	22·4	
22	17·3	18·4	19·5	20·6	21·7	22·2	22·7	2
24	17·6	18·7	19·8	20·9	22·0	22·5	23·1	2
26	17·9	19·0	20·1	21·2	22·4	22·9	23·5	2
28	18·2	19·3	20·5	21·6	22·8	23·4	24·0	2
30	18·6	19·7	20·9	22·1	23·3	23·9	24·5	2
31	18·8	20·0	21·1	22·3	23·5	24·1	24·7	2
32	19·0	20·2	21·4	22·6	23·8	24·4	25·0	2
33	19·2	20·4	21·6	22·9	24·1	24·7	25·3	
34	19·4	20·6	21·9	23·1	24·4	25·0	25·6	
35	19·7	20·9	22·2	23·4	24·7	25·3	26·0	
36	19·9	21·2	22·5	23·7	25·0	25·7	26·3	
37	20·2	21·5	22·8	24·1	25·4	26·0	26·7	
38	20·5	21·8	23·1	24·4	25·7	26·4	27·1	2
39	20·8	22·1	23·4	24·8	26·1	26·8	27·5	2
40	21·1	22·4	23·8	25·2	26·5	27·2	27·9	2

are when the centre of the sun is on the horizon. However due to two low altitude effects, one being refraction, the moment of true sunrise is when the visible sun is a radius above the horizon.

A compass bearing is taken with the sun in this position at both rising or setting, converted to true and compared with the true bearing found using the amplitude. The difference is the compass error, e.g.:

latitude	26°
declination	17°N
amplitude	19°

As the declination is north the sun will rise and set north of east and west in both north or south latitudes.

	Sunrise	*Sunset*
	090°	270°
Amplitude	19°–	19°+
True bearing	071°	289°

If the declination was 17° south, the sun would rise and set south of east and west respectively. In this case the bearings would be:

090° + 19° = 109°
270° – 19° = 251°

If the latitude was 20° and sun's declination 16° north, what would the sun's bearing be at true sunrise? The answer is amplitude 17°, bearing 073°.

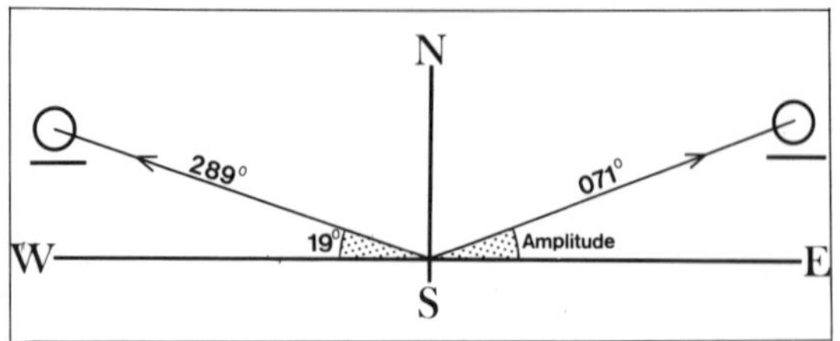

Fig 94
Amplitude

Fig 95
a *Vessel ahead of 1000 DR position*
b *Vessel to port of DR track*

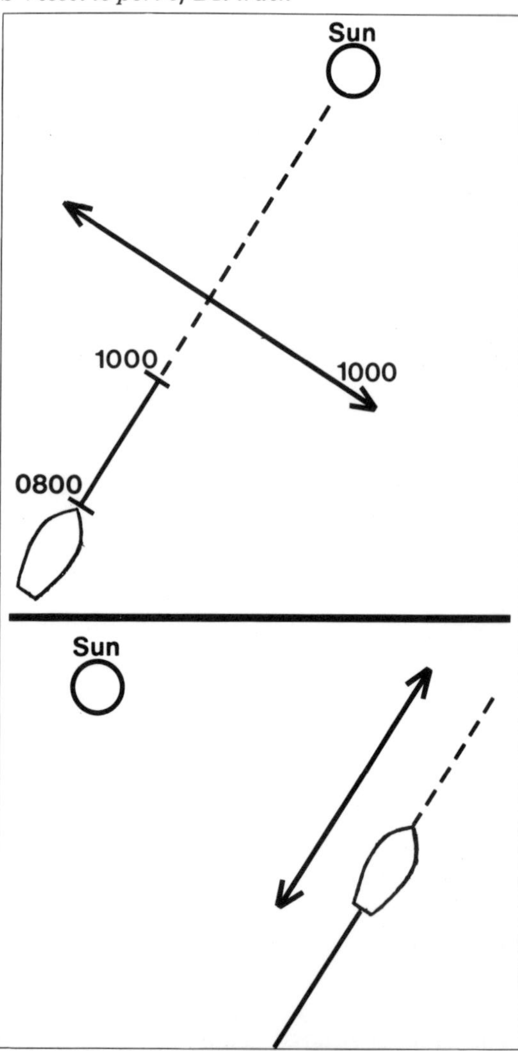

Most useful sun lines

Although a fix using the sun gives the navigator the maximum information for planning each successive stage of the journey, some single position lines in themselves can give very useful information. The navigator is interested in his progress along the intended track and also by how much, if at all, he is being set off the track.

A position line is at right angles to the direction of the sun. If a sight is taken with the sun either directly ahead or directly astern of the boat, the resulting position line will cross the track at 90 degrees i.e. it will indicate progress. If a sight is taken with the sun on either beam the position line will be parallel to the track and will show whether the vessel is on track or if not, which side the vessel is off, and by how much.

Fig 95a shows that the boat is ahead of the 1000 DR position. Fig 95b shows that the boat is to port of the dead reckoning track. Depending on time of year and course, the navigator may find that he is unable to get both these ideal sights each day, but one of them should be obtainable. On a north-south or east-west course, the noon latitude will give the progress along or distance off track respectively.

The day's work is thus a balance between the standard morning, noon and afternoon sights and any additional fixes the navigator may think necessary, either combined with or replaced by the most useful sun lines just discussed.

PRACTICAL SIGHT TAKING

The navigator will be constrained by the layout of his own boat but as far as possible to take a sight he should choose a position protected from spray where he can stand with legs firmly braced but body free to bend or sway from the waist up. In heavy seas it may be a case of hanging on like grim death and grabbing a shot when one can. The main problem for the yachtsman in heavy seas is that the actual horizon may be obscured by large waves or swells close to the boat. The same waves may still be above the horizon even several hundred metres from the craft. Other things being equal, a high position should be used and the sight taken on the up roll to get a clear view of the line of the horizon over the swells. On a dull day the horizon may look firmer from lower down.

Timing the sight

An accurate reading of GMT or Universal Time must be made at the moment the navigator is satisfied he has the sun exactly on the horizon. One watch with a sweep second hand should be assigned completely to the navigator for this purpose. It should be checked against a radio time signal for any error prior to or just after the sight. A watch need not keep perfect time as long as it has a constant error, i.e. gains or loses the same number of seconds each day. Thus even without a time check the total error should be known and then applied to any reading to find accurate GMT. This timepiece should be kept below and a stopwatch used for ordinary purposes. The latter should be started at an exact minute – GMT – and read as each sight is taken. The number of minutes and seconds is then added to the GMT at which the watch was started, e.g.:

Stopwatch started at GMT	10h 23m 00s
Stopwatch reading at moment of sight	7m 46s +
GMT/UT of sunsight	10h 30m 46s

An assistant should read and note the time and the sextant altitude. Make sure this person can read a watch correctly. You might be astounded at just how many people who, in the heat of the moment, would write down the time shown in Fig 96 as 7m 58s. It is of course only 6 m 58 s. That minute error in time would put the resulting position line 15 minutes or a quarter of a degree of longitude in error, and this error will not be apparent in the calculations. If there is a watch with a digital readout on board, this source of error is overcome.

Taking the sight

After ensuring that the assistant is ready with the watch, that the correct sun shades are in place, that the index error has been checked and that the sails are not in the way, bring the sun down to the horizon.

There are raging arguments among navigators as to what happens next. Some take five sights and average them, some draw graphs and some just take one shot. The result is about the same.

In bad weather one has to do the best one can. In good weather the beginner might like to try the following procedure:

1 Having brought the sun near the horizon, look at the sextant altitude. In the morning the sun is rising and in the afternoon it is falling. Set the micrometer to an exact minute

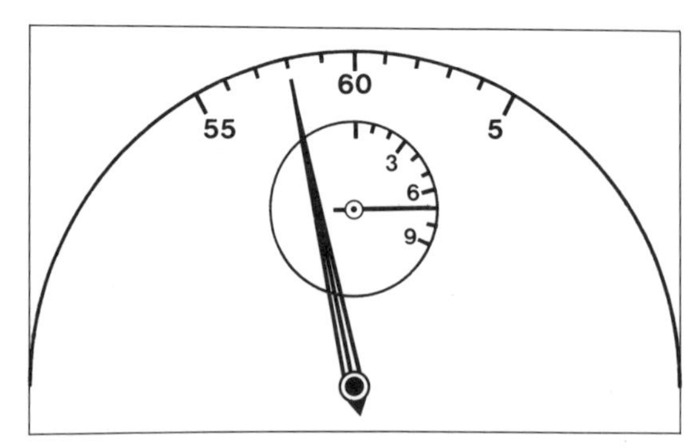

Fig 96
Reading a stopwatch

so that the sun is a little below the horizon in the morning, or a little above in the afternoon. Then rock the sextant and merely watch until the lower limb falls onto or rises up to the horizon.

2 Give the assistant a standby warning and then shout 'stop' or some other previously arranged signal. He reads the watch at this moment.

3 Depending on the time of day, wind the micrometer on or back exactly 5 minutes and repeat the procedure.

4 Repeat the procedure again.

The navigator now has three sextant altitudes with exactly 5 minutes of arc between eachreading, and three times written down. As the difference between each altitude is the same, the times should differ by exactly the same number of seconds. The navigator has pre-averaged the sextant altitudes.

If the two time differences are exactly equal, use any one set of altitude and time for the calculations. If the time differences are only a second or so apart, average the three times, and use the middle altitude, e.g.:

Sextant Altitude	*GMT*	*Time difference*	*Result*
39° 10′.0	10 14 16		
39° 15′.0	10 14 41	25 seconds	A good sight.
39° 20′.0	10 15 06	25 seconds	
23° 30′.0	14 08 45		
23° 25′.0	14 08 59	14 seconds	Not good; repeat.
23° 20′.0	14 09 26	27 seconds	
46° 45′.0	10 59 26		
46° 50′.0	10 59 47	21 seconds	Use middle altitude and average the times.
46° 55′.0	11 00 06	19 seconds	
46° 50′.0	10 59 46		

How long will this take? At first it may be ten minutes or more before the navigator is satisfied that he has a reasonable set of figures. With practice, and assuming constant sunshine during the sight, this should come down to a couple of minutes. What about the one-shot merchants; do they get good results? A qualified 'yes' is the answer, but only after many years' experience.

Using a sextant is a little like using a target rifle. The experienced marksman can sense, probably even before the bullet has left the barrel, that the shot is a good one and is going to hit the bullseye. The experienced sextant handler can also sense that everything about a particular sunshot is just right. He literally feels that the sun was exactly in the right place on the horizon, neither a fraction too high nor a fraction too low.

If he gets this feeling of correctness there is little point in his wasting time taking any further altitudes. But there is no substitute for practice.

Stalking the sun

There are some places in the world, such as the North Atlantic in winter, where the sky can remain overcast for days or even weeks on end with never a sight of even the palest sun. In my experience this does not apply to most of the waters sailed by yachtsmen. The sun always comes out at least once a day, even if only for a minute or two.

The navigator who spends his time below decks, with his sextant locked safely in its box, with the watch stowed safely at the back of a drawer under a pile of charts and who asks the helmsman to call him when the sun comes out deserves to miss these opportunities to find the sun's altitude. The place for the prudent navigator is on deck, with a watch in his pocket, the sextant held loosely in one hand and a cup of coffee in the other, talking to the helmsman.

Once the navigator is competent in using a sextant, and given any sort of reasonable sea conditions, then twenty seconds is all that may be needed to get the sun's altitude. It may not be the most accurate of sights but if upwards of a day has passed without one and there is the distinct possibility of the sun disappearing again for a second longish period, it will be a great morale booster.

The insurance shot

As with any two bearings in a coastal fix there should be a minimum 30-degree angle between any two position lines from the sun, preferably a 40-degree or 50-degree cut. This means that there is about a two-hour wait between any one sight and the next while the sun changes bearing. The navigator might have taken one sight, and ominous clouds may be approaching before the necessary time has quite gone by. Even so he should find the sextant altitude, but not bother to work the sight through. If after an hour or so the sky clears again he can get a good shot of the sun and the 'insurance' shot can be discarded. If not, he has the data available to work out a less than perfect position and if the weather steadily worsens it may be the only fix obtained in that 24-hour period. But at least he's got a fix.

A WORKING DAY AT SEA

The date is 22 February 1978. A typical ocean yacht departed Norfolk Island (29° S, 168° E) a little over 24 hours ago bound for Matthew Island (22° 21′ S, 171° 21′ E). Shortly after leaving harbour the wind freshened and within hours the boat was running under reduced sail before a gale force wind and confused seas. The wind abated overnight and this morning the sun is shining, although moderate swells will make it difficult for the navigator to get accurate results with a sextant. He thinks that his dead reckoning position might be 10 to 15 miles in error. Because of this, he wants to find his position as quickly as possible, even though there are no reefs or shoals ahead.

The true course is 025° and log speed is fluctuating around 7.5 knots. The boat is keeping a time 11 hours ahead of GMT, or zone −11. A time check at 0700 local time showed that the watch kept on GMT is 10 seconds slow. He takes his sextant on deck shortly after 0745 and by 0750 he is satisfied that the results he has obtained are as good as he is going to get in the prevailing sea conditions.

At the moment the sight was taken the watch on GMT read 8h 52m 38s. The navigator has walked into this trap before. His first step is to find the approximate GMT and the date to use in the *Nautical Almanac,* e.g.

Local Time 0753 + 24h	3153
Zone	11 −
GMT/UT	= 2053
	(the previous day)

So the watch was actually reading:

20h 52m 38s on 21 February 1978
Error of watch 10s slow +
Exact GMT 20h 52m 48s on 21 February 1978

The distance reading on the log a minute or so after the sight was 896.1M, and the navigator noted that the sun was bearing almost due east (090°).

The dead reckoning position at 0753 is 26° 20′ S, 169° 20′ E. The sextant altitude is 30° 54′ .7. Dip correction is − 3′.0 and the current index error is + 1′.6.

The sight is worked as follows:

Date at			
Greenwich	21	February	Chosen
GMT	20h	52m 48s	latitude 26°S

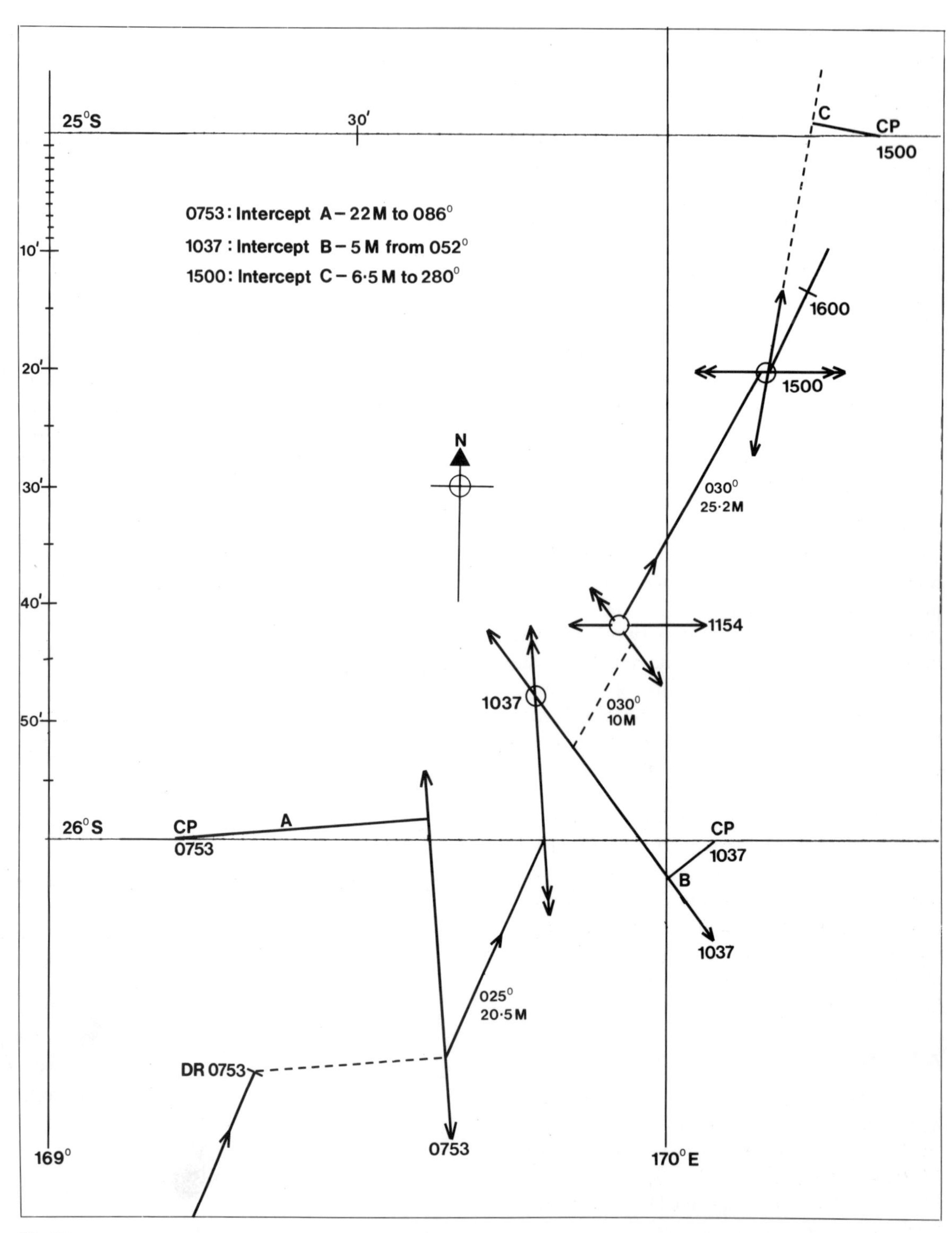

Fig 97
A plot of the sun fixes

Tab GHA	116° 35′.3		
Increment	13° 12′.0		
GHA	129° 47′.3		
Chosen longitude	169° 12′.7 E+		
LHA	299° 00′.0		
Tab dec	S10° 27′.7	d 0.9	
d corr	0′.9 –		
Dec	10° 26′.8		
Tab Hc	30° 21′ d + 24	Z =	94°
d corr	11′ +	Zn =	180° – Z
Hc	30° 32′	=	086°
Sextant altitude	30° 40′.8		
IE and dip	1′.4 –		
App alt	30° 39′.4		
Alt corr (Lower limb)	14′.6 +		
Ho	30° 54′.0		
Hc	30° 32′.0		
Intercept	22′.0	towards	086°

Fig 97 shows the 0753 DR position and the plot of the position line found above. The boat is clearly well to the east of the DR position so the track is restarted from a point on the position line where a perpendicular from the DR meets it. This is shown by the dotted line in the diagram. (This point is exactly the same one as given by an electronic calculator when programmed to work out a Most Probable Position based on a single position line.)

As the navigator can do nothing more until the sun has changed bearing by 30 degrees or more before getting a fix, he decides to work out the time of noon. It is now about 0830. Assuming noon to be 1200, he sets 30 miles on the dividers, which is four hours run at 7.5 knots. By laying this off from the 0753 position he finds that longitude at 1200 will be about 169° 55′ E. He rounds this off to 170° E and does the calculation.

Mer. Pas. for 22 February	12h 14m
Longitude 170° converted to time	11h 20m E –
GMT of Noon	00h 54m (22 Feb)
Zone	11h (ahead)
Local Time	11h 54m

That took him about a minute and a half, and as his sextant was covered in spray while taking the sight at 0754 he spends some time carefully removing the film of salt with fresh water.

After morning coffee at 1000 he instructs one of the new crew members in reading a stopwatch and prepares for the second sight of the day. By 1030 the sea has flattened out and a check on the horizon confirms that the index error is + 1′.6. This time the navigator checks the date and time at Greenwich before taking the sight.

Approximate local time	1035 22 February
Zone	11h –
GMT	2335 21 February

The sextant altitude is 65° 52′.6.

Watch time	23h	37m 10s
Error		10s slow +
GMT	23h	37m 20s 21 February

Dead reckoning position at 1037 local time: 26° 00′ S, 169° 48′ E. Chosen Latitude 26°S

Tab GHA	161° 35′.6		
Inc	9° 20′.0		
GHA	170° 55′.6		
Chosen longitude	170° 04′.4 E+		
LHA	341°		
Tab Dec	S 10°25′.0	d 0′.9	
d correction	0′.6 –		
Dec	10° 24′.4 (same)		
Tab Hc	65° 56′ d + 41	Z	= 128°
d Corr	16′ +	Zn	= 180° – Z
Hc	66° 12′		= 052°

Sextant altitude	65° 52′.6	
IE and dip	1′.4	–
App Alt	65° 51′.2	
Alt Corr (Lower limb)	15′.8	+
Ho	66° 07′.0	
Hc	66° 12′.0	
Intercept	5′.0	from 052°

The position line from this sight is plotted as shown in Fig 97. Based on the GMT the local time to the nearest minute was 1037, and the log reading was 916.6M. Notice that the sun's true bearing changed from 086° at 0754 to 052°, 34° or just over the acceptable 30 degree minimum. Even so, the first sight was taken before the sea had moderated, and the resulting position line may not have been accurate. The distance run between sights is the difference in the two log readings (916.6 – 896.1 = 20.5M).

Using this distance along the boat's course gives the fix shown at 1037. The navigator estimates that this position is accurate to about 4 miles, and that the boat is from 18 to 20 miles to the north-east of the original dead reckoning track. The course being made good (CMG) is closer to 030° than to 025°, the course being steered. Course is maintained for the moment to give an accurate run by dead reckoning between this sight and the noon sight at 1154. The navigator ponders on the fact that if the bad weather had continued he might have found himself over 40 miles off track after 48 hours at sea. It is always difficult to accept just how far a boat can be set from the intended track by bad weather or a wrongly estimated ocean current.

At 1145 the navigator brings the sun onto the horizon in preparation for the noon latitude sight. Five minutes later the altitude has steadied and as there is no further increase in altitude by 1154, he considers the sun is on his meridian. The sextant altitude is 74° 26′.8 and, as he worked out some three hours or more ago, the Greenwich Mean Time of noon is 00h 54min on 22 February (as his watch is 11 hours ahead of GMT). DR latitude: 25°43′S

Noon latitude is:

Sextant altitude	74° 26′.8	Tab Dec.	10°24′.1 S	
IE and dip	–1′.4	d corr	0′.8 –	
App alt	74° 25′.4	Dec	10°23′.3 S	
Alt corr	+15′.9			
True altitude	74° 41′.3			
	90° 00′.0	Log 926.6 at 1154		
Ho	– 74° 41′.3	Log 916.6 at 1037		
Zx	15° 18′.7	Run 10M		
Dec	+ 10° 23′.3			
Latitude	25° 42′ S			

The navigator decides to use a CMG of 30° and the 10M distance run when transferring the 1037 position line up to the latitude found at noon. The angle of cut is 52°. Because of this and, as there was only 1h 17m between sights, he considers that the resulting fix is accurate to a mile. Position at 1154 local time is 25° 42′ S 169° 54′.4 E.

The next and probably final sunshot for the day need not be until mid-afternoon.

The navigator decides to work out the true bearing of the sun at sunset, using the amplitude tables. The compass may have been affected by the bad weather conditions, and needs checking. He remembers that sunset at Norfolk Island was about 1820 two nights ago and there should only have been a few minutes change in the time since then.

Latitude by dead reckoning at sunset is 25° S.

Sunset	1815	Declination at 07h GMT 10° 17′ S
Zone	11 –	
GMT	0715	Amplitude 11°

Fig 98**a**
From the Air Tables, *Vol II, page 150*

N. Lat. {LHA greater than 180°....... Zn=Z; LHA less than 180°.......... Zn=360−Z}

DECLINATION (0°-14°) SAME NAME AS LATITUDE

LHA	0°			1°			2°			3°			4°		
	Hc	d	Z	Hc	d	Z	Hc	d	Z	Hc	d	Z	Hc	d	Z
	° ′	′	°	° ′	′	°	° ′	′	°	° ′	′	°	° ′	′	°
0	65 00	+60	180	66 00	+60	180	67 00	+60	180	68 00	+60	180	69 00	+60	180
1	64 59	60	178	65 59	60	178	66 59	60	177	67 59	60	177	68 59	60	177
2	64 56	59	175	65 55	60	175	66 55	60	175	67 55	60	175	68 55	60	174
3	64 50	60	173	65 50	59	173	66 49	60	172	67 49	59	172	68 48	60	172
4	64 42	60	171	65 42	59	170	66 41	59	170	67 40	59	169	68 39	59	169
5	64 32	+59	168	65 31	+59	168	66 30	+59	167	67 29	+58	167	68 27	+59	166
6	64 20	59	166	65 19	58	166	66 17	58	165	67 15	58	164	68 13	58	164
7	64 06	58	164	65 04	58	163	66 02	57	163	66 59	58	162	67 57	57	161
8	63 50	57	162	64 47	57	161	65 44	57	160	66 41	57	159	67 38	57	159
9	63 32	56	160	64 28	57	159	65 25	56	158	66 21	56	157	67 17	56	156
10	63 12	+56	157	64 08	+56	157	65 04	+55	156	65 59	+55	155	66 54	+55	154
11	62 50	55	155	63 45	55	154	64 40	55	154	65 35	54	153	66 29	54	152
12	62 26	55	153	63 21	54	152	64 15	54	151	65 09	53	150	66 02	53	149
13	62 01	54	151	62 55	53	150	63 48	53	149	64 41	53	148	65 34	52	147
14	61 34	53	150	62 27	53	149	63 20	52	147	64 12	51	146	65 03	51	145
15	61 06	+52	148	61 58	+52	147	62 50	+51	146	63 41	+51	144	64 32	+50	143
16	60 36	51	146	61 27	51	145	62 18	51	144	63 09	49	143	63 58	49	141
17	60 05	50	144	60 55	50	143	61 45	50	142	62 35	48	141	63 23	48	139
18	59 32	50	142	60 22	49	141	61 11	49	140	62 00	47	139	62 47	47	138
19	58 58	49	141	59 47	49	140	60 36	47	139	61 23	47	137	62 10	46	136
20	58 24	+48	139	59 12	+47	138	59 59	+47	137	60 46	+46	136	61 32	+45	134
21	57 48	47	138	58 35	46	137	59 21	46	135	60 07	45	134	60 52	45	133
22	57 10	47	136	57 57	46	135	58 43	45	134	59 28	44	133	60 12	43	131
23	56 32	46	135	57 18	45	134	58 03	44	132	58 47	44	131	59 31	42	130
24	55 53	45	134	56 38	44	132	57 22	44	131	58 06	42	130	58 48	42	128
25	55 14	+44	132	55 58	+43	131	56 41	+43	130	57 24	+41	128	58 05	+41	127
26	54 33	43	131	55 16	43	130	55 59	42	129	56 41	41	127	57 22	40	126
27	53 51	43	130	54 34	42	129	55 16	41	127	55 57	40	126	56 37	40	125
28	53 09	42	129	53 51	41	127	54 32	41	126	55 13	39	125	55 52	39	123
29	52 26	41	127	53 07	41	126	53 48	40	125	54 28	38	124	55 06	38	122
30	51 43	+40	126	52 23	+40	125	53 03	+39	124	53 42	+38	123	54 20	+38	121
31	50 58	40	125	51 38	40	124	52 18	38	123	52 56	37	121	53 33	37	120
32	50 14	39	124	50 53	39	123	51 32	37	122	52 09	37	120	52 46	36	119
33	49 28	39	123	50 07	38	122	50 45	37	121	51 22	36	119	51 58	36	118
34	48 43	38	122	49 21	37	121	49 58	37	120	50 35	35	118	51 10	35	117
35	47 56	+38	121	48 34	+37	120	49 11	+35	119	49 46	+36	118	50 22	+34	116
36	47 09	37	120	47 46	37	119	48 23	35	118	48 58	35	117	49 33	34	115
37	46 22	37	119	46 59	35	118	47 34	35	117	48 09	34	116	48 43	34	115
38	45 35	35	118	46 10	36	117	46 46	34	116	47 20	34	115	47 54	33	114
39	44 47	35	118	45 22	35	116	45 57	34	115	46 31	33	114	47 04	32	113
40	43 58	+35	117	44 33	+34	116	45 07	+34	114	45 41	+33	113	46 14	+32	112
41	43 09	35	116	43 44	34	115	44 18	33	114	44 51	32	113	45 23	32	111
42	42 20	34	115	42 54	34	114	43 28	32	113	44 00	32	112	44 32	31	111
43	41 31	34	114	42 05	32	113	42 37	33	112	43 10	31	111	43 41	31	110
44	40 41	33	114	41 14	33	113	41 47	32	111	42 19	31	110	42 50	30	109
45	39 51	+33	113	40 24	+32	112	40 56	+32	111	41 28	+30	110	41 58	+30	108
46	39 01	33	112	39 34	31	111	40 05	31	110	40 36	31	109	41 07	29	108
47	38 11	32	112	38 43	31	110	39 14	31	109	39 45	30	108	40 15	29	107
48	37 20	32	111	37 52	31	110	38 23	30	109	38 53	30	108	39 23	29	106
49	36 29	31	110	37 00	31	109	37 31	30	108	38 01	30	107	38 31	28	106
50	35 38	+31	110	36 09	+30	109	36 39	+30	107	37 09	+29	106	37 38	+29	105
51	34 47	30	109	35 17	30	108	35 47	30	107	36 17	29	106	36 46	28	105
52	33 55	30	108	34 25	30	107	34 55	29	106	35 24	29	105	35 53	28	104
53	33 03	30	108	33 33	30	107	34 03	29	106	34 32	28	105	35 00	28	103
54	32 11	30	107	32 41	29	106	33 10	29	105	33 39	28	104	34 07	28	103
55	31 19	+30	107	31 49	+29	106	32 18	+28	104	32 46	+28	103	33 14	+27	102
56	30 27	29	106	30 56	29	105	31 25	28	104	31 53	28	103	32 21	27	102
57	29 35	29	105	30 04	28	104	30 32	28	103	31 00	28	102	31 28	27	101
58	28 42	29	105	29 11	28	104	29 39	28	103	30 07	27	102	30 34	27	101
59	27 50	28	104	28 18	28	103	28 46	28	102	29 14	27	101	29 41	26	100
60	26 57	+28	104	27 25	+28	103	27 53	+27	102	28 20	+27	101	28 47	+27	100
61	26 04	28	103	26 32	28	102	27 00	27	101	27 27	27	100	27 54	26	99
62	25 11	28	103	25 39	27	102	26 06	27	101	26 33	27	100	27 00	26	99
63	24 18	27	102	24 45	28	101	25 13	27	100	25 40	26	99	26 06	26	98
64	23 25	27	102	23 52	27	101	24 19	27	100	24 46	26	99	25 12	26	98
65	22 31	+28	101	22 59	+27	100	23 26	+26	99	23 52	+26	98	24 18	+26	97
66	21 38	27	101	22 05	27	100	22 32	26	99	22 58	26	98	23 24	26	97
67	20 44	27	100	21 11	27	99	21 38	26	98	22 04	26	97	22 30	26	96
68	19 51	27	100	20 18	26	99	20 44	26	98	21 10	26	97	21 36	26	96
69	18 57	27	99	19 24	26	98	19 50	26	97	20 16	26	96	20 42	25	95
	0°			1°			2°			3°			4°		

LHA	5°			6°			7°			8°			9°		
	Hc	d	Z	Hc	d	Z	Hc	d	Z	Hc	d	Z	Hc	d	Z
	° ′	′	°	° ′	′	°	° ′	′	°	° ′	′	°	° ′	′	°
0	70 00	+60	180	71 00	+60	180	72 00	+60	180	73 00	+60	180	74 00	+60	180
1	69 59	60	177	70 59	60	177	71 59	59	177	72 58	60	177	73 58	60	176
2	69 55	59	174	70 54	60	174	71 54	60	174	72 54	59	173	73 53	60	173
3	69 48	59	171	70 47	59	171	71 46	60	170	72 46	59	170	73 45	59	169
4	69 38	59	169	70 37	59	168	71 36	59	167	72 35	58	167	73 33	59	166
5	69 26	+58	166	70 24	+59	165	71 23	+58	164	72 21	+57	164	73 18	+58	163
6	69 11	58	163	70 09	58	162	71 07	57	161	72 04	57	160	73 01	56	159
7	68 54	57	160	69 51	57	159	70 48	56	158	71 44	56	157	72 40	56	156
8	68 35	56	158	69 31	56	157	70 27	55	156	71 22	55	154	72 17	54	153
9	68 13	55	155	69 08	55	154	70 03	54	153	70 57	54	152	71 51	53	150
10	67 49	+54	153	68 43	+54	152	69 37	+53	150	70 30	+53	149	71 23	+52	148
11	67 23	53	150	68 16	53	149	69 09	52	148	70 01	52	146	70 53	50	145
12	66 55	53	148	67 48	51	147	68 39	51	146	69 30	50	144	70 20	50	142
13	66 26	51	146	67 17	51	145	68 08	49	143	68 57	49	142	69 46	48	140
14	65 54	51	144	66 45	49	143	67 34	49	141	68 23	48	139	69 11	46	138
15	65 22	+49	142	66 11	+48	140	66 59	+48	139	67 47	+46	137	68 33	+46	136
16	64 47	48	140	65 35	48	138	66 23	46	137	67 09	46	135	67 55	44	134
17	64 11	48	138	64 59	46	137	65 45	45	135	66 30	45	133	67 15	43	132
18	63 34	47	136	64 21	45	135	65 06	44	133	65 50	43	132	66 33	42	130
19	62 56	45	135	63 41	45	133	64 26	43	132	65 09	42	130	65 51	41	128
20	62 17	+44	133	63 01	+44	131	63 45	+42	130	64 27	+41	128	65 08	+40	127
21	61 37	43	131	62 20	42	130	63 02	42	128	63 44	40	127	64 24	39	125
22	60 55	43	130	61 38	41	128	62 19	41	127	63 00	39	125	63 39	38	124
23	60 13	42	128	60 55	40	127	61 35	40	125	62 15	38	124	62 53	37	122
24	59 30	41	127	60 11	40	126	60 51	38	124	61 29	38	123	62 07	36	121
25	58 46	+40	126	59 26	+39	124	60 05	+38	123	60 43	+37	121	61 20	+35	120
26	58 02	39	124	58 41	38	123	59 19	37	122	59 56	36	120	60 32	35	118
27	57 17	38	123	57 55	37	122	58 32	37	120	59 09	35	119	59 44	34	117
28	56 31	38	122	57 09	36	121	57 45	36	119	58 21	34	118	58 55	34	116
29	55 44	37	121	56 21	37	120	56 58	35	118	57 33	33	117	58 06	33	115
30	54 58	+36	120	55 34	+35	118	56 09	+35	117	56 44	+33	116	57 17	+32	114
31	54 10	36	119	54 46	35	117	55 21	33	116	55 54	33	115	56 27	32	113
32	53 22	35	118	53 57	35	116	54 32	33	115	55 05	32	114	55 37	31	112
33	52 34	34	117	53 08	34	115	53 42	33	114	54 15	31	113	54 46	31	111
34	51 45	34	116	52 19	33	115	52 52	32	113	53 24	31	112	53 55	30	110
35	50 56	+34	115	51 30	+32	114	52 02	+32	112	52 34	+30	111	53 04	+30	109
36	50 07	33	114	50 40	32	113	51 12	31	111	51 43	30	110	52 13	29	109
37	49 17	32	113	49 49	32	112	50 21	31	111	50 52	29	109	51 21	29	108
38	48 27	32	112	48 59	31	111	49 30	30	110	50 00	29	109	50 29	29	107
39	47 36	32	112	48 08	31	110	48 39	29	109	49 08	29	108	49 37	28	106
40	46 46	+31	111	47 17	+30	110	47 47	+29	108	48 16	+29	107	48 45	+28	106
41	45 55	30	110	46 25	30	109	46 55	29	108	47 24	29	106	47 53	27	105
42	45 03	31	109	45 34	29	108	46 03	29	107	46 32	28	106	47 00	27	104
43	44 12	30	109	44 42	29	107	45 11	29	106	45 40	27	105	46 07	27	104
44	43 20	30	108	43 50	29	107	44 19	28	106	44 47	27	104	45 14	27	103
45	42 28	+30	107	42 58	+28	106	43 26	+28	105	43 54	+27	104	44 21	+26	102
46	41 36	29	107	42 05	29	105	42 34	27	104	43 01	27	103	43 28	26	102
47	40 44	29	106	41 13	28	105	41 41	27	104	42 08	27	102	42 35	26	101
48	39 52	28	105	40 20	28	104	40 48	27	103	41 15	26	102	41 41	26	101
49	38 59	29	105	39 28	27	104	39 55	27	102	40 22	26	101	40 48	25	100
50	38 07	+28	104	38 35	+27	103	39 02	+26	102	39 28	+26	101	39 54	+25	100
51	37 14	28	104	37 42	27	102	38 09	26	101	38 35	26	100	39 01	25	99
52	36 21	27	103	36 48	27	102	37 15	26	101	37 41	26	100	38 07	25	98
53	35 28	27	102	35 55	27	101	36 22	26	100	36 48	25	99	37 13	25	98
54	34 35	27	102	35 02	26	101	35 28	26	100	35 54	25	99	36 19	25	97
55	33 41	+27	101	34 08	+26	100	34 34	+26	99	35 00	+25	98	35 25	+25	97
56	32 48	27	101	33 15	26	100	33 41	25	99	34 06	25	98	34 31	24	96
57	31 55	26	100	32 21	26	99	32 47	25	98	33 12	25	97	33 37	24	96
58	31 01	26	100	31 27	26	99	31 53	25	98	32 18	25	97	32 43	24	95
59	30 07	26	99	30 33	26	98	30 59	25	97	31 24	25	96	31 49	24	95
60	29 14	+26	99	29 40	+25	98	30 05	+25	97	30 30	+25	96	30 55	+24	95
61	28 20	26	98	28 46	25	97	29 11	25	96	29 36	24	95	30 00	24	94
62	27 26	26	98	27 52	25	97	28 17	25	96	28 42	24	95	29 06	24	94
63	26 32	26	97	26 58	25	96	27 23	25	95	27 48	24	94	28 12	24	93
64	25 38	26	97	26 04	25	96	26 29	24	95	26 53	25	94	27 18	23	93
65	24 44	+25	96	25 09	+25	95	25 34	+25	94	25 59	+24	93	26 23	+24	92
66	23 50	25	96	24 15	25	95	24 40	25	94	25 05	24	93	25 29	24	92
67	22 56	25	95	23 21	25	94	23 46	24	93	24 10	25	92	24 35	23	91
68	22 02	25	95	22 27	25	94	22 52	24	93	23 16	24	92	23 40	24	91
69	21 07	26	94	21 33	24	93	21 57	25	93	22 22	24	92	22 46	23	91
	5°			6°			7°			8°			9°		

LHA	10°			11°			12°			13°			14°			LHA
	Hc	d	Z	Hc	d	Z	Hc	d	Z	Hc	d	Z	Hc	d	Z	
	° ′	′	°	° ′	′	°	° ′	′	°	° ′	′	°	° ′	′	°	
0	75 00	+60	180	76 00	+60	180	77 00	+60	180	78 00	+60	180	79 00	+60	180	360
1	74 58	60	176	75 58	60	176	76 58	60	176	77 58	60	175	78 58	59	175	359
2	74 53	59	172	75 52	60	172	76 52	59	171	77 51	59	171	78 50	60	170	358
3	74 44	59	169	75 43	59	168	76 42	58	167	77 40	59	166	78 39	58	165	357
4	74 32	58	165	75 30	58	164	76 28	57	163	77 25	58	162	78 23	56	160	356
5	74 16	+57	162	75 13	+57	160	76 10	+56	159	77 06	+56	158	78 02	+55	156	355
6	73 57	56	158	74 53	56	157	75 49	55	155	76 44	54	154	77 38	54	152	354
7	73 36	54	155	74 30	55	153	75 25	53	152	76 18	53	150	77 11	51	148	353
8	73 11	54	152	74 05	53	150	74 58	52	148	75 50	50	146	76 40	50	144	352
9	72 44	52	149	73 36	52	147	74 28	50	145	75 18	49	143	76 07	48	141	351
10	72 15	+51	146	73 06	+50	144	73 56	+48	142	74 44	+48	140	75 32	+45	138	350
11	71 43	50	143	72 33	48	141	73 21	47	139	74 08	46	137	74 54	44	135	349
12	71 10	48	141	71 58	47	139	72 45	45	137	73 30	44	135	74 14	43	132	348
13	70 34	47	138	71 21	46	136	72 07	44	134	72 51	42	132	73 33	41	130	347
14	69 57	46	136	70 43	44	134	71 27	43	132	72 10	41	130	72 51	39	127	346
15	69 19	+44	134	70 03	+43	132	70 46	+41	130	71 27	+40	128	72 07	+38	125	345
16	68 39	43	132	69 22	41	130	70 03	40	128	70 43	39	126	71 22	36	123	344
17	67 58	42	130	68 40	40	128	69 20	39	126	69 59	37	124	70 36	35	121	343
18	67 15	41	128	67 56	39	126	68 35	38	124	69 13	36	122	69 49	34	120	342
19	66 32	40	126	67 12	38	125	67 50	36	122	68 26	35	120	69 01	33	118	341
20	65 48	+38	125	66 26	+38	123	67 04	+35	121	67 39	+34	119	68 13	+32	117	340
21	65 03	37	123	65 40	37	121	66 17	34	119	66 51	33	117	67 24	31	115	339
22	64 17	37	122	64 54	35	120	65 29	34	118	66 03	32	116	66 35	30	114	338
23	63 30	36	120	64 06	35	119	64 41	32	117	65 13	32	115	65 45	29	113	337
24	62 43	35	119	63 18	34	117	63 52	32	115	64 24	30	114	64 54	29	112	336
25	61 55	+35	118	62 30	+32	116	63 02	+32	114	63 34	+30	112	64 04	+28	110	335
26	61 07	33	117	61 40	33	115	62 13	30	113	62 43	29	111	63 12	28	109	334
27	60 18	33	116	60 51	31	114	61 22	30	112	61 52	29	110	62 21	27	108	333
28	59 29	32	114	60 01	31	113	60 32	29	111	61 01	28	109	61 29	27	107	332
29	58 39	32	113	59 11	30	112	59 41	29	110	60 10	27	108	60 37	26	107	331
30	57 49	+31	112	58 20	+30	111	58 50	+28	109	59 18	+27	107	59 45	+25	106	330
31	56 59	30	112	57 29	29	110	57 58	28	108	58 26	26	107	58 52	25	105	329
32	56 08	30	111	56 38	28	109	57 06	28	107	57 34	26	106	58 00	24	104	328
33	55 17	29	110	55 46	28	108	56 14	27	107	56 41	26	105	57 07	24	103	327
34	54 25	29	109	54 54	28	107	55 22	27	106	55 49	25	104	56 14	24	103	326
35	53 34	+28	108	54 02	+28	107	54 30	+26	105	54 56	+25	103	55 21	+23	102	325
36	52 42	28	107	53 10	27	106	53 37	26	104	54 03	24	103	54 27	24	101	324
37	51 50	28	107	52 18	26	105	52 44	26	104	53 10	24	102	53 34	23	101	323
38	50 58	27	106	51 25	26	104	51 51	25	103	52 16	25	101	52 41	22	100	322
39	50 05	27	105	50 32	26	104	50 58	25	102	51 23	24	101	51 47	23	99	321
40	49 13	+26	104	49 39	+26	103	50 05	+25	102	50 30	+23	100	50 53	+23	99	320
41	48 20	26	104	48 46	26	102	49 12	24	101	49 36	23	100	49 59	23	98	319
42	47 27	26	103	47 53	25	102	48 18	24	100	48 42	24	99	49 06	22	98	318
43	46 34	26	102	47 00	25	101	47 25	24	100	47 49	23	98	48 12	22	97	317
44	45 41	25	102	46 06	25	100	46 31	24	99	46 55	23	98	47 18	21	96	316
45	44 47	+26	101	45 13	+24	100	45 37	+24	99	46 01	+22	97	46 23	+22	96	315
46	43 54	25	101	44 19	24	99	44 43	24	98	45 07	22	97	45 29	22	95	314
47	43 01	24	100	43 25	25	99	43 50	23	97	44 13	22	96	44 35	22	95	313
48	42 07	25	99	42 32	24	98	42 56	23	97	43 19	22	96	43 41	21	94	312
49	41 13	25	99	41 38	24	98	42 02	23	96	42 25	22	95	42 47	21	94	311
50	40 19	+25	98	40 44	+24	97	41 08	+22	96	41 30	+23	95	41 53	+21	93	310
51	39 26	24	98	39 50	23	97	40 13	23	95	40 36	22	94	40 58	21	93	309
52	38 32	24	97	38 56	23	96	39 19	23	95	39 42	22	94	40 04	21	93	308
53	37 38	24	97	38 02	23	96	38 25	23	94	38 48	22	93	39 10	21	92	307
54	36 44	24	96	37 08	23	95	37 31	22	94	37 53	22	93	38 15	21	92	306
55	35 50	+23	96	36 13	+24	95	36 37	+22	94	36 59	+22	92	37 21	+21	91	305
56	34 55	24	95	35 19	23	94	35 42	23	93	36 05	21	92	36 26	22	91	304
57	34 01	24	95	34 25	23	94	34 48	22	93	35 10	22	91	35 32	21	90	303
58	33 07	24	94	33 31	23	93	33 54	22	92	34 16	22	91	34 38	21	90	302
59	32 13	23	94	32 36	23	93	32 59	23	92	33 22	21	91	33 43	21	89	301
60	31 19	+23	93	31 42	+23	92	32 05	+22	91	32 27	+22	90	32 49	+21	89	300
61	30 24	24	93	30 48	23	92	31 11	22	91	31 33	22	90	31 55	21	89	299
62	29 30	23	93	29 53	23	91	30 16	22	90	30 38	22	89	31 00	21	88	298
63	28 36	23	92	28 59	23	91	29 22	22	90	29 44	22	89	30 06	21	88	297
64	27 41	24	92	28 05	22	91	28 27	23	90	28 50	22	89	29 12	21	87	296
65	26 47	+23	91	27 10	+23	90	27 33	+22	89	27 55	+22	88	28 17	+22	87	295
66	25 53	23	91	26 16	23	90	26 39	22	89	27 01	22	88	27 23	21	87	294
67	24 58	23	90	25 21	23	89	25 44	23	88	26 07	22	87	26 29	21	86	293
68	24 04	23	90	24 27	23	89	24 50	22	88	25 12	22	87	25 34	22	86	292
69	23 09	24	90	23 33	23	89	23 56	22	88	24 18	22	87	24 40	22	85	291
	10°			11°			12°			13°			14°			

S. Lat. {LHA greater than 180°....... Zn=180−Z; LHA less than 180°.......... Zn=180+Z}

DECLINATION (0°-14°) SAME NAME AS LATITUDE

LAT 25°

N. Lat. {LHA greater than 180°....... Zn=Z; LHA less than 180°........... Zn=360−Z}

DECLINATION (0°-14°) SAME NAME AS LATITUDE

LAT 26°

LHA	0° Hc	d	Z	1° Hc	d	Z	2° Hc	d	Z	3° Hc	d	Z	4° Hc	d	Z	5° Hc	d	Z	6° Hc	d	Z	7° Hc	d	Z
	° ′	′	°	° ′	′	°	° ′	′	°	° ′	′	°	° ′	′	°	° ′	′	°	° ′	′	°	° ′	′	°
0	64 00	+60	180	65 00	+60	180	66 00	+60	180	67 00	+60	180	68 00	+60	180	69 00	+60	180	70 00	+60	180	71 00	+60	180
1	63 59	60	178	64 59	60	178	65 59	60	178	66 59	60	177	67 59	60	177	68 59	60	177	69 59	60	177	70 59	60	177
2	63 56	60	175	64 56	59	175	65 55	60	175	66 55	60	175	67 55	60	175	68 55	60	175	69 55	59	174	70 54	60	174
3	63 50	60	173	64 50	60	173	65 50	59	173	66 49	60	172	67 49	59	172	68 48	60	172	69 48	59	171	70 47	60	171
4	63 43	59	171	64 42	60	171	65 42	59	170	66 41	59	170	67 40	59	169	68 39	59	169	69 38	59	169	70 37	59	168
5	63 33	+59	169	64 32	+59	168	65 31	+59	168	66 30	+59	167	67 29	+59	167	68 28	+58	166	69 26	+59	166	70 25	+58	165
6	63 22	58	167	64 20	59	166	65 19	58	166	66 17	59	165	67 16	58	164	68 14	58	164	69 12	58	163	70 10	57	162
7	63 08	58	164	64 06	58	164	65 04	58	163	66 02	58	163	67 00	58	162	67 58	57	161	68 55	57	160	69 52	57	159
8	62 53	57	162	63 50	58	162	64 48	57	161	65 45	57	160	66 42	57	159	67 39	56	159	68 35	57	158	69 32	56	157
9	62 35	57	160	63 32	57	160	64 29	57	159	65 26	56	158	66 22	56	157	67 18	56	156	68 14	55	155	69 09	55	154
10	62 16	+57	158	63 13	+56	157	64 09	+56	157	65 05	+55	156	66 00	+55	155	66 55	+55	154	67 50	+55	153	68 45	+54	152
11	61 55	56	156	62 51	55	155	63 46	56	154	64 42	54	154	65 36	55	153	66 31	54	152	67 25	53	150	68 18	53	149
12	61 32	56	154	62 28	54	153	63 22	55	152	64 17	54	151	65 11	53	150	66 04	53	149	66 57	52	148	67 49	52	147
13	61 08	54	152	62 02	54	151	62 56	54	150	63 50	53	149	64 43	53	148	65 36	52	147	66 28	51	146	67 19	51	145
14	60 42	54	150	61 36	53	149	62 29	53	149	63 22	52	147	64 14	52	146	65 06	51	145	65 57	50	144	66 47	50	143
15	60 15	+53	149	61 08	+52	148	62 00	+52	147	62 52	+51	146	63 43	+51	144	64 34	+50	143	65 24	+49	142	66 13	+49	140
16	59 46	52	147	60 38	52	146	61 30	51	145	62 21	50	144	63 11	50	142	64 01	49	141	64 50	48	140	65 38	48	139
17	59 16	51	145	60 07	51	144	60 58	50	143	61 48	49	142	62 37	49	141	63 26	49	139	64 15	47	138	65 02	46	137
18	58 44	51	144	59 35	50	142	60 25	49	141	61 14	49	140	62 03	48	139	62 51	47	138	63 38	46	136	64 24	46	135
19	58 12	49	142	59 01	49	141	59 50	49	140	60 39	48	139	61 27	47	137	62 14	46	136	63 00	45	135	63 45	45	133
20	57 38	+49	140	58 27	+48	139	59 15	+47	138	60 02	+47	137	60 49	+47	136	61 36	+45	134	62 21	+44	133	63 05	+44	131
21	57 03	48	139	57 51	47	138	58 38	47	137	59 25	46	135	60 11	45	134	60 56	45	133	61 41	44	131	62 25	42	130
22	56 27	47	137	57 14	47	136	58 01	46	135	58 47	45	134	59 32	44	133	60 16	44	131	61 00	43	130	61 43	41	128
23	55 50	46	136	56 36	46	135	57 22	45	134	58 07	45	132	58 52	43	131	59 35	43	130	60 18	42	128	61 00	41	127
24	55 12	45	135	55 57	46	133	56 43	44	132	57 27	44	131	58 11	42	130	58 53	42	128	59 35	41	127	60 16	40	126
25	54 33	+45	133	55 18	+44	132	56 02	+44	131	56 46	+43	130	57 29	+42	128	58 11	+41	127	58 52	+40	126	59 32	+39	124
26	53 53	44	132	54 37	44	131	55 21	43	130	56 04	42	128	56 46	41	127	57 27	41	126	58 08	39	124	58 47	39	123
27	53 13	43	131	53 56	43	130	54 39	42	128	55 21	42	127	56 03	40	126	56 43	40	125	57 23	39	123	58 02	37	122
28	52 31	43	130	53 14	42	128	53 56	42	127	54 38	41	126	55 19	39	125	55 58	39	123	56 37	38	122	57 15	37	121
29	51 49	43	128	52 32	41	127	53 13	41	126	53 54	40	125	54 34	39	124	55 13	38	122	55 51	38	121	56 29	36	119
30	51 07	+41	127	51 48	+41	126	52 29	+40	125	53 09	+40	124	53 49	+38	122	54 27	+38	121	55 05	+36	120	55 41	+36	118
31	50 24	40	126	51 04	41	125	51 45	39	124	52 24	39	123	53 03	38	121	53 41	37	120	54 18	36	119	54 54	35	117
32	49 40	40	125	50 20	40	124	51 00	38	123	51 38	38	122	52 16	38	120	52 54	36	119	53 30	36	118	54 06	34	116
33	48 55	40	124	49 35	39	123	50 14	38	122	50 52	38	121	51 30	36	119	52 06	36	118	52 42	35	117	53 17	34	115
34	48 10	39	123	48 49	39	122	49 28	37	121	50 05	37	120	50 42	36	118	51 18	36	117	51 54	34	116	52 28	34	114
35	47 25	+38	122	48 03	+38	121	48 41	+37	120	49 18	+37	119	49 55	+35	117	50 30	+35	116	51 05	+34	115	51 39	+33	113
36	46 39	38	121	47 17	37	120	47 54	37	119	48 31	36	118	49 07	35	116	49 42	34	115	50 16	33	114	50 49	33	113
37	45 52	38	120	46 30	37	119	47 07	36	118	47 43	35	117	48 18	35	116	48 53	33	114	49 26	33	113	49 59	32	112
38	45 06	37	119	45 43	36	118	46 19	35	117	46 54	35	116	47 29	34	115	48 03	34	113	48 37	32	112	49 09	31	111
39	44 18	37	118	44 55	36	117	45 31	35	116	46 06	34	115	46 40	34	114	47 14	32	113	47 46	32	111	48 18	32	110
40	43 31	+36	118	44 07	+35	117	44 42	+35	115	45 17	+34	114	45 51	+33	113	46 24	+32	112	46 56	+32	111	47 28	+30	109
41	42 43	35	117	43 18	35	116	43 53	34	115	44 27	34	113	45 01	33	112	45 34	31	111	46 05	32	110	46 37	30	109
42	41 55	35	116	42 30	34	115	43 04	34	114	43 38	33	113	44 11	32	111	44 43	32	110	45 15	30	109	45 45	30	108
43	41 06	34	115	41 40	34	114	42 14	34	113	42 48	32	112	43 20	32	111	43 52	32	110	44 24	30	108	44 54	30	107
44	40 17	34	114	40 51	34	113	41 25	33	112	41 58	32	111	42 30	31	110	43 01	31	109	43 32	30	108	44 02	30	106
45	39 28	+33	114	40 01	+34	113	40 35	+32	112	41 07	+32	110	41 39	+31	109	42 10	+31	108	42 41	+30	107	43 11	+29	106
46	38 38	34	113	39 12	32	112	39 44	32	111	40 16	32	110	40 48	31	109	41 19	30	107	41 49	30	106	42 19	28	105
47	37 48	33	112	38 21	33	111	38 54	32	110	39 26	31	109	39 57	30	108	40 27	30	107	40 57	29	106	41 26	29	105
48	36 58	33	112	37 31	32	111	38 03	32	109	38 35	30	108	39 05	31	107	39 36	29	106	40 05	29	105	40 34	28	104
49	36 08	32	111	36 40	32	110	37 12	31	109	37 43	31	108	38 14	30	107	38 44	29	106	39 13	29	104	39 42	28	103
50	35 18	+31	110	35 49	+32	109	36 21	+31	108	36 52	+30	107	37 22	+30	106	37 52	+29	105	38 21	+28	104	38 49	+28	103
51	34 27	31	110	34 58	32	109	35 30	30	108	36 00	30	106	36 30	29	105	36 59	29	104	37 28	28	103	37 56	28	102
52	33 36	31	109	34 07	31	108	34 38	30	107	35 08	30	106	35 38	29	105	36 07	29	104	36 36	28	103	37 04	27	101
53	32 45	31	108	33 16	30	107	33 46	30	106	34 16	30	105	34 46	29	104	35 15	26	103	35 43	28	102	36 11	27	101
54	31 53	31	108	32 24	30	107	32 54	30	106	33 24	29	105	33 53	29	104	34 22	28	103	34 50	28	101	35 18	27	100
55	31 02	+30	107	31 32	+30	106	32 02	+30	105	32 32	+29	104	33 01	+28	103	33 29	+28	102	33 57	+28	101	34 25	+26	100
56	30 10	31	107	30 41	29	106	31 10	30	105	31 40	28	103	32 08	29	102	32 37	27	101	33 04	27	100	33 31	27	99
57	29 19	30	106	29 49	29	105	30 18	29	104	30 47	29	103	31 16	28	102	31 44	27	101	32 11	27	100	32 38	27	99
58	28 27	29	105	28 56	30	104	29 26	28	103	29 54	29	102	30 23	28	101	30 51	27	100	31 18	27	99	31 45	26	98
59	27 35	29	105	28 04	29	104	28 33	29	103	29 02	28	102	29 30	28	101	29 58	27	100	30 25	26	99	30 51	27	98
60	26 42	+30	104	27 12	+28	103	27 40	+29	102	28 09	+28	101	28 37	+27	100	29 04	+27	99	29 31	+27	98	29 58	+26	97
61	25 50	29	104	26 19	29	103	26 48	28	102	27 16	28	101	27 44	27	100	28 11	27	99	28 38	26	98	29 04	26	97
62	24 58	28	103	25 26	29	102	25 55	28	101	26 23	27	100	26 50	28	99	27 18	26	98	27 44	27	97	28 11	26	96
63	24 05	29	103	24 34	28	102	25 02	28	101	25 30	27	100	25 57	27	99	26 24	27	98	26 51	26	97	27 17	26	96
64	23 12	29	102	23 41	28	101	24 09	28	100	24 37	27	99	25 04	27	98	25 31	26	97	25 57	27	96	26 24	25	95
65	22 20	+28	102	22 48	+28	101	23 16	+27	100	23 43	+27	99	24 10	+27	98	24 37	+27	97	25 04	+26	96	25 30	+25	95
66	21 27	28	101	21 55	27	100	22 22	28	99	22 50	27	98	23 17	27	97	23 44	26	96	24 10	26	95	24 36	26	94
67	20 34	28	101	21 02	27	100	21 29	27	99	21 56	27	98	22 23	27	97	22 50	26	96	23 16	26	95	23 42	26	94
68	19 41	27	100	20 08	28	99	20 36	27	98	21 03	27	97	21 30	26	96	21 56	27	95	22 23	25	94	22 48	26	93
69	18 47	28	100	19 15	27	99	19 42	27	98	20 09	27	97	20 36	27	96	21 03	26	95	21 29	26	94	21 55	25	93

LHA	8° Hc	d	Z	9° Hc	d	Z	10° Hc	d	Z	11° Hc	d	Z	12° Hc	d	Z	13° Hc	d	Z	14° Hc	d	Z	LHA
	° ′	′	°	° ′	′	°	° ′	′	°	° ′	′	°	° ′	′	°	° ′	′	°	° ′	′	°	
0	72 00	+60	180	73 00	+60	180	74 00	+60	180	75 00	+60	180	76 00	+60	180	77 00	+60	180	78 00	+60	180	360
1	71 59	59	177	72 58	60	177	73 58	60	176	74 58	60	176	75 58	60	176	76 58	60	176	77 58	60	175	359
2	71 54	60	174	72 54	59	173	73 53	60	173	74 53	59	173	75 52	60	172	76 52	59	171	77 51	60	171	358
3	71 47	59	171	72 46	59	170	73 45	59	169	74 44	59	169	75 43	59	168	76 42	59	167	77 41	58	166	357
4	71 36	59	167	72 35	59	167	73 34	58	166	74 32	58	165	75 30	58	164	76 28	58	163	77 26	57	162	356
5	71 23	+58	164	72 21	+58	164	73 19	+57	163	74 16	+58	162	75 14	+57	161	76 11	+56	159	77 07	+56	158	355
6	71 07	57	161	72 04	57	160	73 01	57	159	73 58	56	158	74 54	56	157	75 50	55	155	76 45	54	154	354
7	70 49	56	159	71 45	56	157	72 41	55	156	73 36	55	155	74 31	55	154	75 26	53	152	76 19	53	150	353
8	70 28	55	156	71 23	55	155	72 18	54	153	73 12	54	152	74 06	53	150	74 59	52	148	75 51	51	147	352
9	70 04	55	153	70 59	53	152	71 52	54	150	72 46	52	149	73 38	52	147	74 30	50	145	75 20	49	143	351
10	69 39	+53	150	70 32	+53	149	71 25	+51	148	72 16	+52	146	73 08	+50	144	73 58	+49	142	74 47	+47	140	350
11	69 11	52	148	70 03	52	147	70 55	50	145	71 45	50	143	72 35	49	141	73 24	47	139	74 11	46	137	349
12	68 41	51	146	69 32	51	144	70 23	49	142	71 12	48	141	72 00	48	139	72 48	45	137	73 33	45	135	348
13	68 10	50	143	69 00	49	142	69 49	48	140	70 37	47	138	71 24	46	136	72 10	44	134	72 54	43	132	347
14	67 37	49	141	68 26	47	140	69 13	47	138	70 00	46	136	70 46	44	134	71 30	43	132	72 13	42	130	346
15	67 02	+48	139	67 50	+46	137	68 36	+46	136	69 22	+45	134	70 07	+43	132	70 50	+41	130	71 31	+40	128	345
16	66 26	47	137	67 13	45	135	67 58	45	134	68 43	43	132	69 26	42	130	70 08	40	128	70 48	39	126	344
17	65 48	46	135	66 34	44	133	67 18	44	132	68 02	42	130	68 44	40	128	69 24	40	126	70 04	37	124	343
18	65 10	44	133	65 54	44	132	66 38	42	130	67 20	41	128	68 01	39	126	68 40	38	124	69 18	36	122	342
19	64 30	43	132	65 13	43	130	65 56	41	128	66 37	40	126	67 17	38	125	67 55	37	122	68 32	35	120	341
20	63 49	+43	130	64 32	+41	128	65 13	+40	127	65 53	+39	125	66 32	+37	123	67 09	+36	121	67 45	+34	119	340
21	63 07	42	128	63 49	40	127	64 29	39	125	65 08	38	123	65 46	37	121	66 23	35	119	66 58	33	117	339
22	62 24	41	127	63 05	40	125	63 45	38	124	64 23	37	122	65 00	35	120	65 35	34	118	66 09	33	116	338
23	61 41	40	125	62 21	38	124	62 59	38	122	63 37	36	120	64 13	34	119	64 47	34	117	65 21	31	115	337
24	60 56	39	124	61 35	38	122	62 13	37	121	62 50	35	119	63 25	34	117	63 59	32	115	64 31	31	113	336
25	60 11	+39	123	60 50	+37	121	61 27	+35	120	62 02	+35	118	62 37	+33	116	63 10	+32	114	63 42	+30	112	335
26	59 26	37	121	60 03	36	120	60 39	35	118	61 14	34	117	61 48	33	115	62 21	31	113	62 52	29	111	334
27	58 39	37	120	59 16	36	119	59 52	34	117	60 26	33	115	60 59	32	114	61 31	30	112	62 01	29	110	333
28	57 52	36	119	58 28	35	118	59 03	34	116	59 37	32	114	60 09	32	113	60 41	29	111	61 10	29	109	332
29	57 05	35	118	57 40	35	116	58 15	33	115	58 48	31	113	59 19	31	112	59 50	29	110	60 19	28	108	331
30	56 17	+35	117	56 52	+33	115	57 25	+33	114	57 58	+31	112	58 29	+30	111	58 59	+29	109	59 28	+27	107	330
31	55 29	34	116	56 03	33	114	56 36	32	113	57 08	31	111	57 39	29	110	58 08	28	108	58 36	27	106	329
32	54 40	34	115	55 14	32	113	55 46	31	112	56 17	31	110	56 48	29	109	57 17	27	107	57 44	27	106	328
33	53 51	33	114	54 24	32	113	54 56	31	111	55 27	30	110	55 57	28	108	56 25	27	106	56 52	26	105	327
34	53 02	32	113	53 34	31	112	54 05	31	110	54 36	29	109	55 05	28	107	55 33	27	106	56 00	26	104	326
35	52 12	+32	112	52 44	+31	111	53 15	+30	109	53 45	+28	108	54 13	+28	106	54 41	+27	105	55 08	+25	103	325
36	51 22	31	111	51 53	31	110	52 24	29	109	52 53	29	107	53 22	27	106	53 49	26	104	54 15	25	103	324
37	50 31	31	110	51 02	30	109	51 32	29	108	52 01	29	106	52 30	27	105	52 57	25	103	53 22	25	102	323
38	49 40	31	110	50 11	30	108	50 41	29	107	51 10	27	106	51 37	27	104	52 04	26	103	52 30	24	101	322
39	48 50	30	109	49 20	29	108	49 49	29	106	50 18	27	105	50 45	26	103	51 11	26	102	51 37	24	101	321
40	47 58	+30	108	48 28	+29	107	48 57	+28	105	49 25	+27	104	49 52	+26	103	50 18	+26	101	50 44	+24	100	320
41	47 07	30	107	47 37	28	106	48 05	28	105	48 33	27	103	49 00	26	102	49 26	24	101	49 50	24	99	319
42	46 15	30	107	46 45	28	105	47 13	27	104	47 40	27	103	48 07	25	101	48 32	25	100	48 57	24	99	318
43	45 24	29	106	45 53	28	105	46 21	27	103	46 48	26	102	47 14	25	101	47 39	25	99	48 04	23	98	317
44	44 32	28	105	45 00	28	104	45 28	27	103	45 55	26	101	46 21	25	100	46 46	24	99	47 10	24	98	316
45	43 40	+28	105	44 08	+27	103	44 35	+27	102	45 02	+26	101	45 28	+25	100	45 53	+24	98	46 17	+23	97	315
46	42 47	28	104	43 15	28	103	43 43	26	102	44 09	26	100	44 35	24	99	44 59	24	98	45 23	23	96	314
47	41 55	28	103	42 23	27	102	42 50	26	101	43 16	25	100	43 41	25	98	44 06	24	97	44 30	22	96	313
48	41 02	28	103	41 30	27	102	41 57	26	100	42 23	25	99	42 48	24	98	43 12	24	97	43 36	23	95	312
49	40 10	27	102	40 37	27	101	41 04	25	100	41 29	25	99	41 54	25	97	42 19	23	96	42 42	23	95	311
50	39 17	+27	102	39 44	+26	100	40 10	+26	99	40 36	+25	98	41 01	+24	97	41 25	+23	96	41 48	+23	94	310
51	38 24	27	101	38 51	26	100	39 17	26	99	39 43	24	97	40 07	24	96	40 31	24	95	40 55	22	94	309
52	37 31	27	100	37 58	26	99	38 24	25	98	38 49	25	97	39 14	24	96	39 38	23	95	40 01	22	93	308
53	36 38	26	100	37 04	26	99	37 30	25	98	37 55	25	96	38 20	24	95	38 44	23	94	39 07	22	93	307
54	35 45	26	99	36 11	26	98	36 37	25	97	37 02	24	96	37 26	24	95	37 50	23	94	38 13	23	92	306
55	34 51	+27	99	35 18	+25	98	35 43	+25	97	36 08	+25	95	36 33	+23	94	36 56	+23	93	37 19	+23	92	305
56	33 58	26	98	34 24	26	97	34 50	24	96	35 14	25	95	35 39	23	94	36 02	23	93	36 25	23	92	304
57	33 05	26	98	33 31	25	97	33 56	25	96	34 21	24	94	34 45	23	93	35 08	23	92	35 31	23	91	303
58	32 11	26	97	32 37	25	96	33 02	25	95	33 27	24	94	33 51	24	93	34 15	23	92	34 38	22	91	302
59	31 18	25	97	31 43	26	96	32 09	24	95	32 33	24	93	32 57	24	92	33 21	23	91	33 44	22	90	301
60	30 24	+26	96	30 50	+25	95	31 15	+24	94	31 39	+24	93	32 03	+24	92	32 27	+23	91	32 50	+22	90	300
61	29 30	26	96	29 56	25	95	30 21	24	94	30 45	24	93	31 09	24	91	31 33	23	90	31 56	22	89	299
62	28 37	25	95	29 02	25	94	29 27	25	93	29 52	23	92	30 15	24	91	30 39	23	90	31 02	22	89	298
63	27 43	25	95	28 08	25	94	28 33	25	93	28 58	24	92	29 22	23	91	29 45	23	90	30 08	22	88	297
64	26 49	25	94	27 14	25	93	27 39	25	92	28 04	24	91	28 28	23	90	28 51	23	89	29 14	22	88	296
65	25 55	+26	94	26 21	+24	93	26 45	+25	92	27 10	+24	91	27 34	+23	90	27 57	+23	89	28 20	+23	88	295
66	25 02	25	93	25 27	25	92	25 52	24	91	26 16	24	90	26 40	23	89	27 03	23	88	27 26	23	87	294
67	24 08	25	93	24 33	25	92	24 58	24	91	25 22	24	90	25 46	23	89	26 09	23	88	26 32	23	87	293
68	23 14	25	92	23 39	25	91	24 04	24	90	24 28	24	89	24 52	23	88	25 15	24	87	25 39	22	86	292
69	22 20	25	92	22 45	25	91	23 10	24	90	23 34	24	89	23 58	24	88	24 22	23	87	24 45	23	86	291

S. Lat. {LHA greater than 180°....... Zn=180−Z; LHA less than 180°........... Zn=180+Z}

DECLINATION (0°-14°) SAME NAME AS LATITUDE

As this is the southern hemisphere summer, the sun is rising and setting south of east and west respectively.

Bearing at sunset	270° – Amplitude
	270° – 11°
Sun's true bearing	259°

Several times during the afternoon, when in casual conversation with the helmsman, the navigator notices that the boat's head is continually falling off to starboard and that, although the helmsman keeps bringing the boat back on to course 025°, he is steering a mean course of about 028°. As there is probably still a slight set to starboard off the track, due to the past weather conditions, the navigator makes a mental note to use a course made good of 030° again when running the noon latitude to the afternoon sun line.

At 1500 in calm seas and blazing sunshine with a good clear horizon, the navigator takes a single sight and works out his position. Being a little cocky at this stage of the day, he forgets to change local time to GMT. His intercept is ridiculous, some hundreds of miles long. In his anxiety to find the mistake he goes from *Nautical Almanac* to *Air Tables* in ever-decreasing circles.

But at least he has already learned two things. First, when working out a celestial sight, only an optimist uses a ballpoint pen. Pencil is much easier to erase and results in a cleaner finished product. Secondly, in any set of circumstances when the figures in the books start to blur and the brain goes into overdrive trying to sort the mess out there is only one thing to do – stop! Make a nice cup of coffee and go on deck in the good fresh air and drink it. Then after ten minutes or so when the blood pressure has eased, go back to the books. The mistake usually hits you straight in the eye.

The reader might like to help the navigator out by working the sight. Watch error, index error and dip as before.

Time by watch on GMT	04h 00m 03s	22 Feb
Sextant altitude	43° 01′.7	
Position by dead reckoning at 1500	25° 20′ S	170° 06′ E

(Correction to sun's GHA for 00min 13sec is 0° 03′.3)

Answers:

Chosen latitude	25°S	Hc 43° 09′
Chosen longitude	170° 20′.8E	Ho 43° 15′.5
LHA	47°	True Bg 280°
Log reading at 1500 local time	951.8M	
CMG	030°	
Position at 1500	25° 20′ S	170° 09′.6E

If this navigator took starsights, then civil twilight would be at 1840. Otherwise his day's work is done, except to check the compass at sunset. However, if the wind was favourable, the boat's course would be altered overnight back towards Matthew Island. At 1500 the boat was 190M from the island and at 7.5 knots the ETA would be 1630 the following day. The dead reckoning track would be plotted overnight to give a position for the first sunsight. No doubt the navigator would try to get another sun fix at about 1030, so that any slight alteration of course needed could be made some six hours prior to arrival.

If the reader has not been on an ocean cruise before, then I hope this chapter has given him some idea of the practicalities of navigation at sea. There are many variations on the theme but the events given above are fairly realistic. Once a pattern of work is established, subject to weather the same cycle is repeated each day.

Planned deviation from track

Earlier in the coastal section of the book (p.33) the concept of deliberately finding some above-water rocks to ensure avoiding some

1978 FEBRUARY 21, 22, 23 (TUES., WED., THURS.)

G.M.T.	SUN G.H.A.	SUN Dec.	MOON G.H.A.	v	MOON Dec.	d	H.P.
d h	° ′	° ′	° ′	′	° ′	′	′
21 00	176 33.9	S10 45.8	20 46.9	12.7	N13 53.6	6.4	54.8
01	191 33.9	44.9	35 18.6	12.8	13 47.2	6.4	54.8
02	206 34.0	44.0	49 50.4	12.8	13 40.8	6.5	54.8
03	221 34.1	·· 43.1	64 22.2	12.8	13 34.3	6.6	54.8
04	236 34.1	42.2	78 54.0	12.8	13 27.7	6.7	54.9
05	251 34.2	41.3	93 25.8	12.8	13 21.0	6.7	54.9
06	266 34.3	S10 40.4	107 57.6	12.8	N13 14.3	6.8	54.9
07	281 34.4	39.5	122 29.4	12.8	13 07.5	6.8	54.9
TUESDAY 08	296 34.4	38.6	137 01.2	12.8	13 00.7	6.9	54.9
09	311 34.5	·· 37.7	151 33.0	12.8	12 53.8	7.0	54.9
10	326 34.6	36.8	166 04.8	12.9	12 46.8	7.1	55.0
11	341 34.7	35.9	180 36.7	12.8	12 39.7	7.1	55.0
12	356 34.7	S10 35.0	195 08.5	12.9	N12 32.6	7.1	55.0
13	11 34.8	34.1	209 40.4	12.8	12 25.5	7.2	55.0
14	26 34.9	33.1	224 12.2	12.9	12 18.3	7.3	55.0
15	41 34.9	·· 32.2	238 44.1	12.9	12 11.0	7.4	55.1
16	56 35.0	31.3	253 16.0	12.9	12 03.6	7.4	55.1
17	71 35.1	30.4	267 47.9	12.9	11 56.2	7.5	55.1
18	86 35.2	S10 29.5	282 19.8	12.9	N11 48.7	7.5	55.1
19	101 35.3	28.6	296 51.7	12.9	11 41.2	7.6	55.1
20	116 35.3	27.7	311 23.6	12.9	11 33.6	7.6	55.1
21	131 35.4	·· 26.8	325 55.5	12.9	11 26.0	7.7	55.2
22	146 35.5	25.9	340 27.4	12.9	11 18.3	7.8	55.2
23	161 35.6	25.0	354 59.3	12.9	11 10.5	7.8	55.2
22 00	176 35.6	S10 24.1	9 31.2	13.0	N11 02.7	7.9	55.2
01	191 35.7	23.2	24 03.2	12.9	10 54.8	7.9	55.2
02	206 35.8	22.3	38 35.1	12.9	10 46.9	8.0	55.3
03	221 35.9	·· 21.4	53 07.0	13.0	10 38.9	8.0	55.3
04	236 35.9	20.5	67 39.0	12.9	10 30.9	8.1	55.3
05	251 36.0	19.5	82 10.9	13.0	10 22.8	8.2	55.3
06	266 36.1	S10 18.6	96 42.9	13.0	N10 14.6	8.2	55.3
07	281 36.2	17.7	111 14.9	12.9	10 06.4	8.2	55.3
WEDNESDAY 08	296 36.3	16.8	125 46.8	13.0	9 58.2	8.3	55.4
09	311 36.3	·· 15.9	140 18.8	13.0	9 49.9	8.4	55.4
10	326 36.4	15.0	154 50.8	12.9	9 41.5	8.4	55.4
11	341 36.5	14.1	169 22.7	13.0	9 33.1	8.5	55.4
12	356 36.6	S10 13.2	183 54.7	13.0	N 9 24.6	8.5	55.4
13	11 36.7	12.3	198 26.7	13.0	9 16.1	8.5	55.5
14	26 36.7	11.4	212 58.7	13.0	9 07.6	8.6	55.5
15	41 36.8	·· 10.4	227 30.7	13.0	8 59.0	8.7	55.5
16	56 36.9	09.5	242 02.7	13.0	8 50.3	8.7	55.5
17	71 37.0	08.6	256 34.7	13.0	8 41.6	8.7	55.5
18	86 37.1	S10 07.7	271 06.7	12.9	N 8 32.9	8.8	55.6
19	101 37.2	06.8	285 38.6	13.0	8 24.1	8.8	55.6
20	116 37.2	05.9	300 10.6	13.0	8 15.3	8.9	55.6
21	131 37.3	·· 05.0	314 42.6	13.0	8 06.4	8.9	55.6
22	146 37.4	04.1	329 14.6	13.0	7 57.5	9.0	55.6
23	161 37.5	03.1	343 46.6	13.0	7 48.5	9.0	55.7
23 00	176 37.6	S10 02.2	358 18.6	13.0	N 7 39.5	9.1	55.7
01	191 37.7	01.3	12 50.6	13.0	7 30.4	9.1	55.7
02	206 37.7	10 00.4	27 22.6	13.0	7 21.3	9.1	55.7
03	221 37.8	9 59.5	41 54.6	13.0	7 12.2	9.2	55.7
04	236 37.9	58.6	56 26.6	13.0	7 03.0	9.2	55.8
05	251 38.0	57.7	70 58.6	13.0	6 53.8	9.2	55.8
06	266 38.1	S 9 56.7	85 30.6	13.0	N 6 44.6	9.3	55.8
07	281 38.2	55.8	100 02.6	13.0	6 35.3	9.3	55.8
THURSDAY 08	296 38.3	54.9	114 34.6	12.9	6 26.0	9.4	55.8
09	311 38.3	·· 54.0	129 06.5	13.0	6 16.6	9.4	55.9
10	326 38.4	53.1	143 38.5	13.0	6 07.2	9.4	55.9
11	341 38.5	52.2	158 10.5	13.0	5 57.8	9.5	55.9
12	356 38.6	S 9 51.3	172 42.5	12.9	N 5 48.3	9.5	55.9
13	11 38.7	50.3	187 14.4	13.0	5 38.8	9.5	55.9
14	26 38.8	49.4	201 46.4	12.9	5 29.3	9.6	56.0
15	41 38.9	·· 48.5	216 18.3	13.0	5 19.7	9.6	56.0
16	56 39.0	47.6	230 50.3	12.9	5 10.1	9.6	56.0
17	71 39.0	46.7	245 22.2	13.0	5 00.5	9.7	56.0
18	86 39.1	S 9 45.7	259 54.2	12.9	N 4 50.8	9.7	56.0
19	101 39.2	44.8	274 26.1	12.9	4 41.1	9.7	56.1
20	116 39.3	43.9	288 58.0	12.9	4 31.4	9.8	56.1
21	131 39.4	·· 43.0	303 29.9	12.9	4 21.6	9.7	56.1
22	146 39.5	42.1	318 01.8	12.9	4 11.9	9.8	56.1
23	161 39.6	41.2	332 33.7	12.9	4 02.1	9.9	56.1
	S.D. 16.2	d 0.9	S.D. 15.0		15.1		15.2

Lat.	Twilight Naut.	Twilight Civil	Sunrise	Moonrise 21	Moonrise 22	Moonrise 23	Moonrise 24
°	h m	h m	h m	h m	h m	h m	h m
N 72	05 45	07 03	08 16	14 17	15 59	17 40	19 22
N 70	05 47	06 57	08 02	14 40	16 13	17 47	19 23
68	05 47	06 52	07 50	14 57	16 24	17 53	19 23
66	05 48	06 47	07 41	15 11	16 33	17 57	19 24
64	05 49	06 44	07 33	15 22	16 41	18 01	19 24
62	05 49	06 40	07 26	15 32	16 47	18 05	19 24
60	05 49	06 37	07 20	15 40	16 53	18 08	19 25
N 58	05 49	06 34	07 15	15 47	16 58	18 11	19 25
56	05 49	06 32	07 10	15 54	17 02	18 13	19 25
54	05 49	06 30	07 06	15 59	17 06	18 15	19 26
52	05 48	06 27	07 02	16 04	17 10	18 17	19 26
50	05 48	06 25	06 58	16 09	17 13	18 19	19 26
45	05 47	06 21	06 51	16 19	17 20	18 23	19 26
N 40	05 45	06 17	06 44	16 27	17 26	18 26	19 27
35	05 44	06 13	06 39	16 34	17 31	18 28	19 27
30	05 42	06 10	06 34	16 41	17 35	18 31	19 27
20	05 37	06 03	06 25	16 51	17 43	18 35	19 28
N 10	05 32	05 56	06 18	17 01	17 50	18 39	19 28
0	05 25	05 49	06 10	17 10	17 56	18 42	19 29
S 10	05 16	05 41	06 03	17 18	18 02	18 46	19 29
20	05 06	05 32	05 55	17 28	18 09	18 49	19 30
30	04 52	05 21	05 46	17 38	18 16	18 53	19 30
35	04 43	05 14	05 40	17 44	18 21	18 56	19 31
40	04 32	05 06	05 34	17 51	18 26	18 59	19 31
45	04 19	04 56	05 27	18 00	18 31	19 02	19 31
S 50	04 01	04 44	05 18	18 09	18 38	19 05	19 32
52	03 53	04 38	05 14	18 14	18 41	19 07	19 32
54	03 43	04 31	05 10	18 19	18 45	19 09	19 33
56	03 32	04 24	05 05	18 24	18 49	19 11	19 33
58	03 19	04 16	04 59	18 30	18 53	19 13	19 33
S 60	03 03	04 06	04 53	18 37	18 58	19 16	19 34

Lat.	Sunset	Twilight Civil	Twilight Naut.	Moonset 21	Moonset 22	Moonset 23	Moonset 24
°	h m	h m	h m	h m	h m	h m	h m
N 72	16 13	17 26	18 44	07 51	07 46	07 41	07 37
N 70	16 27	17 32	18 43	07 28	07 31	07 32	07 33
68	16 38	17 37	18 42	07 10	07 19	07 25	07 31
66	16 48	17 41	18 41	06 55	07 08	07 19	07 28
64	16 56	17 45	18 40	06 43	07 00	07 14	07 26
62	17 03	17 48	18 40	06 33	06 52	07 09	07 24
60	17 08	17 51	18 40	06 24	06 46	07 05	07 23
N 58	17 14	17 54	18 39	06 16	06 40	07 02	07 22
56	17 18	17 56	18 40	06 09	06 35	06 58	07 20
54	17 22	17 59	18 40	06 03	06 31	06 56	07 19
52	17 26	18 01	18 40	05 58	06 26	06 53	07 18
50	17 30	18 03	18 40	05 52	06 23	06 51	07 17
45	17 37	18 07	18 41	05 42	06 14	06 45	07 15
N 40	17 43	18 11	18 42	05 32	06 08	06 41	07 14
35	17 49	18 15	18 44	05 25	06 02	06 37	07 12
30	17 54	18 18	18 46	05 18	05 57	06 34	07 11
20	18 02	18 25	18 50	05 06	05 47	06 28	07 08
N 10	18 10	18 31	18 56	04 55	05 39	06 23	07 06
0	18 17	18 38	19 02	04 45	05 32	06 18	07 04
S 10	18 24	18 46	19 10	04 35	05 24	06 13	07 02
20	18 32	18 55	19 21	04 25	05 16	06 08	07 00
30	18 41	19 06	19 35	04 13	05 07	06 02	06 58
35	18 46	19 12	19 43	04 06	05 01	05 58	06 56
40	18 52	19 21	19 54	03 57	04 55	05 54	06 55
45	19 00	19 30	20 07	03 48	04 48	05 50	06 53
S 50	19 08	19 42	20 24	03 36	04 39	05 44	06 51
52	19 12	19 48	20 33	03 31	04 35	05 42	06 50
54	19 16	19 54	20 42	03 25	04 31	05 39	06 48
56	19 21	20 01	20 53	03 19	04 26	05 36	06 47
58	19 27	20 10	21 06	03 11	04 20	05 32	06 46
S 60	19 33	20 19	21 21	03 03	04 14	05 28	06 44

Day	SUN Eqn. of Time 00ʰ	SUN Eqn. of Time 12ʰ	SUN Mer. Pass.	MOON Mer. Pass. Upper	MOON Mer. Pass. Lower	Age	Phase
	m s	m s	h m	h m	h m	d	
21	13 45	13 41	12 14	23 21	10 57	14	○
22	13 38	13 34	12 14	24 07	11 44	15	
23	13 30	13 26	12 13	00 07	12 30	16	

Fig 99 *From the 1978* Nautical Almanac, *page 45 (Feb. 21, 22, 23, Tue, Wed, Thurs)*

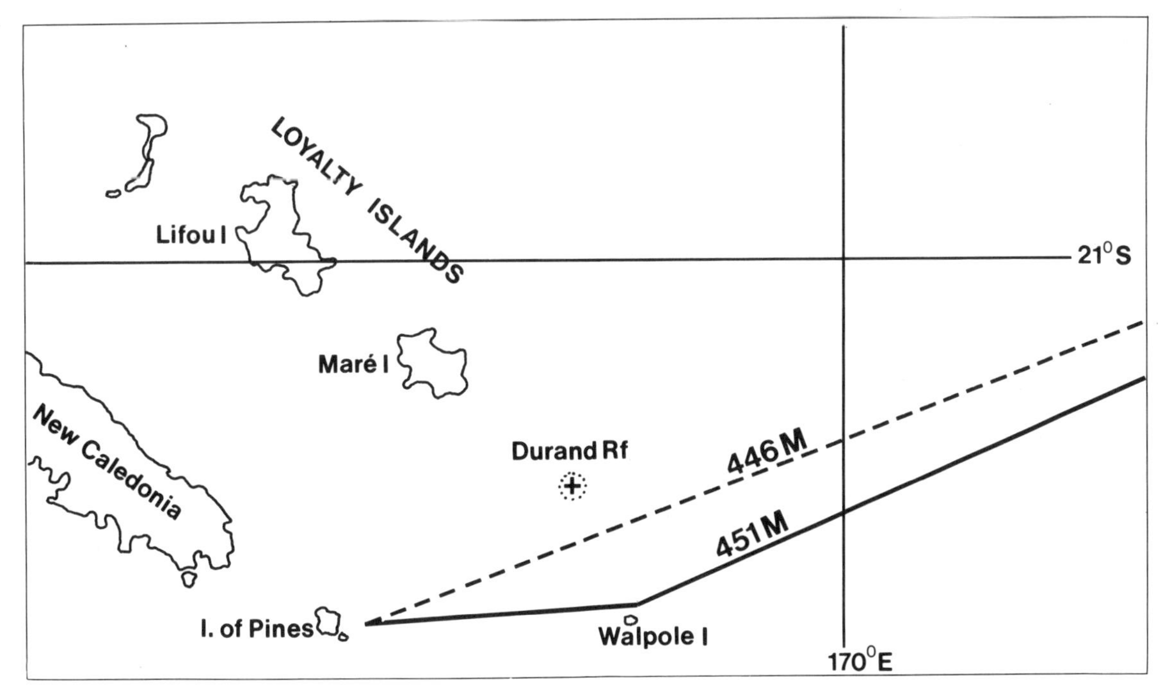

Fig 100
Planned deviation from track

underwater dangers was discussed. The same idea can be used in an ocean passage to prove the boat's position by land fix up to a day before arrival at the main destination. This may be particularly desirable if overcast skies have prevented the navigator from obtaining good celestial fixes and if the destination is surrounded by off-lying reefs or banks.

In Fig 100 a boat has come from the Fiji Islands and is going to the Isle of Pines off New Caledonia. The direct track from a position at latitude 20° S, 175°E is shown as a broken line. This track passes less than 15 miles to the east of Durand Reef. For most of the year there is a general westerly set in this area, which is likely to take the boat even closer to the danger.

The Admiralty Pilot has this to say about the reef:

> 'It is particularly dangerous because the sea does not always break on it, the soundings give no warning of its proximity and half a mile westward of the breakers is a depth of 384 metres (210 fathoms). In 1972, the reef was reported to lie 4 miles west-south-westward of its charted position.'

The continuous track in Fig 100 is a slight deviation from the direct route which passes further to the east of Durand Reef, but more importantly leads to Walpole Island. It is 100 metres high and there are no off-lying dangers. Being about 75 miles east of the Isle of Pines, a good check on position should be possible less than a day before arrival at the destination. The increase in total distance is just 5 miles. There are some banks between Walpole Island and the Reef with depths ranging from 10 to 36 metres, which are not dangerous except in a heavy swell. The direct track goes within 5 miles of these. If the navigator decided that in the prevailing conditions he preferred to pass to the south-east of the island, the old trick of aiming well to one side then sailing to the latitude and turning west along the parallel past Walpole and on to the Isle of Pines could be considered. This might put 10 to 15 miles on the distance.

Landfall

The first sight of land after any ocean passage is always a thrill. The tension associated with the routine running of any craft, especially if bad weather has been encountered, starts to ease with the mere presence of good old *terra firma*.

But once the initial and justifiable elation has passed the navigator should realise that what for him could be the most difficult part of the whole voyage is just beginning. This is no time to relax; that same *terra firma* will tear a hole in the bottom of the boat if the craft is not guided safely into harbour. The navigator's job finishes when the anchor goes down or the first line goes ashore on to the jetty.

There is no need to switch abruptly from celestial to coastal navigation just because there happens to be a piece of land covering a small part of the horizon. For example, in Fig 101 the navigator has been able to get a bearing on a prominent lighthouse, but the angle is so fine on the bow that a running fix might take some time to complete if the boat speed is low. However the horizon is quite clear for finding a noon latitude and the resulting fix will enable him to clear the dangerous coral safely.

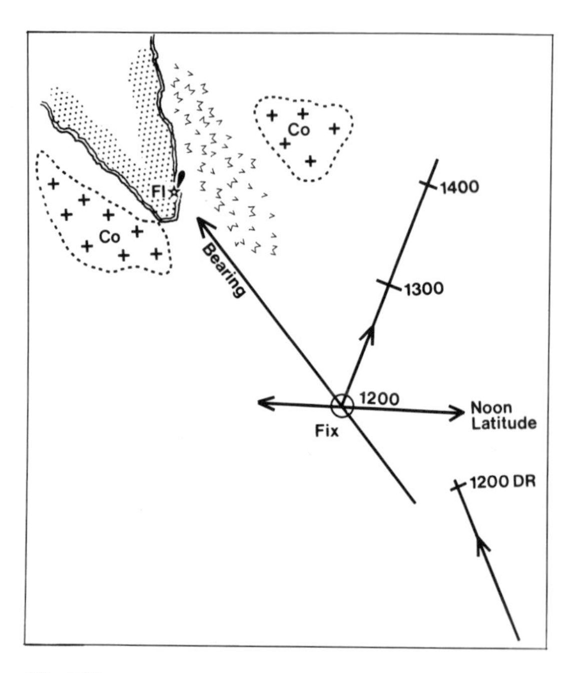

Fig 101
Crossing a shore bearing with a noon latitude to obtain a fix

If landfall is made on a featureless coastline with no fixing marks, even a single celestial line can be most useful. In Fig 102, the position line from the sun is along the same bearing that leads into harbour, i.e. parallel to the required track. By running a dead reckoning track at a broad angle – preferably 90 degrees – the navigator can choose the moment to turn and run in to the harbour. Although the boat's position along the sun line is not known, running the same distance from any point on the line means that it will turn on to the desired track.

Fig 102
Use of single position line

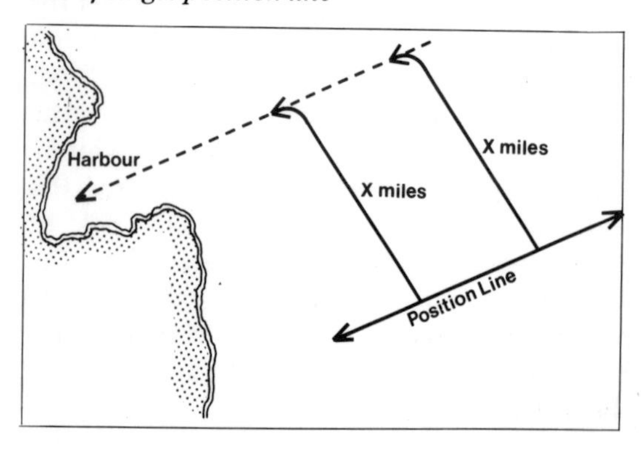

Any position line parallel to the coast will give a good indication of how far offshore the boat is. In the example illustrated in Fig 103, a mid-morning sight has given a sun line running NW to SE parallel to the coast. If this were in a region of prevailing east to south-east winds with a consequent surface current setting west towards the shore, the navigator could get an idea of the strength of the set. If the position line showed that the boat was closer to land than the DR or estimated position for the time of the sight, the current would be stronger than anticipated. Even without an actual fix, this type of information is extremely valuable.

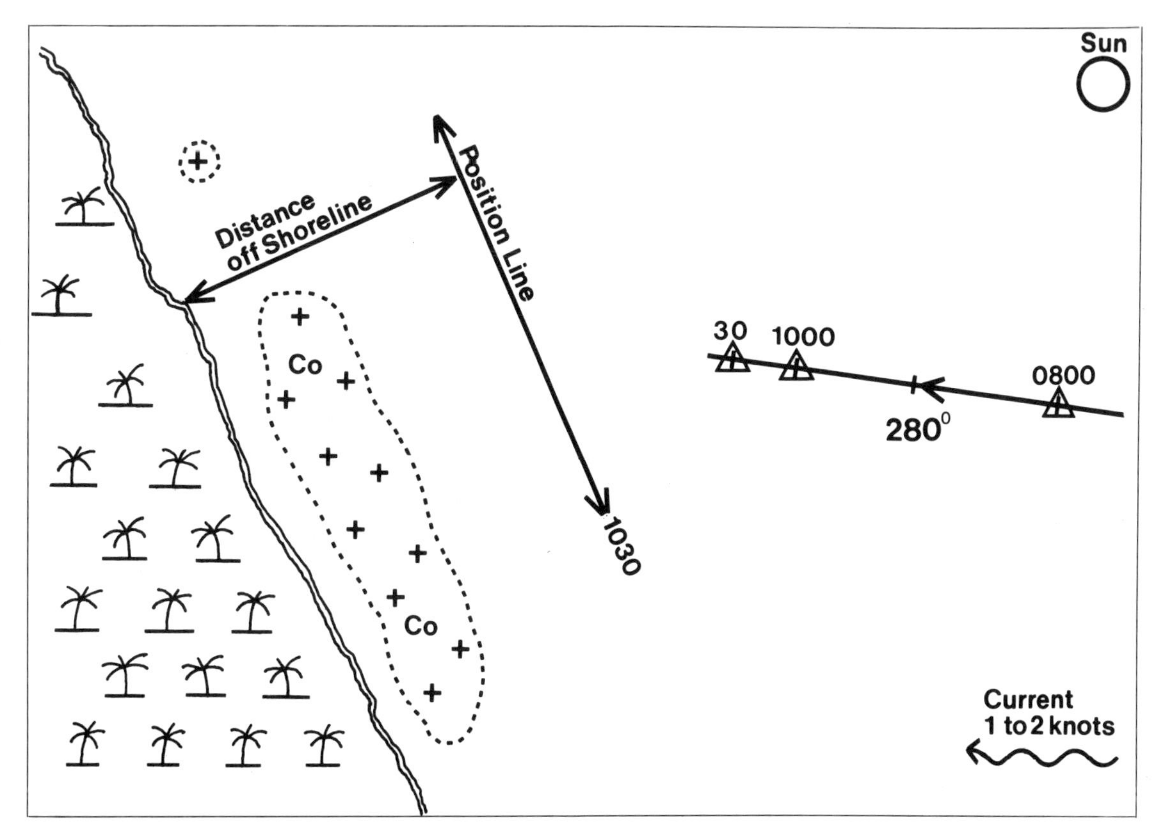

Fig 103
Use of single celestial position line to find distance off a dangerous coast

If a celestial position line is obtained shortly before land is sighted, it can be crossed with the bearing of a shore navigation mark by use of the running fix in the same way that one sun line is run up to the time of the subsequent sun line. In Fig 104 the celestial position line found at 0930 has been crossed with a bearing of the conspicuous chimney taken at 1000.

Preparation for a voyage

The navigator can do a great deal in harbour prior to departure to ease the work at sea. I am not only referring to the obvious things such as providing the right charts, embarking the sextant, watch, drawing instruments and other paraphernalia of the trade, nor do I mean making sure the *Nautical Almanac* and other tables are on board, although these are essential items. More than one person has suddenly realised in horror that his navigation tables are still sitting on the kitchen table. I am more concerned with some aspects that may not occur to the reader, or which he might only learn by bitter experience.

Any navigator, whether amateur or professional, loses speed in using the tables when not at sea. This speed can be regained fairly quickly, but far better to re-work some old sights at home than to go through the drama of trying to remember what you're supposed to do next during the first few days in a bouncing yacht.

Why not go one better? Work out the calculated altitude of the sun for say 1000 on your proposed date of departure. Use the position of your mooring in harbour as the dead reckoning position. The answer will at least give a good idea as to what time the first sight should be taken at sea to give that 50-degree cut with the noon latitude.

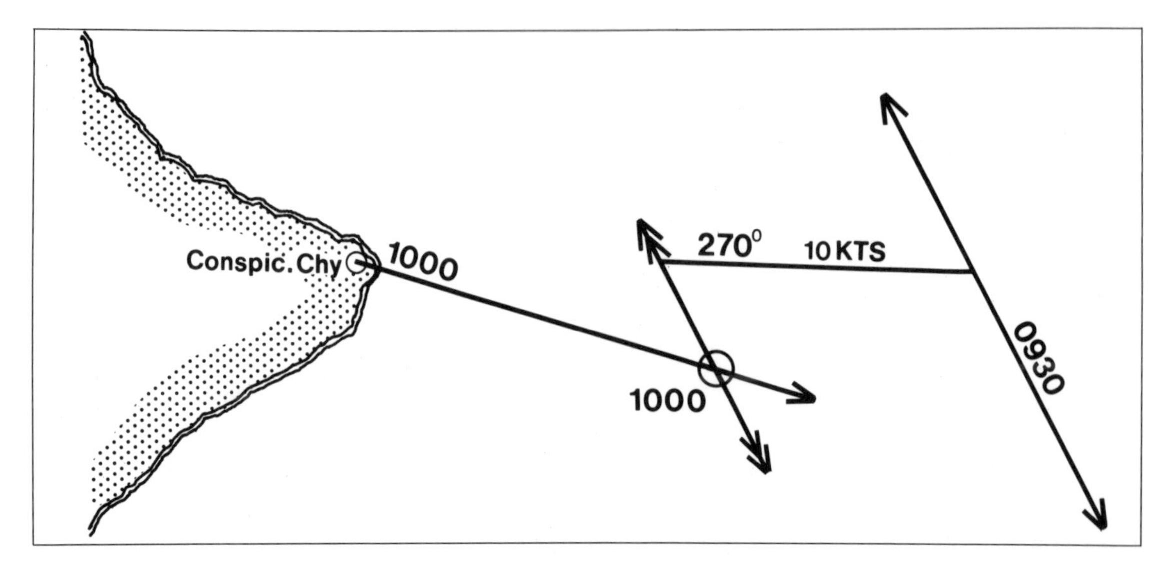

Fig 104
Running the celestial position line to give a fix with the bearing of a shore object

Work out the time of noon for the first day out. This could be done weeks before departure date. If you aim to get away on the early morning tide, then a midday dead reckoning position can be found and the longitude used will not be greatly in error. It's all good practice.

Work out the time of noon for the whole voyage; this is quite feasible with a roughly north or south track. Remember the time of meridian passage is quite independent of latitude. If longitude changes only three to four degrees over the whole voyage, it should be possible to calculate the times accurate to a couple of minutes a day.

You could work out the bearings of sunrise and sunset for the whole voyage using the amplitude tables. The latitude and declination used to enter the table have to be correct only to half a degree or so.

You can also use the latitude of your home port and work a noon latitude sight backwards. Again, this would be in the comfort of your own home, and at least the working will show whether Dec and ZX have to be added or subtracted to find latitude. Except on the odd occasion when a boat crosses the equator or passes near the sun's GP if the one has to be added to the other on the first day out, you'll be doing exactly the same on the last day of the journey.

Everything mentioned above will have to be done again at sea, but think of the practice involved, the speed that will have been acquired and the confidence with which the first day's work on the boat will be attacked.

The sextant will have been checked for side error and the current value of index error found during one of those trial runs when the new sails were hoisted for the first time. This is the opportunity to regain that smooth motion in bringing the sun down to the horizon.

Charts are a fine size for use on an ocean liner, but nothing is more infuriating than when they are just too big for the chart table drawer of a small yacht. Trim off that excess two or three inches of useless border. It's amazing how much smaller and more manageable they become.

Decide which way the clocks will have to be altered before leaving harbour, and the approximate stages of the journey at which this should be done. From the navigator's point of view, it is quite a good idea to keep Summer Time on board. If meridian passage is at approximately 1200 each day, then the navigator will be busy working out the noon

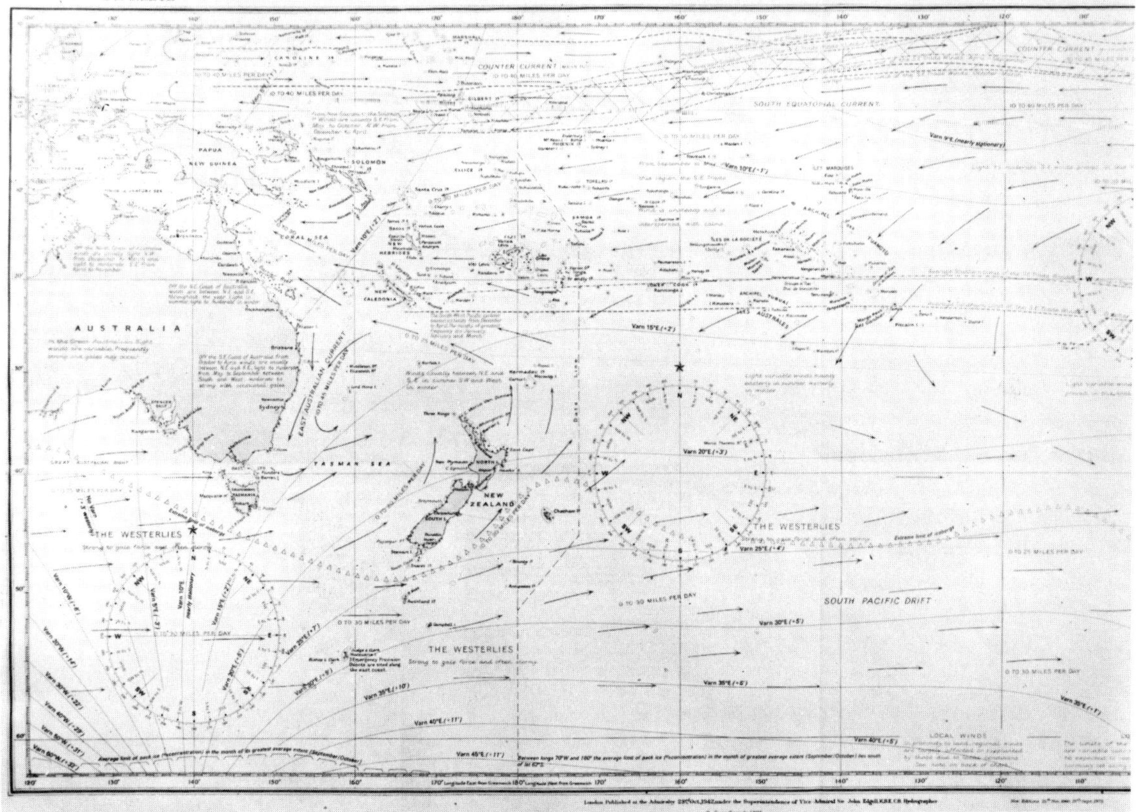

Fig 105
A lifeboat chart

latitude while everybody else is eating lunch. With daylight saving the navigator can have a leisurely meal before taking the noon sight at about 1300. The rest of the crew can be conned by assuring them how much they will enjoy the long sunny evenings, which is true anyway.

Ocean currents

During the preparation and planning for an ocean passage, the decision between sailing a rhumb line track or using the shorter great circle will have to be made. Many ocean winds such as the trades, and some of the currents are relatively constant and predictable. The yacht navigator may find that a deviation from the direct track to reach a belt of favourable winds or to get into a current that will boost the speed made good by two knots or more is well worth the extra distance. In making this decision the likely winds and currents and the great circle distance should be known.

Current and wind charts

Detailed charts showing winds and currents for various months of the year in the world's major oceans are published in both the United Kingdom and the United States. These can be purchased from chart agents in most countries of the western world, including Australia and New Zealand. HM Stationery Office, London also publishes a volume entitled *Ocean Passages of the World* which is probably the definitive work for anyone planning a long voyage. Part Two of this book deals exclusively with sailing routes of the world and contains sailing lore going back to the time of the clipper ships on the UK to Australia and the China routes. The last clipper, the *Cutty Sark*, launched in 1869, is preserved in London.

Lifeboat charts

Fig 105 shows a lifeboat chart which, although not as detailed as the ones just discussed, shows the general winds and currents in each major ocean. As the name implies, their primary purpose is for use in boats whose parent ship has sunk. However, printed on the back of the chart in a very compact form is an explanation of basic navigation principles. There are also instructions on how to find latitude at noon using a protractor and a pencil, with a table of the sun's declination for each month of the year. Lifeboat charts are good value.

The Admiralty *Pilots* or *Sailing Directions* are published in a number of volumes, each containing information for specific ocean areas and countries, e.g. the *Pacific Islands Pilot Vol.II* covers the central groups, including New Caledonia, the Fiji Islands and the Tonga, Samoa and Tokelau Islands, as well as many others. Although these *Pilots* are designed for big ship use and contain rather more detailed information than the yacht navigator might need, they do discuss the climate in the area and give information on winds, currents and tidal streams near the coast which are not shown on the more general wind and current ocean charts. The Hydrographer of the Royal Navy publishes a companion volume to any or all the *Pilots* called *The Mariner's Handbook*. This gives details of all navigational charts and books available, the use of charts, a chapter on navigational hazards and, of most interest, a chapter called 'Natural Conditions'. This includes general maritime meteorology, colour of the sea and coral waters.

Great circle course and distance

Frankly, for any ocean passage under 1500 miles it is a waste of time even bothering to find the great circle distance. The overall saving might be less than 10 miles. For example the great circle distance from the North Cape of New Zealand to Brisbane is 1072 miles, while the rhumb line distance is 1078 miles. Coupled with a saving of just 6 miles, the great circle passes only a few miles south of the notorious Middleton Reef and between Middleton and Elizabeth Reefs. The former has claimed more than one fishing boat, a yacht or two, and the hulk of the freighter *Runic* is there to this day. Whether any of these was actually trying to sail the great circle track is not at issue – the point is

Fig 107
Laying off the track

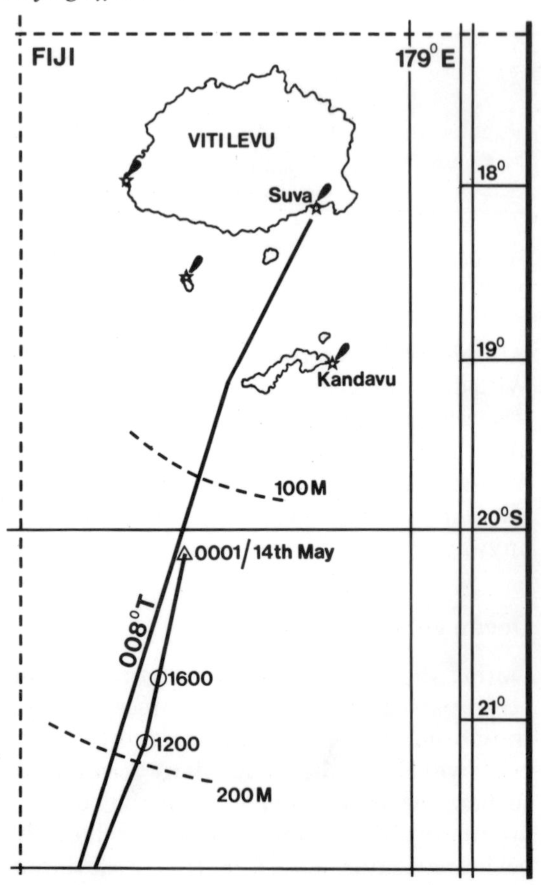

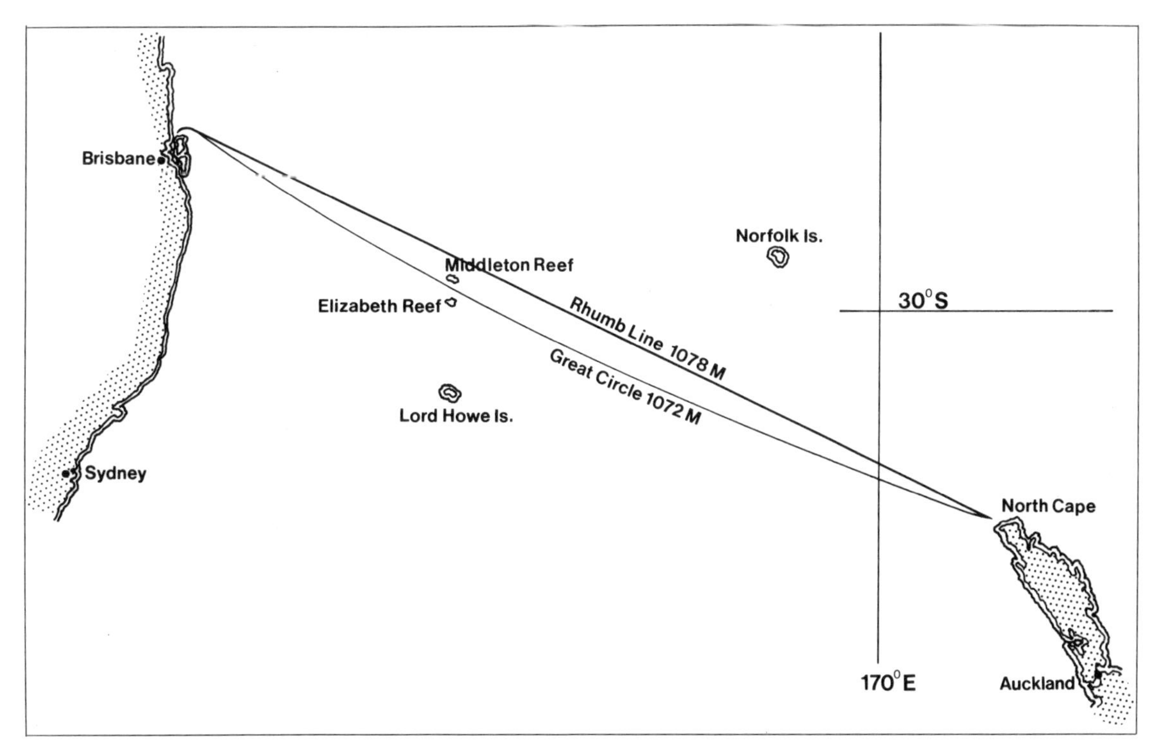

Fig 106
Comparison between a great circle track and a rhumb line

that a reef is a good place to stay away from.

The fractionally longer rhumb line passes about 25 miles north of both of them. Even aiming to pass 40 miles north would put less than 5 miles on the total distance. If the reader looks back to Fig 8, the saving in distance between Bermuda and England is only a little over 50 miles in a voyage of just on 3 000 miles.

Laying off the track

The yacht navigator may not be able to sail exactly along a track laid off on the chart, but it is useful to show the route so that deviations from it are immediately clear when the daily sunsight fixes are plotted. The distances to go to the destination should be noted say every hundred miles back along the track to the start point. This does away with any need continually to measure off or calculate these distances while at sea. The total rhumb line distance is also found. If the navigator suspects that the great circle will give an appreciable saving, the *Air Tables* can be used to find this distance.

Finding great circle distance

Look at Fig 78 (page 81) which shows the PZX triangle. The side ZX is the distance between the point Z and the sun's GP. The tables are entered with latitude, declination (which is the sun's latitude) and LHA, i.e. two latitudes and the difference in longitude between the two points. Fig 108 shows exactly the same sort of triangle, except that F and T are two ports. As their latitudes and longitudes are known, the *Air Tables* can be used to find the side FT, which is the great circle distance between them. To do this, call:

The latitude of one port, latitude;

The latitude of the other port, declination;

The difference between the two longitudes, LHA.

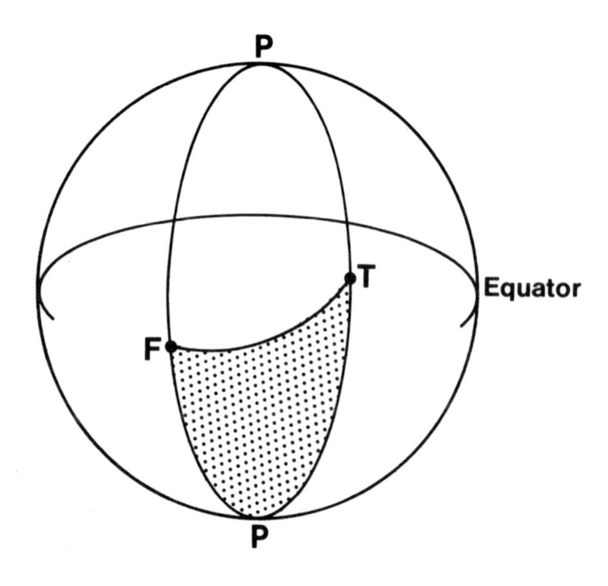

Fig 108
Finding great circle distance

For example, find the great circle distance between Sydney (33° 52′S 151° 13′E) and Suva (18° 09′S 178° 26′E). These two positions have been taken from a list of ports of the world. The latitudes and longitudes given in such lists are usually for a prominent navigation mark (such as a lighthouse) or a building (such as an observatory). The actual departure and arrival positions are plotted on a chart outside the harbour entrance. The latitude and LHA used in the *Air Tables* must be to an exact degree. With these points in mind, the following latitudes and longitudes will be used as being the start and finish of the great circle track.

Sydney 34° 00′S 151° 26′E
Suva 18° 20′S 178° 26′E

The difference in longitude between Sydney and Suva is:
178° 26′ E
151° 26′ E –

27°

The values to enter the tables then become:

Latitude	34°
Declination	18° 20′ (same)
LHA	27°

Hc	61° 05′ d + 37
Correction (Table 5)	12′ +
Hc	61° 17′
Distance	90° minus Hc
	= 90° - 61° 17′
	= 28° 43′

This is converted to nautical miles, i.e. (28° x 60) + 43′. The great circle distance from Sydney to Suva is therefore 1 723 miles.

What is the great circle distance from a position just south of Sao Miguel Island in the Azores (37°N 25° 30′W) to Barbados in the West Indies (13°N 59° 30′W)?

Latitude + declination same name, Hc 51° 18′, distance 2 322M.

If the navigator decides to plot the great circle track, a gnomonic chart of the particular ocean should be obtained from a chart agent. A straight line is drawn between the start and finish points, and this line represents the shortest track between the two. Meridians of longitude for every exact 5 or 10 degrees are shown on the gnomonic chart, and positions on the line are transferred to a Mercator chart by reading off the latitudes at the points of intersection with these meridians. These points will form the curve of the great circle on the Mercator chart. A rhumb line course is then sailed between each of these transferred points.

However, the overriding considerations for the yacht navigator will always be the favourable wind patterns and currents and the avoidance of reefs and shoals by the widest possible margin.

Appendix One
Selected Stars

Volume I of the *Air Tables* contains the altitudes and true azimuths (Zn) of seven selected stars at any latitude and for any moment of time. The advantages in using this volume for solving starsights instead of the other volumes of the *Air Tables* are that:

1 No declination correction is needed when finding altitude.

2 No calculation is needed to find the true bearing of the star as Zn is given directly.

3 Stars can be identified from information in the tables.

4 The GHA required can be found without recourse to the *Nautical Almanac* if necessary.

These advantages reduce by half the number of steps needed in calculating the altitude of a star. Volume I cannot be used for planet sights.

First point of Aries

The first point of Aries, or Aries as it is usually known, is the point in the heavens directly behind the sun on 21 March – the equinox – when the sun's declination is 0 degrees. To us a star is a fixed point of light, and as Aries is a fixed point in the heavens it can be treated as if a star was there, and its geographical position with respect to Greenwich can be predicted.

The Greenwich hour angle of Aries is tabulated in the left-hand column of the left-hand page of the *Nautical Almanac*. Using GHA Aries and a chosen longitude in the normal way, the local hour angle of Aries can be found. Volume I is entered with chosen latitude, and LHA Aries for the time of each starsight. Notice here that declination is not needed, although star declinations are given in the *Nautical Almanac*.

Finding LHA Aries

As mentioned above GHA Aries is tabulated in the *Nautical Almanac* against GMT and an extract for 21 February 1978 is shown in Fig 109. Chosen latitude is 26°S and DR longitude 166° 40′E. Civil twilight is at about 1905 local time, which is 11 hours ahead of GMT.
To find LHA Aries at 08h 05min GMT:

GHA Aries for 08h GMT	270°	53′.3	
Increment for 05 m	1°	15′.2	+
GHA Aries	272°	08′.5	
Chosen longitude	166°	51′.5 E	+
LHA Aries	439°	00′.0	
	360°		–
LHA Aries	79°		

There is a separate column for the increment to GHA Aries in the tinted pages of the *Nautical Almanac*. GHA Aries can also be found from Table 4 at the back of Volume I of the *Air Tables*.

Identifying stars

Nothing other than the *Air Tables* is needed to identify stars. The extract in Fig 110 is from the page for latitude 26°S. The most suitable seven stars at any given moment are tabulated against LHA Aries, which in the example above is 79°. This will increase by 1 degree every four minutes. As the altitude and true bearing are tabulated, each star can be found by looking along the bearing at the right altitude. Alternatively, the altitude can be set on the sextant and by looking at the horizon along the

G.M.T.	ARIES
	G.H.A.
d h	° ′
21 00	150 33.6
01	165 36.0
02	180 38.5
03	195 41.0
04	210 43.4
05	225 45.9
06	240 48.4
07	255 50.8
08	270 53.3
T 09	285 55.8
U 10	300 58.2
E 11	316 00.7
S 12	331 03.2
D 13	346 05.6
A 14	1 08.1
Y 15	16 10.5
16	31 13.0
17	46 15.5
18	61 17.9
19	76 20.4
20	91 22.9
21	106 25.3
22	121 27.8
23	136 30.3

Fig 109
Tabulation of GHA Aries. From the 1978 Nautical Almanac, *page 44*

right bearing, the star should be visible in the telescope. The best three stars to give a fix with good angles of cut are marked with an asterisk. Those in capital letters, such as Betelgeuse, are the brightest, while those in smaller letters, such as Hamal, are not quite as bright and will probably not be visible until about ten minutes after civil twilight. A minimum of three stars should be taken, but preferably four. As long as the sights are completed within ten minutes or so, the fact that the boat has moved between each shot can be ignored.

Starsight working

Exactly the same page contains the answers when working out the sights as was used in preparation. Fig 111 shows the working for the three best stars taken between 1905 and 1910 local time on 21 February 1978. All three should be worked together. This saves three separate looks at the *Nautical Almanac* when the required information for all stars can be taken out at the same time. Dip correction is −3′.0; there is no index error. As a star is a point source of light, the only correction to apparent altitude is for refraction. The star correction table is in the front of the *Nautical Almanac*.

LAT 26°S

LHA ♈	Hc	Zn	Hc	Zn	Hc	Zn	Hc	Zn	Hc	Zn	Hc	Zn	Hc	Zn
	BETELGEUSE		PROCYON		•Suhail		CANOPUS		•ACHERNAR		Hamal		•ALDEBARAN	
75	54 08	023	40 33	056	37 36	126	59 04	155	42 30	215	25 06	316	47 05	351
76	54 28	022	41 18	056	38 19	126	59 27	156	41 59	215	24 28	315	46 56	350
77	54 48	020	42 02	055	39 03	126	59 48	157	41 28	215	23 50	314	46 46	348
78	55 05	018	42 46	054	39 47	126	60 09	158	40 57	215	23 11	314	46 34	347
79	55 21	017	43 29	053	40 30	126	60 28	159	40 26	215	22 32	313	46 21	346
80	55 36	015	44 12	052	41 14	126	60 47	160	39 55	216	21 52	312	46 07	344
81	55 49	013	44 54	051	41 58	126	61 05	161	39 23	216	21 12	311	45 52	343
82	56 01	012	45 36	050	42 41	126	61 22	162	38 52	216	20 31	311	45 35	342
83	56 11	010	46 17	049	43 25	126	61 38	164	38 20	216	19 50	310	45 18	340
84	56 19	008	46 57	048	44 08	126	61 52	165	37 48	216	19 09	309	44 59	339
85	56 26	006	47 36	047	44 52	126	62 06	166	37 16	216	18 27	309	44 39	338
86	56 31	004	48 15	046	45 35	126	62 19	167	36 44	216	17 45	308	44 18	336
87	56 34	003	48 53	044	46 19	126	62 30	168	36 12	216	17 02	308	43 56	335
88	56 36	001	49 31	043	47 02	127	62 40	170	35 40	217	16 19	307	43 33	334
89	56 36	359	50 07	042	47 45	127	62 50	171	35 08	217	15 36	306	43 08	333

Fig 110
Most suitable seven stars tabulated against LHA Aries. From the Air Tables, *Vol I, page 212*

	Suhail	Achernar	Aldebaran
GMT	08h05m40s	08h07m20s	08h09m48s
GHA Aries	270°53′.3	270°53′.3	270°53′.3
Increment	1°25′.2	1°50′.3	2°27′.4
GHA Aries	272°18′.5	272°43′.6	273°20′.7
Chosen Longitude	166°41′.5	166°16′.4	166°39.3 - E+
LHA Aries	439°	439°	440°
	360°−	360°−	360°−
LHA Aries	79°	79°	80°
Sext Alt	40°47′.1	40°35′.1	45°49′.3
IE and Dip	3′ −	3′ −	3′ −
App Alt	40°44′.1	40°32′.1	45°46′.3
Alt Corr	1′.1 −	1′.1 −	0′.9 −
Ho	40°43′	40°31′	45°45′.4
Hc*	40°30′	40°26′	46°07′.0
Intercept	13 to	5 to	21.6 from
Zn*	126°	215°	344°

*Hc and Zn direct from *Air Tables.*
The fix would be at 1908 local time.

Once the intercept has been found in the normal manner, the stars are plotted, each from its own chosen position as shown in Fig 111. If the reader has already had some experience with sunsights before tackling starsights, the plotting can be speeded up by dispensing with the intercept line. If the parallel rulers are set at right angles to the star's true bearing, the distance set on a pair of compasses and a small arc inscribed, then the rulers stepped across to the tangent point with the arc, the position line can be drawn in.

Precession and nutation

The current edition of the *Air Tables,* Volume I, is for Epoch 1975, and the tables are correct for that year.

Although the stars are considered fixed in the heavens, the planes of reference from the earth, i.e. the celestial equator and the extension of the earth's axis through the Poles, fluctuate very slowly and the first point of Aries moves. This movement of Aries is called the precession of the equinoxes, and is the reason why the former has moved away from the constellation of Aries in which it was situated when the term was first devised.

Nutation is a short-term oscillation superimposed on precession. These effects are allowed for when preparing data for the *Nautical Almanac,* and do not have to be considered when using Volume II or Volume III of the *Air Tables.* However, when using Volume I, a small correction for the effects of nutation and precession may have to be made. The fix is moved according to the information given in Table 5 at the back of Volume I. This correction could be as much as 4 miles, depending on LHA and latitude. The 1980 Epoch edition of the *Air Tables,* Volume I, should be on sale by mid-1979.

Direction from the stars

Zn, or the true bearing of any of the seven selected stars, can be found from the *Air Tables* for any time of the night. All that is needed is LHA Aries to the nearest whole degree. So any low altitude star listed could be used to get a compass check.

Fig 111
The plotted three-star fix

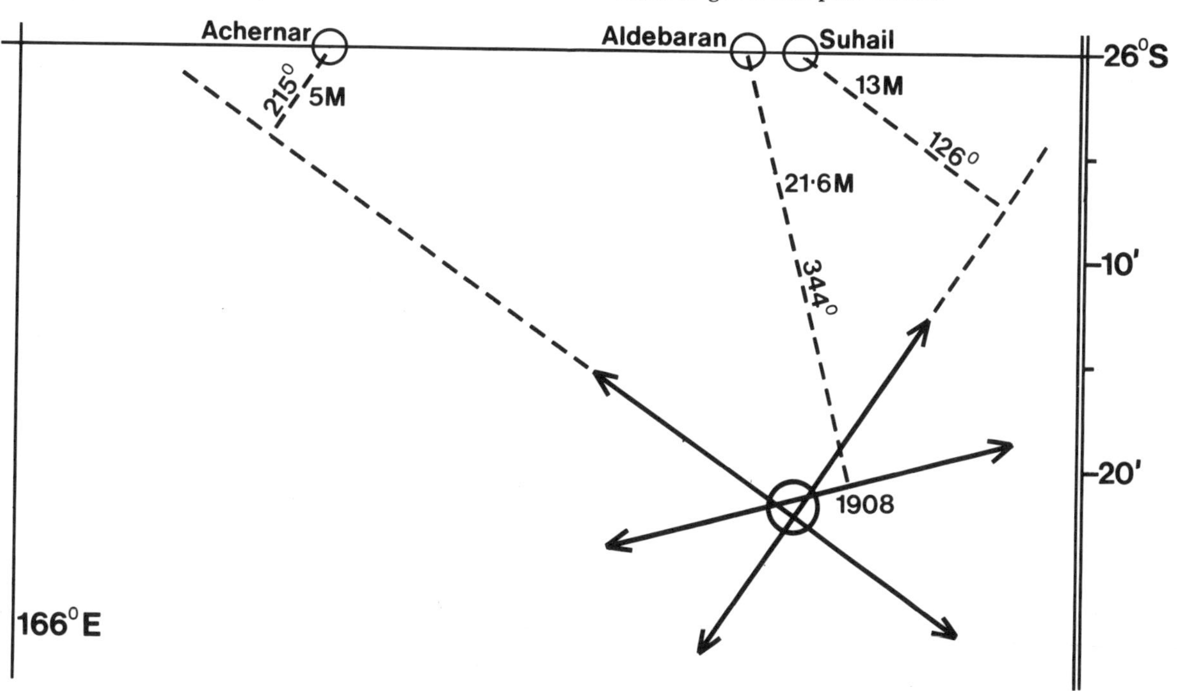

Although there is no equivalent to the Pole Star in the southern hemisphere, the direction of true south can be found using the Southern Cross and the star Achernar. The latter was one of the selected stars used in the example. The cross is identified by the two stars that act as pointers. The brightest of these is Rigel Kent, used for starsights. The star at the base of the cross, Acrux, is also used. If the observer follows the long axis through Acrux in a very slight curve across the sky, he will come to Achernar, which is by itself and easily recognised. The South Celestial Pole is a fraction to the left of the point halfway between the two stars. This doesn't sound very accurate. I suggest the reader finds true south with a hand bearing compass or other means one evening, and then identifies Acrux and Achernar and gets the correct point in his mind's eye. He should find that it is possible to judge the correct spot to an accuracy of a degree or so on future occasions.

In the northern hemisphere Polaris, the Pole Star, circles the extension of the earth's axis of spin, and its bearing is never more than 2 degrees from true north. It is not a particularly bright star, but can be identified by finding the constellation called the Plough and using the northern pointers shown in Fig 113.

Fig 113
The Pole Star and the northern pointers

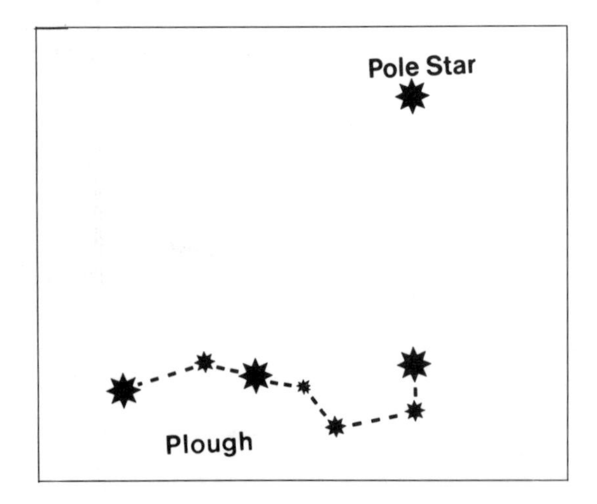

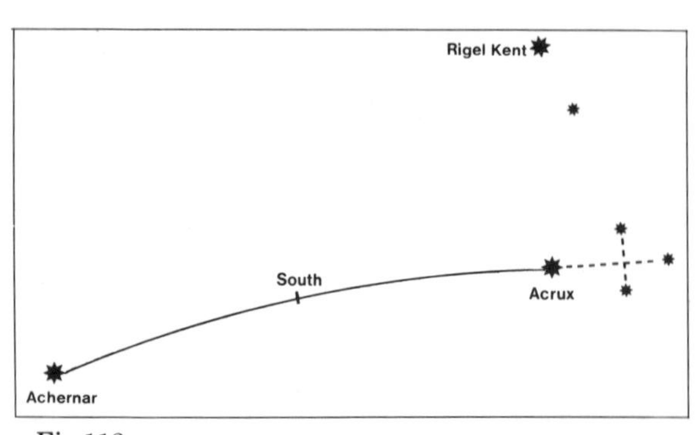

Fig 112
Finding the direction of true south in the southern hemisphere

Latitude from Polaris

In Fig 114 the observer's latitude = ZQ.
PZ + PN = 90° and
PZ + ZQ = 90°

As PZ is common to both the above, by substitution PN = ZQ i.e. the altitude of the pole = the latitude of the observer. So if Polaris was actually at the pole the navigator could find his latitude by simply finding the true altitude of the Pole Star. However its declination is about 89°, which is why it describes a small circle around the pole, and the altitude of Polaris is not quite equal to latitude.

The *Nautical Almanac* contains pole star tables, immediately preceding the tinted pages, by which a pole star altitude can be easily converted into a latitude using three corrections called a_0, a_1, and a_2. To do this, the LHA of Aries is worked out for the GMT of the sight. (Seconds of time can be ignored). Using this LHA, a_0 is found from the tables. By going down the same column just used, a_1 and a_2 will be found using the DR latitude and the month of the year respectively. These corrections are added to the true altitude, but 1° must then be subtracted from the answer just obtained to give latitude, e.g.

On 21 February 1978, at 17h 50m GMT, in DR position 58° 20′N, 2° 00′W the true altitude of Polaris was found to be 59° 10′.

Fig 115
Pole Star Table. From the 1978 Nautical Almanac, *page 276*

POLARIS (POLE STAR) TABLES, 1978

FOR DETERMINING LATITUDE FROM SEXTANT ALTITUDE AND FOR AZIMUTH

L.H.A. ARIES	240°–249°	250°–259°	260°–269°	270°–279°	280°–289°	290°–299°	300°–309°	310°–319°	320°–329°	330°–339°	340°–349°	350°–359°
	a_0	a_0	a_0	a_0	a_0	a_0	a_0	a_0	a_0	a_0	a_0	a_0
°	° ′	° ′	° ′	° ′	° ′	° ′	° ′	° ′	° ′	° ′	° ′	° ′
0	1 43·3	1 38·8	1 33·0	1 26·2	1 18·5	1 10·3	1 01·6	0 52·9	0 44·4	0 36·3	0 28·8	0 22·3
1	42·9	38·2	32·3	25·4	17·7	09·4	1 00·8	52·1	43·5	35·5	28·1	21·7
2	42·5	37·7	31·7	24·7	16·9	08·6	0 59·9	51·2	42·7	34·7	27·4	21·1
3	42·1	37·2	31·0	24·0	16·1	07·7	59·0	50·3	41·9	33·9	26·8	20·5
4	41·7	36·6	30·4	23·2	15·3	06·8	58·2	49·5	41·1	33·2	26·1	20·0
5	1 41·2	1 36·0	1 29·7	1 22·4	1 14·5	1 06·0	0 57·3	0 48·6	0 40·3	0 32·4	0 25·4	0 19·4
6	40·8	35·4	29·0	21·7	13·6	05·1	56·4	47·8	39·4	31·7	24·8	18·9
7	40·3	34·8	28·3	20·9	12·8	04·3	55·5	46·9	38·6	31·0	24·1	18·4
8	39·8	34·2	27·6	20·1	11·9	03·4	54·7	46·1	37·8	30·2	23·5	17·9
9	39·3	33·6	26·9	19·3	11·1	02·5	53·8	45·2	37·0	29·5	22·9	17·4
10	1 38·8	1 33·0	1 26·2	1 18·5	1 10·3	1 01·6	0 52·9	0 44·4	0 36·3	0 28·8	0 22·3	0 16·9
Lat.	a_1	a_1	a_1	a_1	a_1	a_1	a_1	a_1	a_1	a_1	a_1	a_1
°	′	′	′	′	′	′	′	′	′	′	′	′
0	0·5	0·4	0·3	0·3	0·2	0·2	0·2	0·2	0·2	0·3	0·4	0·4
10	·5	·4	·4	·3	·3	·2	·2	·2	·3	·3	·4	·5
20	·5	·5	·4	·4	·3	·3	·3	·3	·3	·4	·4	·5
30	·5	·5	·5	·4	·4	·4	·4	·4	·4	·4	·5	·5
40	0·6	0·5	0·5	0·5	0·5	0·5	0·5	0·5	0·5	0·5	0·5	0·6
45	·6	·6	·6	·5	·5	·5	·5	·5	·5	·6	·6	·6
50	·6	·6	·6	·6	·6	·6	·6	·6	·6	·6	·6	·6
55	·6	·6	·7	·7	·7	·7	·7	·7	·7	·7	·6	·6
60	·7	·7	·7	·8	·8	·8	·8	·8	·8	·7	·7	·7
62	0·7	0·7	0·8	0·8	0·8	0·8	0·9	0·8	0·8	0·8	0·7	0·7
64	·7	·7	·8	·8	·9	0·9	0·9	0·9	·9	·8	·8	·7
66	·7	·8	·8	0·9	0·9	1·0	1·0	1·0	0·9	·9	·8	·7
68	0·7	0·8	0·9	1·0	1·0	1·1	1·1	1·0	1·0	0·9	0·9	0·8
Month	a_2	a_2	a_2	a_2	a_2	a_2	a_2	a_2	a_2	a_2	a_2	a_2
	′	′	′	′	′	′	′	′	′	′	′	′
Jan.	0·5	0·5	0·5	0·5	0·5	0·6	0·6	0·6	0·6	0·6	0·7	0·7
Feb.	·4	·4	·4	·4	·4	·4	·4	·5	·5	·5	·5	·6
Mar.	·4	·4	·4	·3	·3	·3	·3	·3	·3	·4	·4	·4
Apr.	0·5	0·5	0·4	0·3	0·3	0·3	0·2	0·2	0·2	0·2	0·3	0·3
May	·7	·6	·5	·4	·4	·3	·3	·2	·2	·2	·2	·2
June	·8	·7	·7	·6	·5	·4	·4	·3	·3	·2	·2	·2
July	0·9	0·9	0·8	0·7	0·7	0·6	0·5	0·5	0·4	0·3	0·3	0·3
Aug.	1·0	·9	·9	·9	·8	·8	·7	·6	·6	·5	·4	·4
Sept.	0·9	·9	·9	·9	·9	·9	·8	·8	·7	·7	·6	·6
Oct.	0·8	0·9	0·9	0·9	0·9	0·9	0·9	0·9	0·9	0·9	0·8	0·8
Nov.	·7	·8	·8	·9	·9	·9	1·0	1·0	1·0	1·0	0·9	0·9
Dec.	0·5	0·6	0·7	0·7	0·8	0·8	0·9	0·9	1·0	1·0	1·0	1·0
Lat.	AZIMUTH											
°	°	°	°	°	°	°	°	°	°	°	°	°
0	0·4	0·6	0·7	0·7	0·8	0·8	0·8	0·8	0·8	0·7	0·6	0·5
20	0·5	0·6	0·7	0·8	0·8	0·9	0·9	0·9	0·8	0·8	0·7	0·5
40	0·6	0·7	0·9	1·0	1·0	1·1	1·1	1·1	1·0	0·9	0·8	0·7
50	0·7	0·9	1·0	1·1	1·2	1·3	1·3	1·3	1·2	1·1	1·0	0·8
55	0·8	1·0	1·1	1·3	1·4	1·4	1·5	1·4	1·4	1·2	1·1	0·9
60	0·9	1·1	1·3	1·5	1·6	1·6	1·7	1·6	1·6	1·4	1·3	1·0
65	1·0	1·3	1·5	1·7	1·9	1·9	2·0	1·9	1·8	1·7	1·5	1·2

Latitude = Apparent altitude (corrected for refraction) $- 1° + a_0 + a_1 + a_2$

The table is entered with L.H.A. Aries to determine the column to be used; each column refers to a range of 10°. a_0 is taken, with mental interpolation, from the upper table with the units of L.H.A. Aries in degrees as argument; a_1, a_2 are taken, without interpolation, from the second and third tables with arguments latitude and month respectively. a_0, a_1, a_2 are always positive. The final table gives the azimuth of *Polaris.*

GHA Aries for 17h GMT	= 46° 15′.5
Increment for 50m	= 12° 32′.1
GHA Aries	= 58° 47′.6
Longitude	= 2° 00′.0 W –
LHA Aries	= 56° 47′.6

True Alt.	59° 10′.0
a_0	0° 13′.2
a_1	0′.6
a_2	0′.8
	59° 24′.6
	-1°
Latitude	58° 24′.6 N

Fig 114
The earth viewed from above the observer's zenith – northern hemisphere

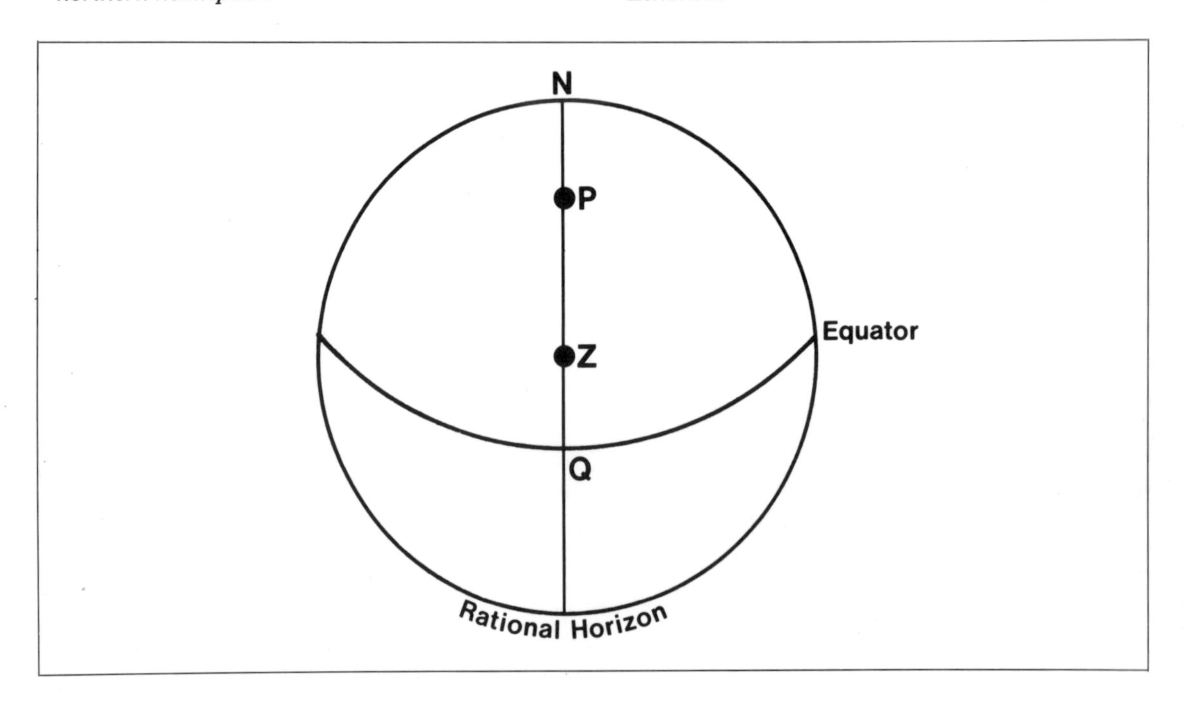

Appendix Two

Moon and Planet Sights

MOON

The moon is often visible during the day and the position line resulting from a moon sight can be crossed with a sun line taken at the same time to give a fix. Moon sights are as easy to take as sunsights, except that the lower limb is used part of each month while the upper limb is all that is visible for the remainder of the time. During full moon it may be necessary to use the lightest shade over the index mirror to get a sharp outline of the moon's disc if a sight is taken near dawn or dusk.

The moon's distance from the earth varies during each month and so does its speed around the earth. Consequently the GHA changes at different rates. Although this is provided for in the daily pages of the *Nautical Almanac,* the increment tables at the back are for the slowest hourly rate of change. To avoid having several sets of increment tables, the data for the moon includes a column headed v. Based on this, a small correction is added to the tabulated GHA. By comparison with the sun the hourly change of declination, d, is quite significant. Although rays from the sun to any part of the earth's surface can be considered parallel, the moon is so close, averaging a mere 230 000 miles, that this assumption cannot be made. A correction called horizontal parallax (HP) has to be applied to the sextant altitude to allow for the resulting error.

1978 DECEMBER 9,

G.M.T.		SUN		MOON				
		G.H.A.	Dec.	G.H.A.	v	Dec.	d	H.P.
d	h	° ′	° ′	° ′	′	° ′	′	′
9	00	101 59.3	S22 45.6	66 16.9	11.7	N 3 02.5	10.4	57.6
	01	196 59.0	45.8	80 47.6	11.6	3 12.9	10.5	57.6
	02	211 58.7	46.1	95 18.2	11.7	3 23.4	10.4	57.6
	03	226 58.5	· · 46.3	109 48.9	11.6	3 33.8	10.3	57.5
	04	241 58.2	46.6	124 19.5	11.7	3 44.1	10.4	57.5
	05	256 57.9	46.8	138 50.2	11.7	3 54.5	10.3	57.5
	06	271 57.6	S22 47.1	153 20.9	11.7	N 4 04.8	10.3	57.5
	07	286 57.4	47.3	167 51.6	11.7	4 15.1	10.2	57.4
S	08	301 57.1	47.6	182 22.3	11.8	4 25.3	10.3	57.4
A	09	316 56.8	· · 47.8	196 53.1	11.7	4 35.6	10.2	57.4
T	10	331 56.5	48.1	211 23.8	11.7	4 45.8	10.1	57.4
U	11	346 56.2	48.3	225 54.5	11.8	4 55.9	10.2	57.3
R	12	1 56.0	S22 48.6	240 25.3	11.7	N 5 06.1	10.1	57.3
D	13	16 55.7	48.8	254 56.0	11.8	5 16.2	10.0	57.3
A	14	31 55.4	49.1	269 26.8	11.7	5 26.2	10.1	57.3
Y	15	46 55.1	· · 49.3	283 57.5	11.8	5 36.3	10.0	57.3
	16	61 54.8	49.6	298 28.3	11.8	5 46.3	9.9	57.2
	17	76 54.6	49.8	312 59.1	11.7	5 56.2	10.0	57.2
	18	91 54.3	S22 50.0	327 29.8	11.8	N 6 06.2	9.9	57.2
	19	106 54.0	50.3	342 00.6	11.8	6 16.1	9.8	57.2
	20	121 53.7	50.5	356 31.4	11.8	6 25.9	9.8	57.1
	21	136 53.5	· · 50.8	11 02.2	11.7	6 35.7	9.8	57.1
	22	151 53.2	51.0	25 32.9	11.8	6 45.5	9.7	57.1
	23	166 52.9	51.2	40 03.7	11.8	6 55.2	9.7	57.1

Fig 116
Extract from the 1978 Nautical Almanac, *page 239*

The moon's GHA is tabulated against each exact hour. GMT and v are taken from the column immediately to the right. This is the value for the whole hour, and the proportion for the minutes and seconds of time can be found in the increment pages. Using the same page that contains the increment for the moon's GHA, go down the column headed v or d. Find the appropriate value of v, and immediately opposite is the correction. The correction for d is found on the same page in a similar manner.

The altitude correction tables for the moon are at the back of the *Almanac* and contain an explanation on their use for either an upper or lower limb sight. The corrections for apparent altitude and HP are taken from the same column.

Because of the moon's slightly irregular orbit and the number of relatively large corrections needed, the resulting position line may not be quite as accurate as other celestial position lines.

Apart from the additional corrections involved, a moon sight is worked exactly the same way as a sunsight. Although the moon may rise at different times of the day or night during the year, like all heavenly bodies it comes up in the eastern part of the sky. So the navigator can find the approximate true azimuth before doing any calculations.

For example: Afternoon moon sight. Approximate bearing 105°. Lower Limb. Position by dead reckoning at 1630, 20° 16′N, 150° 25′W. Clocks 10 hours behind GMT. 8 December 1978. No index error. Dip -3′.

Local time	1630 8 December
Zone	10 +
GMT	2630
GMT	0230 9 December

Date at Greenwich, 9 December 1978. Chosen latitude 20°N.

	v 11′.7	
Moon Tab GHA	95°18′.2	
Inc	7°09′.5 +	
v correction	5′.9 +	
GHA	102°33′.6	
	360° +	
	462°33′.6	
Chosen longitude	150°33′.6 W -	
LHA	312°	
d	10′.4	
Tab Dec	N 3°23′.4 (Increasing)	
d corr	5′.2 +	
Dec	3°28′.6 same	
Sext alt	39°26′	
IE and dip	3′ -	
App alt	39°23′	HP
Alt corr	54′.1	57′.6
HP corr	4′.9	
True alt. Ho	40°22′	
Tab Hc	40°14′	d +24
d corr	12′ +	
Hc	40°26′	Z 104°
		Zn = Z

Hc	40°26′
Ho	40°22′
	Intercept 4M from 104°

PLANET SIGHTS

The *Nautical Almanac* has a page of notes near the front which indicate when the planets will be visible during the year, and whether they are morning or evening stars. By far the most useful are Venus and Jupiter. If they are evening stars, both can be seen by the time of sunset, and Venus is often visible an hour or more beforehand.

Planet sights are worked in exactly the same way as the sun, except that there is a small v correction to be applied to the GHA. This is occasionally minus for Venus, but is shown in the *Almanac*. The only correction to the apparent altitude is for refraction and is taken from the stars and planets table in the front of the book.

Next to the sun and moon, Venus is the brightest object in the sky. As with the moon, it is sometimes useful to use the lightest shade if taking a sight of Venus at or after the time of sunset. The planet then appears as a pinpoint of light, which is the exact centre of the body, and this can be brought down to the horizon to give an accurate sextant altitude.

Meridian passage of Venus

Latitude can be found when any of the navigational bodies cross the observer's meridian in the same way as for the sun. If the stars or minor planets are on or close to the meridian, the position line can be found by using the *Air Tables* in the normal way. However, at certain times of the year, a daytime latitude by meridian passage of Venus is possible. A fix from a sun line and a Venus latitude can prove most useful.

The times of meridian passage of all the planets are given at the bottom of the left-hand page in the *Almanac*.

When the times of the meridian passage of Venus and that of the Sun are approximately the same, the planet will not be visible during the day. But, for example in early September 1978, mer. pass. Venus was 1430 and in December just after 0900. The local time of meridian passage Venus is found in exactly the same manner as for the sun.

For example, on 5 September 1978 in longitude 174° E in a vessel keeping 12 hours ahead of GMT:

mer. pass. Venus (*Nautical Almanac*)	1444
Longitude 174°E converted to time	−1136
GMT of mer. pass. at longtitude 174°E	0308
Zone	+12
	1508

Local time of mer. pass. Venus

Finding Venus during the day can prove a bit tricky, but as with the sun it will be either due north or due south at meridian passage, which at least limits the relevant part of the sky to a few degrees either side of those directions. A few slow sweeps up and down with a pair of binoculars usually achieves the required result. Using the naked eye, the planet looks like a pale white pinhead in the sky. Once sighted, you usually realise that you've been looking directly at it for about five minutes. Don't try too hard. If one looks casually around it suddenly appears quite plainly in view. On the other hand if you look so intently that your eyes water, stop for a minute or so before trying again.

Another method of finding Venus is to set the expected altitude of the planet at meridian passage on the sextant, and look at the north or south point of the horizon. Due to the magnification of the telescope, Venus should then be visible. The expected altitude is found by starting with the latitude by dead reckoning at the time the planet will be on the meridian. A latitude sight is then worked in reverse, ending with the approximate sextant altitude.

Latitude from meridian passage of Venus

On 16 December 1978 at the time of meridian passage of Venus in dead reckoning position 34°N, 16° 14′ E, the planet's true altitude was found to be 42° 56′.6. The zenith distance and declination of Venus are combined in the same manner as for the sun, to give latitude.

Mer. pass. Venus	0907
Longitude	0105 E -
GMT	0802
Zone	1h ahead +
Local time	09 02
	90° 00′
True altitude	42° 56′.6 -
ZX	47° 03′.4
Dec at 0802 GMT	12° 57′.4 -
Latitude at 0902	34° 06′.0N

Appendix Three
Traditional Procedures

Solution of the PZX triangle

Prior to the introduction of the short tabular solutions over forty years ago, one of the two most common methods of solving the spherical triangle was the St Hilaire or intercept method. The existing *Marine and Air Tables* use the intercept method, but are worked and plotted from a *chosen position*, which means a minimum of interpolation is needed. The various tabulated altitudes and azimuths in the body of the tables have been precalculated, using the same formula employed by the mariner in the logarithmic computation of sights. These were worked using the *dead reckoning position* in both the calculations and when plotting the position line. This is convenient in starsights inasmuch as all the stars are plotted from the one point, but involves interpolation for the minutes of latitude and local hour angle derived from the longitude.

If the calculated zenith distance is known, the calculated altitude can be found from the relationship:

Altitude = 90° - Zenith Distance (ZX)
The cosine-haversine formula is used to find ZX:
Nat.Hav. ZX =
Nat.Hav.A + Nat.Hav. (Lat ± Dec.)
where A is given by:
Log.Hav.A =
Log.Hav.LHA + Log.Cos.Lat + Log.Cos.Dec.

Latitude and declination are added if they have contrary names and subtracted if they have the same names.

The azimuth angle is found from the ABC tables in a book of *Nautical Tables,* or by using an azimuth diagram available through chart agents. This is then converted to a true azimuth or bearing.

The sight on page 101 is reworked here as an example.

DR position. 26° 00′S, 169° 48′E. GMT 23h 37m 20s on 21 February 1978. True altitude was 66° 07′ and Dec 10° 24′.4 S.

GHA	170° 55′.6	
Longitude	169° 48′.0 E +	
LHA	340° 43′.6	Log Hav 8.447 51
Latitude	26° 00′.0 S	Log Cos 9.953 66
Declination	10° 24′.4 S	Log Cos 9.992 80 +
		Log Hav 8.393 97
		convert to:
		Nat Hav 0.024 77
(Lat - Dec)	15° 35′.6	Nat Hav 0.018 40 +
		Nat Hav 0.043 17
		ZX = 23° 58′.0
Hc	= (90° – ZX)	
	= (90° – 23° 58′.0)	A = 1.41N
	= 66° 02′	B = 0.55S
		C = 0.86N
Ho	66° 07′	Azimuth = N52°.3E
Hc	66° 02′	
Intercept	5′ towards 052°	

As mentioned above, the intercept is now plotted from the dead reckoning position and the position line drawn in the usual way. The standard corrections are applied to sextant altitude to find true altitude. There are rather more calculations needed than with the *Air Tables.* Despite the use of logarithmic tables accurate to five decimal places, the position line is only as accurate as Ho, i.e. the sextant altitude.

Appendix Four
Precision Fixing

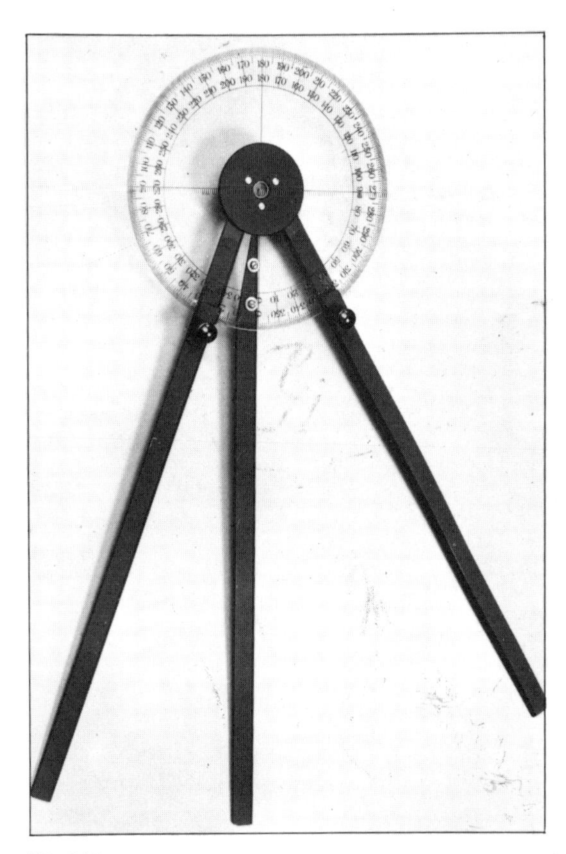

Fig 117
The three-armed protractor or station pointer

Horizontal sextant angle (HSA) fixes can be plotted very quickly and accurately with an instrument called a station pointer, or three-armed protractor, shown in Fig 117. It consists of a circle graduated in degrees and three arms, the bevelled edges of each radiating from the centre of the circle. The centre leg is fixed. Each of the outer legs is movable and can be clamped in any position. When a HSA fix is taken, each of the outer legs is set at the required angle. The bevelled edge of the fixed centre leg is placed over the centre object on the chart and the station pointer adjusted until the bevelled edges of all three legs are over the three fixing objects. The centre of the circle is indicated by a small nick or hole, and this is the fix position. The instrument is moved into the correct position on the chart in the same manner as described for a HSA fix using tracing paper in Chapter Two.

There are some plastic three-armed protractors on the market which are rather less expensive than the metal models.

A quite satisfactory instrument for the yachtsman's use in plotting HSA fixes is shown in Fig 118 and is sometimes called a Douglas protractor. It is graduated around the edge from 0° to 359°. At the centre is a hole large enough to take the point of a sharp pencil. Pencil lines can be drawn on the underside, which has a matt surface. The engraved line from the centre to north is used, as is the fixed centre leg of the station pointer and the two angles drawn in pencil. The protractor is then placed matt side down on the chart so that the pencil lines and engraved N - S line run through the three fixing marks. In Fig 118 pencil lines are shown for an angle of 40° between the centre and right-hand fixing mark and the other angle is 50°. As the protractor has to be turned over to pencil in the lines, the angles have to be reversed when they are laid off. Full instructions are included with the instrument, which can also be used for reading off courses or bearings and can be used in lieu of a parallel ruler.

Be warned. Get the 255 mm square model (Model 10). There are smaller ones, but the lines will not reach far enough across the chart if trying to plot a HSA fix.

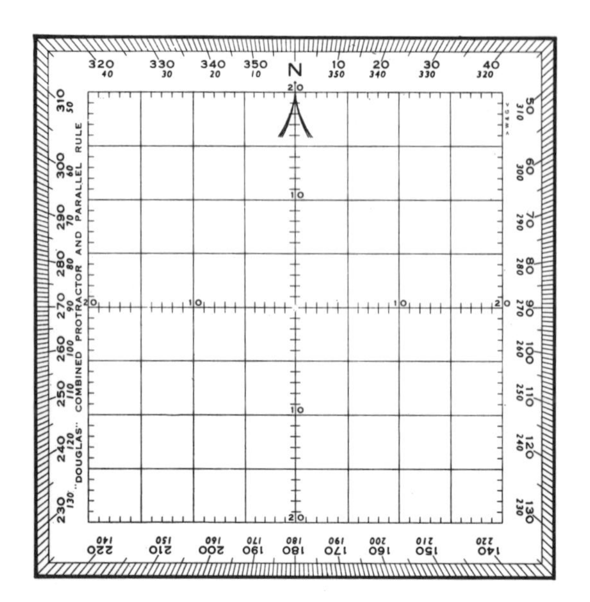

Fig 118
The Douglas protractor (255 mm model)

Horizontal sextant angle lattice

The accuracy achieved with HSA fixing is probably not often required by the yachtsman, but there may be special occasions when a club or yachting organisation wants to lay a mark or buoy with particular precision. Although the station pointer is accurate, it does need constant practice to use it with any speed. HSA fixes can be plotted rapidly without the use of instruments. In ideal conditions a positional accuracy of 6 metres can be achieved with fixing marks up to 5 miles from the boat.

In Chapter Two it was explained that for any angle between two objects there is a circle which goes through the objects, and the angle between them is the same anywhere on the circle. These circles are curves of equal subtended angle. If two pairs of objects are selected and the curves for various angles drawn in on the chart beforehand, each fix is where the appropriate curves for the HSA angles are found to intersect. This is called a horizontal sextant angle lattice, and, although tedious to draw up, it lasts for the life of the chart.

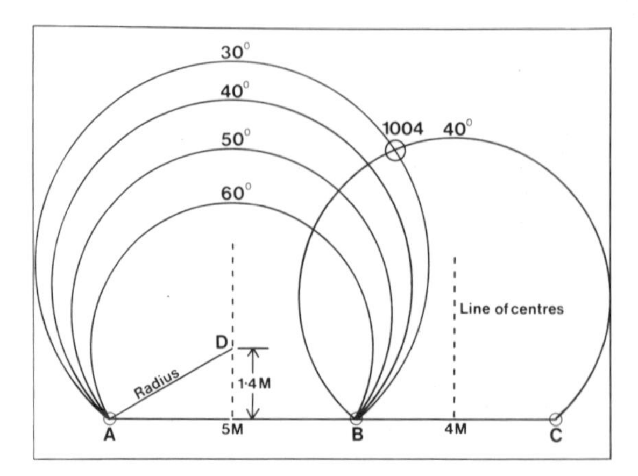

Fig 119
Part of a horizontal sextant angle lattice

The lattice can be drawn up either geometrically or with the use of diagram D6472. The latter is the easiest and the diagram can be purchased through major chart agents. D6472 comes with instructions on its use. To construct a lattice without the diagram, consider the pattern of arcs generated from one pair of objects. The centres of these arcs all lie along the perpendicular bisector of the baseline joining the two objects. This is called the line of centres. The distance of the centre of the arc from the baseline for any angle (θ) is given by

$$\tfrac{1}{2}\, d \cot \theta$$

where 'd' is the length of the baseline. The interval of angle for which the curves are to be drawn in is first decided, the idea being to have a reasonable density of lattice line while preserving clarity. The centre of each arc is found from the formula. With radius from the centre to one object, the arc can be drawn in using compasses and a hard pencil. The arcs should preferably be inked with a different colour for each pair of objects.

As I said, it is a little tedious drawing up the lattice, but because the only plotting required at sea to find position is to ring the intersection of the two arcs, the fix can be put on the chart in 3 to 6 seconds. The practical problem is identifying the marks, but once the initial angle is found with the sextant, it is

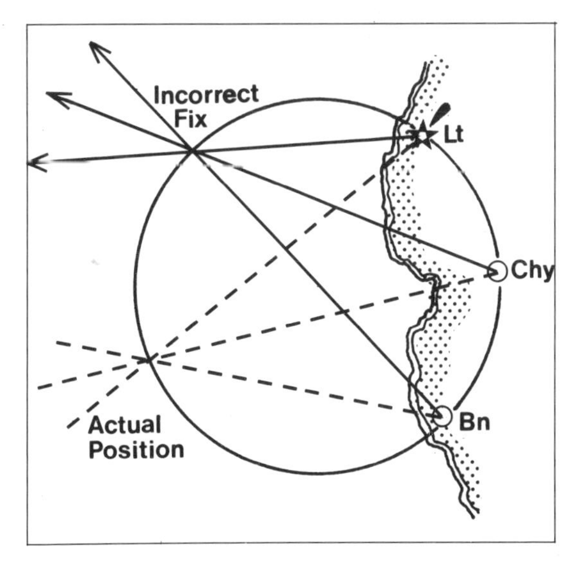

Fig 120
Incorrect fix, if the three marks and the boat lie on the same circle

only a matter of winding the micrometer wheel to keep the objects together. The greatest speed is achieved if two sextants are used. The persons adjust their sextants from time to time, and the navigator should get the two angles within seconds of asking for a fix.

Fig 119 shows three charted objects. A and B are 5M apart and B and C are 4M apart. The circles for HSA angles 30°, 40°, 50° and 60° between A and B are drawn in. The 40° arc through B and C is also shown. The line of centres from each baseline is dotted in. The centre of the 60° arc is 1.4 miles from the baseline at D. This arc was drawn in by using centre D and radius DA or DB. Using the formula, the distance was found as follows:

½ d Cot θ		
½(5M) Cot 60°	Log 2.5	0.397 94
2.5M Cot 60°	Log Cot 60°	9.761 44 +
	Log Distance	10.159 38
		0.159 38
	Distance	1.443M
	=	1.44M

As this has to be done for each angle, using the diagram is a lot quicker!

The fix shown in Fig 119 at 1004 results from HSA angles of 30° between A and B and 40° between B and C. Once the curves are drawn in on the chart, the baselines and lines of centres can be erased.

Choosing the objects

As with any HSA fix, the three marks should either be in a straight line on the chart, or the centre object of the three should be the closest. If the two outer marks are closest to the boat, it is possible for all three objects and the boat to lie on one and the same circle, as shown in Fig 120. In this case the angles between the two sets of marks are exactly the same anywhere on the circle. When such a fix is plotted, it would be sheer coincidence as to which part of the circle the navigator chose, and the fix could be grossly in error.

Caution: the same thing can happen in a fix by cross bearings if the three objects lie on the same circle, and there is an unknown error in the compass.

Glossary of Terms

abeam in a direction at right angles to the fore and aft line of a craft in the horizontal plane.

altitude The vertical angle of a celestial body above the horizon.

apparent altitude The observed altitude corrected for index error and dip.

apparent time Time by the true sun. An apparent day varies in length, i.e. it is not a fixed interval of time.

azimuth Direction measured in the horizontal plane.

azimuth angle Angle at the zenith between the observer's meridian and the direction of a celestial body.

bearing The direction of one point from another.

celestial horizon See rational horizon.

chosen or assumed position A position based on the DR, chosen so as to reduce the number of calculations required to work a celestial sight.

civil twilight The time after sunset or before sunrise at which stars and the horizon are both visible.

cocked hat The triangle resulting from the intersection of three position lines that do not meet at a point.

compass An instrument used for indicating direction.

course The angle between the meridian and the fore and aft line of a craft, measured 0° to 360° clockwise from north.

course made good (CMG) The actual direction of travel of a craft.

cut (angle of) The angle between any pair of position lines in the same fix.

dead reckoning The forecasting ahead of a boat's probable position based on speed, elapsed time and course being steered.

dead reckoning position (DR) The position on the chart resulting from dead reckoning.

declination Latitude of the geographical position of a celestial body.

dip Correction applied to a sextant altitude to allow for the height of eye of an observer above sea level.

deviation The angle between the direction of magnetic north and the direction of north as indicated by a magnetic compass.

estimated position The DR position adjusted for the known or estimated effects of current, tidal stream or leeway.

equinox The time at which the sun crosses the equator. Its declination is 0°.

first point of Aries The point in the heavens at which the sun's declination changes from south to north on 21 March at the vernal (spring) equinox.

fix A position found from two or more intersecting position lines.

fore and aft line The longitudinal axis of a boat. Generally taken as the centre line between bow and stern.

geographical position (GP) Point on the surface of the earth at which an imaginary line from the centre of a celestial body to the centre of the earth passes through the earth's crust.

gnomonic chart A chart on the gnomonic projection in which great circles appear as straight lines but rhumb lines and parallels of latitude are curves.

great circle A circle whose plane passes through the centre of a sphere dividing it into two equal halves – the earth may be represented as a sphere.

Greenwich hour angle (GHA) Longitude of the geographical position of a celestial body, but measured 0° to 360° west from the meridian through Greenwich.

Greenwich Mean Time (GMT) Time by the mean sun related to the Greenwich meridian.

heading ship's head The direction in which the bow is pointing at any given moment.

index error (IE) A small but consistent error in the reading on a sextant because the two mirrors are not parallel when the scale is set to zero.

intercept The difference between the true altitude of a celestial body found by an observer and that calculated for a chosen position at the same instant of time.

latitude Angular distance north or south of the equator measured at the earth's centre.

lattice The pattern formed on a chart by pre-plotted position lines that intersect.

leeway Sideways movement of a craft through the water due to the effect of wind.

local hour angle (LHA) The longitude of the geographical position of a celestial body measured 0° to 360° westward from an observer or a chosen position.

log An instrument which indicates boat speed and distance travelled through the water.

longitude Angular distance between the Greenwich meridian and the meridian passing through a place. Measured at the centre of the earth in the plane of the equator 0° to 180° E or W.

Loran C Long Range Navigation aid. Low frequency hyperbolic fixing system based on pulse and phase comparisons.

magnetic compass A compass employing the earth's magnetic field as the directional force.

magnetic north The direction of the north magnetic Pole at any place.

mean day An artificial unit of constant length, based on the average of all apparent days over a period of years.

mean sun An imaginary body which travels at a constant rate thus giving a mean day of constant length.

mean time Time based on the mean sun.

Mercator chart A chart on the Mercator projection. Rhumb lines appear as straight lines, whereas great circles are curves.

meridian A straight line joining the true North Pole and the true South Pole.

meridian passage The moment of transit of the sun across the meridian at a place; noon.

observer All-embracing term used to describe any person engaged in celestial or terrestial observation of phenomena or events used in the practice of navigation at sea.

observed altitude Altitude obtained using a sextant.

Omega A very low frequency, long range, hyperbolic fixing system.

parallax in altitude The angle at the body between the lines from the celestial body to an observer and to the centre of the earth. Stars are so distant that they have no parallax, the sun's parallax is too small to be significant, but the moon's parallax must be allowed for.

plot Diagrammatic representation of the progress of a craft, usually on a chart.

position line or line of position (LOP) A line on the chart on which the boat lies or has lain. It may be straight, curved or irregular in shape.

prime meridian The Greenwich meridian.

projection The representation on the plane surface of a chart of all or any part of the curved surface of the earth.

radar Use of reflected radio waves to find distance and/or bearing of objects. Initial letters of Radio Aid to Detection And Ranging.

rational horizon Great circle 90° from the zenith, parallel to the sensible horizon.

refraction The bending of light rays as they pass through the earth's atmosphere.

relative (direction) Direction in the horizontal plane with reference to the bow of a boat. An object dead ahead is 0° REL. Measured clockwise through 360°, or through 180° to port or starboard, when it may be prefixed red or green.

rhumb line A line which cuts all meridians at the same angle; line followed by craft sailing on one course.

running fix A fix in which position lines are not obtained simultaneously, but the first is run or transferred to the time of the second.

semi-diameter Radius of the sun. Correction applied to allow for the fact that the observed altitude is found using the upper or lower limb whereas the true altitude is to the centre of the sun.

sensible horizon The sea level plane at right angles to the vertical through the observer's position. The visible horizon to an observer with no height of eye.

set (of current) The direction of movement of a current or tidal stream.

side error An error in the sextant due to the horizon mirror not being perpendicular to the frame of the instrument.

solstice Either time (about 21 June or 22 December) at which the sun reaches its maximum north or south declination and appears to pause before reversing direction.

sub-stellar point See geographical position.

track The future or intended path of a vessel, e.g. the intended rhumb line track plotted on a chart.

transit (range – USA) Any two fixed objects in line as seen from a craft.

true altitude The angular distance of the centre of a celestial body above the rational horizon. For the sun and stars, this can be assumed to be their angle above the sensible horizon without loss of accuracy.

true azimuth True direction of a celestial body from an observer. Exactly equal to the true bearing of the body's geographical position from an observer.

true direction Direction measured clockwise from true north from 0° to 360°.

true north The direction from any point on the earth to the true North Pole.

variation (magnetic) The angle at a place between the direction of true north and the direction of magnetic north.

visible horizon To an observer at sea, the line appearing to mark the intersection of sea and sky.

zenith The point in the heavens directly above an observer.

zenith distance Angular distance of a celestial body from an observer's zenith. (90° – true altitude). On the earth, the distance between the observer and the geographical position of the body.

Index

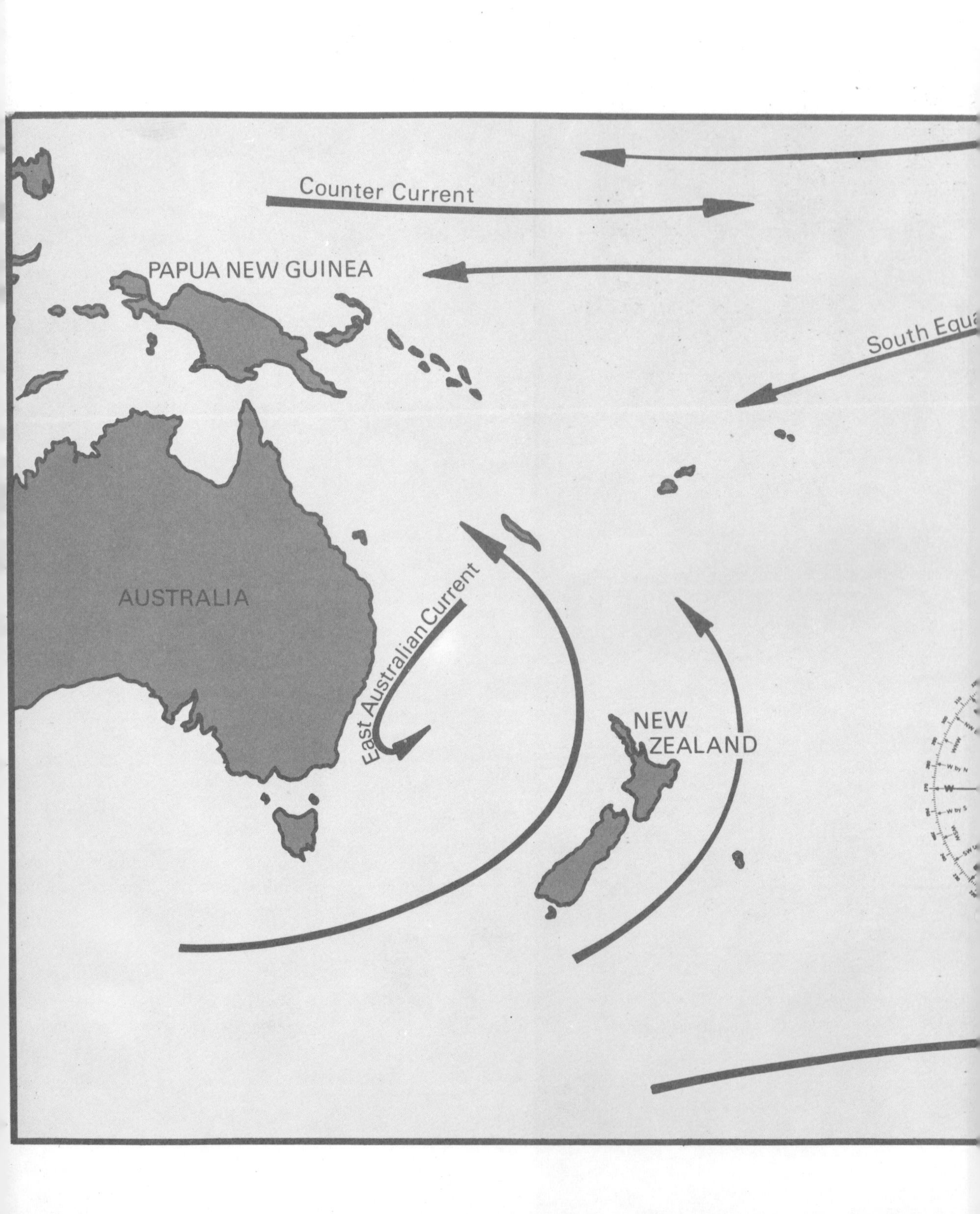
Counter Current
PAPUA NEW GUINEA
South Equa
AUSTRALIA
East Australian Current
NEW
ZEALAND